Ceramics and Glass:
a basic technology

Ceramics and Glass: a basic technology

by
Charles Bray

Published by
Society of Glass Technology
Don Valley House
Savile Street East
Sheffield S4 7UQ

Ceramics and Glass: a basic technology by Charles Bray

Charles Bray was Principal Lecturer responsible for ceramics and glass in the Faculty of Art and Design at Sunderland Polytechnic, now the University of Sunderland. He was responsible for initiating the degree course in glass and ceramics and was involved in the setting up of the first Glass Centre in Sunderland. He organised many conferences and these various activities stimulated much of the development of the major glass interest in the area.

He was active for many years as treasurer and membership secretary of British Artists in Glass, and its first elected life member.

He served on the panel of Northern Arts for many years, is a Fellow of the Society of Glass Technology, is an honorary Fellow of the University of Sunderland and is a Fellow of the Royal Society of Arts.

He now has work in most of the major glass collections and exhibits mostly in Europe. He has been invited to take part in several international exhibitions and in many exhibitions of British Glass.

The objects of the Society of Glass Technology are to encourage and advance the study of the history, art, science, design, manufacture, after treatment, distribution and end use of glass of any and every kind. These aims are furthered by meetings, publications, the maintenance of a library and the promotion of association with other interested persons and organisations.

Society of Glass Technology
Don Valley House
Savile Street East
Sheffield S4 7UQ, UK
Tel   +44(0)114 263 4455
Fax   +44(0)114 263 4411
Email   books@sgt.org
Web   http://www.sgt.org

The Society of Glass Technology is a registered charity no. 237438.

ISBN 0-900682-30-2 (hardback)
ISBN 0-900682-32-9 (paperback)

Preface

This book has been written for students, potters and glassmakers working individually or in small studios. It is intended to be a source of understandable information. Most books on glass and ceramic technology are aimed at technologists or at students of technology, and as a result, are often not easily understood by many people who have little or no scientific background. It has been very difficult to write at an appropriate level.

For some people it may be pitched too low and for others it may be a little too high. I have assessed this on my own needs and personal experience as a working glassmaker and potter. The book deliberately brings together the two areas because there is much information, normally attributed to one area which seriously affects the other.

I am very grateful for the help and advice given by Dr Doug Crozier of the Society of Glass Technology, Dr Collin Gill of the University of Sunderland and by David Moore of the Society of Glass Technology.

Contents

I.
Introduction

At first sight the two crafts of producing pottery and making articles in glass seem to be completely separate entities yet, in fact, they have a great deal in common. Many of the earliest glassmaking techniques evolved from those already in use for making pottery and most of the people who started the studio glass movement were established potters. At a basic level, both activities involve the manipulation of malleable materials into specific forms, one using a process which involves the cold working of a plastic material which becomes permanently hardened by firing whilst the other consisting largely of operating with a very hot molten material which hardens on cooling. There are further connections. Clay when fired to a biscuit state is still fairly porous and usually needs to be glazed if it is necessary to make the ceramic form impervious to water. The glazing process consists of firing a very thin layer of glass on to the surface of the biscuit form. Clay can also be fired further until in the production of stoneware and porcelain many of the constituent particles turn to glass which will then seal and fill the pores of the material.

In a similar manner the materials from which both glass and most ceramics originate are strongly related. The major difference in the underlying structure of glass and ceramics is that most ceramics retain a complex crystal structure, but sometimes containing glassy material, whereas glass, which is formed by melting particular crystalline materials, becomes non-crystalline and any crystals which may occur are usually regarded as defects and as a considerable nuisance. There are particular exceptions to this in that crystals are sometimes deliberately cultivated in glazes to form an interesting range of what are called crystalline glazes and as very fine crystals evenly distributed in glass to form a range of materials called glass ceramics. These are proving to have a remarkable range of properties, the best known being those which result in excellent resistance to both thermal and physical shock. Such relatively new materials are constantly being extended and are proving to be of great benefit to both science and to industry.

Another area in which potters and glassmakers share technology is that of constructing their own furnaces and kilns. In order to do this successfully they need to understand the essential parameters and behaviour of a wide range of refractory and insulation materials. The great majority of these are based on fired clay or clay related products such as ceramic fibre, sillimanite and mullite. When one looks at the underlying structure of both ceramics and glass it becomes obvious that there is much more in common than is generally understood.

Moving away from the basic premise of simple pottery and glassmaking into modern industrial practice there is a considerably greater relationship between the two activities. The way in which glasses melt, ceramic materials bond together and refractories withstand corrosion at high temperature are all inter-related. They produce articles which have properties, whether they be strength, transparency, colour or shape which when matched to the application require understanding and appreciation of both glass and ceramic technology.

It must be obvious that at one level, work in both areas has been produced for many thousands of years and can still be produced relying solely on crafts-manship and a simple awareness of the behaviour of a limited range of basic materials. It is when problems arise, when native curiosity takes over, or when, as with the development of materials like glass ceramics, there is a wish to extend possibilities, it suddenly becomes necessary to understand the how and why in greater depth.

It is intended that this book will undertake to explain the characteristics of the materials involved, their relationships with each other and with many of the problems that arise as a result of this. It is also intended to generate greater understanding of both materials and principles involved in the ceramics and glassmaking processes.

Detail from Glass Carpet by John Patsalides

The plastic nature of clay is well demonstrated by its universal use as a modelling material

General considerations

Clay can be described as a hydrated silicate of aluminium. This simply means that ideally it contains one part of alumina (aluminium oxide) and two parts of silica (silicon dioxide) It also means that it contains two parts of water which are tied to the chemical structure and released as steam during the firing process. The clay which we use, however, is most unlikely to conform strictly to the standard formula that is usually presented because the variations in this material are enormous. When it is dug from the ground it can contain silica and various rock particles in the form of sand, mica and feldspar, etc, all of which contribute to the character and behaviour of the clay. Brick clays, for example, may only contain a small proportion of material which could even be loosely described as being clay.

Glass is also a material with a considerable variation in content but almost all glass used today contains silica, usually introduced in the form of sand, which acts as the glass former, together with other materials known as network modifiers which are likely to include a little alumina, fluxing materials to lower the melting temperature and some calcium carbonate or similar material to stabilise the result. From the above it can be seen that both clay and glass are

Porcelain bottle by Lucie Rie. Courtesy of the Eagle collection at the Shipley Art Gallery, Gateshead, Tyne and Wear Museums. Private loan

likely to contain silica in quantity. There is also a large amount of alumina in clay, rather less in glaze and very much less, usually less than two per cent, in glass. In most cases additional materials are included which tend to modify both the behaviour and the result. From the above it will be seen that both clay and glass are likely to contain silica in quantity. There is also a lot of alumina in clay, rather less in a glaze and normally, very much less, usually less than two percent, in glass. In most cases additional materials are included which tend to modify both the behaviour and the result.

Much also depends on the temperature to which they are eventually taken, the rate at which they are then cooled and the use for which the particular glass or ceramic has been designed. Many of the refractories we use in glassmaking today are based on clay. As clays contain a high proportion of silica they will become molten if taken to a sufficiently high temperature. Whether they then form a ceramic material or a glass depends on how quickly the molten mass is cooled. This is a phenomenon which occurs naturally as a result of volcanic action. Silica rich lava usually cools slowly and consolidates into a wide range of crystalline rock forms but it occasionally cools sufficiently rapidly to produce the natural black glass known as obsidian which was used for making knives and various tools by the pre-Hispanic tribes of Central America. If in the process of cooling gas becomes trapped in the lava, it can form the foamed volcanic glass known as pumice, used as an abrasive and as a polishing material by glassworkers. If there are strong winds, threads of molten material can be blown into the natural glass fibres known as "Goddesses' Hair".

From this it can easily be deduced that a glass is formed when some crystalline materials such as silica are melted and then cooled too quickly to be able to regain a crystalline form. In this case the silica is said to have become vitrified. If on the other hand the molten silica cools slowly and reverts to a crystal form it is said to have been devitrified. In other words something which has become a glass is said to have vitrified and something which has been glass but has reverted to being a crystalline material is said to have become devitrified. A natural form of this is the rock basalt. This is material which often forms as a glass but then devitrifies into a crystalline material. The two terms occur frequently in reference to both ceramics and glass but are sometimes used rather loosely. For instance, stoneware and porcelain are often described as being vitrified, yet they only contain sufficient glassy particles to seal the pores. Similarly, glass is often said to have been devitrified when only a small proportion of the material may have been affected.

One important matter for the potter or studio glassmaker is that of understanding chemical formulae. These are quoted in most books and are essential to composition calculations and to the development and understanding of melting and firing processes. The various minerals that are used are often quite complex mixtures or compounds of various elements. These elements are all given an abbreviation to correspond to the name. For instance Na is short for the Greek word natron and is used to describe the element sodium. K (kalium) describes potassium and perhaps more obviously O describes oxygen and H hydrogen, and so on. This facilitates the construction of equations to describe the various compounds which are formed when elements combine together. When the atoms of elements react together they form molecules.

Chemical equations are a very convenient shorthand to describe quite complex compounds and many of them soon become immediately recognisable. They are also useful because they give a precise definition. In ceramics and in glassmaking there are many terms which mean different things to different people. "Potash" is an obvious example. It actually refers to potassium carbonate (K_2CO_3) but many people think of it as meaning potassium oxide (K_2O), probably because this is the active material to be considered in forming glass and glazes and is the material which is left after carbon dioxide (CO_2) is driven off from the potassium carbonate as batch or glaze is being heated.

The term "lime" also turns up regularly and, depending entirely on the circumstances and the person using the material, this can translate as limestone, chalk, quicklime, slaked lime, etc, whereas names such as calcia or calcium carbonate or their chemical formulae have precise meanings. This vague use of terms is common throughout ceramic and glassmaking and even today recipes for compiling batch, glaze and clay bodies are often presented in ways that are open to misinterpretation. This can cause some confusion and a possible creation of errors when calculating material requirements for various processes.

The description in words of every chemical reaction would be very tedious. Chemical formulae are used in a similar style to algebraic equations to express precisely in shorthand the starting materials (reactants) and end materials (products) of a chemical reaction.

Examples

A common example of this which is often quoted is that hydrochloric acid (HCl) reacts violently with caustic soda, chemical name sodium hydroxide (NaOH) to form sodium chloride (NaCl) and water (H_2O). The chemical equation for this is:-

$$HCl + NaOH = NaCl + H_2O$$

A more relevant example to glass or glaze making is that heating sodium carbonate produces sodium oxide and carbon dioxide giving the following chemical equation:-

$$Na_2CO_3 = Na_2O + CO_2$$

Much of the formation of glass and ceramics depends considerably on the nature of the basic crystalline source material, the various other minerals that may be present, the amount of heat to which they have been subjected and the rate at which they have been cooled.

Crystalline material

Many solid materials have a crystalline character which may or may not be obvious. Crystals result from the fact that the structure of a crystalline material is in the form of a regular repetitive lattice of atoms, relatively simple in the case of sand and rather more complex in the case of clay. When such material is heated sufficiently the atoms become agitated, bonds are broken, until eventually as the heat increases, the atoms lose their ability to retain a regular structural lattice and the network becomes completely random and forms an amorphous liquid. If this liquid cools slowly it tries to regain a regular lattice structure but when cooled quickly it cannot do so and will form a glass. A glass, therefore, is a material which in converting from a liquid to a solid state has retained the random structure characteristic of the liquid. An understanding of the relationship between a crystalline material and a glass is fundamental to an appreciation of much of the underlying technology relating to both glass and ceramics.

Lattices

The term "Lattice" which is used considerably in reference to ceramics and to a lesser extent in reference to glass materials is commonly used to describe the regular placing of atoms or molecules on specific points in a three-dimensional structure. Such a regular three-dimensional structure describes a crystalline material. A "Network," which is also a common term can refer to a lattice if the arrangements of the atoms or molecules are regular. If the arrangement concerned is not regular then it is usually called a "Random Network" and will refer to an amorphous substance such as glass.

Sand and clay are two of the most abundant materials on earth. Clay and some sands originate from feldspathic rock that itself makes up approximately 60% of the minerals on the crust of the earth and which have decomposed into various clay materials and quartz grains. Many of these have been gradually abraded, carried by rivers and glaciers and deposited elsewhere in large areas as sand and clay. The sand is almost wholly composed of silica (SiO_2), a compound of one part of silicon and two parts of oxygen. In a silica crystal such as quartz the structure is one of a simple but regular repetitive pattern of tetrahedra.

Clay is a much more varied substance but in the basic clay material (kaolinite) the silica bonds together with gibbsite (alumina) to form flat irregular hexagonal plates stacked together like playing cards. These are held together with an electrical charge and the chemically bonded water between the layers. They are lubricated by more water which is not chemically bonded. It is the presence of this water that provides much of the plasticity. The amount of this water can vary considerably and accounts for much of the wide variation in the plasticity of clays.

In a glass or a glaze the molecules assume a much more haphazard arrangement to produce a three-dimensional network in which no unit repeats itself at regular distances. Silica is a material which can be melted at high temperatures and formed into a glass with particularly useful and individual properties, but most glass in general use contains other materials which are introduced to lower the melting point, to stabilise the finished glass, and/or to produce a wide range of properties such as colour, opacity, strength, high resistance to thermal shock, etc.

Glass and glaze can be regarded as a form of supercooled liquid which has no regular molecular structure. As explained earlier, it exists when certain materials are unable to regain their original crystalline form after cooling from a molten state. Almost all glasses and glazes are based on silica, sometimes in conjunction with boric oxide which, whilst it acts as a glass former, melts at a low temperature is often introduced to aid further melting of the batch materials or to produce particular qualities such as a strong resistance to physical and thermal shock.

As crystalline silica has a melting temperature of 1713°C (3115°F), this is far too high for most glassmaking processes both in terms of the cost of firing and in the ability of normally available furnace refractories to remain solid.

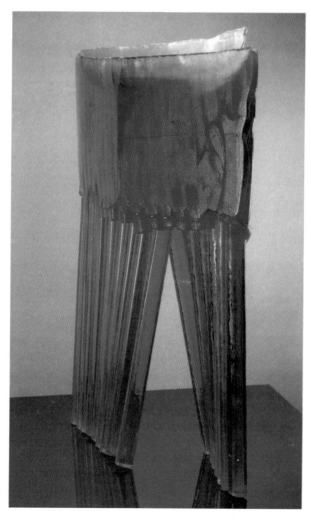

Cast glass sculpture by Gisela Sabokova, Czech Republic. Photograph by Karel Bartonicek

Because of this it is usually mixed with other materials, known as fluxes or network modifiers, to bring own the melting temperature and to stabilise the resulting glass.

Basic glass materials

Three relatively common materials, sand, soda ash and limestone provide most of the minerals used in the making of commercial soda–lime–silica glass. Silica, sodium oxide and limestone are also commonly present in many glazes. A little alumina will almost certainly be present in glass and rather more in a glaze.

Engineering components made from silicon nitride (Photograph courtesy of Tenmat)

The alumina in a glaze stiffens it so that whilst it softens sufficiently to form a glass layer which will bond to the ceramic body, the layer remains sufficiently viscous to stay in place without running off the form. Potters experimenting with glazes are often tempted to reduce the alumina content in order to achieve some particular colour or effect but the result can easily turn out to be a pot which is firmly cemented to a kiln shelf by a layer of glass. There are many other minerals in general use that are described in greater detail under batch materials, batch melting and glaze composition.

The making of pottery and glass has developed over the centuries. Until comparatively recently this has been largely by a long process of trial and error rather than any depth of understanding of chemical and physical processes. Both crafts have evolved from a gradual awareness of a small range of natural materials and related, simple, firing processes. We still rely heavily on natural minerals but there are now several other materials such as silicon nitride, silicon carbide, uranium dioxide, etc, which are used, particularly in industry, and can hardly be considered to be naturally occurring materials. Forming processes have also changed considerably to embrace a wider range of techniques.

A further change concerns the term "Ceramics" which once referred to pottery articles, refractories, bricks and tiles, etc, produced by the process of firing clay. It is now difficult to define ceramics simply in terms of composition and the name now seems to relate more to a much wider range of materials having a refractory nature processed by the application of heat. For the purposes of this text, however, the term will be used in its original context unless otherwise stated.

There is also a small difference in terminology between that used by potters and that used by glassmakers which might cause some confusion. Materials

Earthenware vessel with copper lustre

which reduce the melting temperature of a glaze and/or fuse the body in the firing process tend to be called fluxes whilst in glassmaking they now tend to be known as network modifiers.

Whilst there are many potters and glassmakers who have a deep understanding of the technology of their craft, there are considerable numbers who do not have any depth of knowledge or understanding of the underlying chemistry nor do they feel inclined to try to develop this, but the basic technology can be approached simply without any great necessity for becoming deeply involved. At this level, however, it is well worth the effort of trying to understand a little of the underlying structure as so much of what happens can only be explained properly in these terms. Because of this, whenever it is possible to explain something simply, without recourse to complex theory, this will be done. There are, however, matters which need reference to the underlying physics and chemistry so some basic theory is explained, hopefully at a level at which it will be readily understood by those who have little or no background in these subjects.

II.
Material origins

A great proportion of the minerals used in studio ceramics and some of those used in glassmaking result from the formation of igneous rock from hot magma pushing up towards the surface of the earth. Where this did not actually reach the surface it formed large domes which whilst cooling were often attacked from below by hot gases.

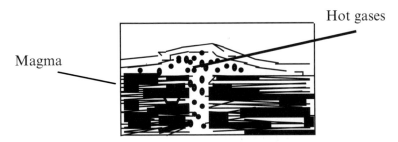

Hot gases

Magma

This created a complex situation in which a considerable amount of cooling took place. The cooling magma which was not affected or was affected very little became hard granites and feldspars. Some materials that were success-fully attacked tended to form much softer rock which included clay. The proc-ess was one in which hard granitic rock was attacked by hot and often corrosive gases, such as carbonic acid and various compounds of boron and fluorine together with superheated acidic steam. This caused it to decompose into feld-spar plus various salts and silicates. These, in turn, decomposed forming sheets of alumina which, together with the results of further substitution turner into kaolinite, accompanied by mica and quartz.

The action could be demonstrated in a simplified form as:-

Feldspar + water +carbon dioxide
    turning into Clay + silica + potassium carbonate

From this, much of the potassium carbonate would be washed away. In fact, various metal ions present also became removed as carbonates or bicarbonates. Some of the silica would be held as free particles in the clay and some would be separated into quartz particles often in colloidal gel form, and would also be washed away. Igneous rocks other than the granites were also attacked and decomposed in a similar manner but the clay which resulted from this process tends to have a high proportion of other minerals and is a less pure clay than that originating from granite.

Much of the quartz was eroded eventually into the silica sands used for glassmaking. The kaolinite, after various processes of erosion, movement and redeposit formed most of the various types of clay as we know them today.

The nature of these clays depend on the composition of the rocks from which they originated, the various mineral and organic impurities which they accumulated in their travels and the abrasion, weathering and leaching to which they have been subjected. As a result, a very wide range of clays has been created, each with vastly different qualities and usually readily available but often requiring some modification to suit the various forming processes that have evolved. From the nature of the composition of the surface of the earth and the forces which act upon it there is a huge continuing provision of the various clays, sands and other minerals used in both ceramics and in glass-making though some of these, particularly the best of them are not as readily available as they were.

The term "clay" does not have a precise meaning and covers a huge variety of natural substances with considerable differences in appearance, physical and chemical composition and texture. Some of them contain as much as 90% actual clay material whereas in others the content can be as little as 30%. The only thing that they have in common is that they are plastic when they are wet, become rigid when they are dry, become plastic again when re-wetted and can be fired to become permanently non-plastic.

Residual or primary clay

The purest clay or that least contaminated by other minerals is residual clay which is deposited at or near to the place where it originated from the decomposed igneous and metamorphic rock. It is known as primary clay or china clay and contains a high proportion of kaolinite. This is a refractory clay which because of its lack of impurities, particularly iron oxide, is white when fired but lacks plasticity. Because of this, it is usually necessary to mix it with other more plastic clays to make it into a material that is more easily worked.

Bentonite is a very useful material that is also formed at this stage. It is clay-like in its plasticity because of its similar plate structure and is much used in the oil industry as a lubricant for rock drilling. It is really a montmorillonite rather than a clay but is often used by potters to increase the plasticity of clay, additions of up to 2% having a marked effect. Introductions of more than this are rarely practical because they are likely to create high shrinkage.

As the primary clay is washed from its place of origin and redeposited it becomes broken into finer particles by abrasion and by the action of water and ice. It also picks up various minerals, in particular ferric oxide which produces grey, cream and brown colours and organic matter which darkens the clay, often gives it a characteristic smell and, in quantity, aids the firing and the plasticity. The organic matter usually burns out without having any significant effect on the colour of the fired clay. These clays are known as secondary clays and include the very plastic ball clays and most of the refractory fireclays.

Glassmaking sands

The sands used for glassmaking go through a similar process. Many of them also very much depend on the nature of the rock from which they were originally formed. Geologists classify sands as being between 0·2 and 2 mm in diameter. The particle size in the sands is important and as a general rule the grains of sand for pot melting should be between 0·15 and 0·5 mm in diameter whilst those for tank melting can be somewhat larger and up to about 1·5 mm. Another important factor is the degree to which they have been affected by other minerals, especially ferric oxide and to a lesser extent chromic oxide. This can become crucial to the extent that many sands may become unsuitable for glassmaking largely because even a small iron and/or chrome content can have a considerable effect on the colour. As a result much of the sand in Britain is either unusable without appropriate chemical treatment or can only be used for the production of some coloured glass. Whilst there is much silica rich sand and rock in the world, the best and relatively pure silica sands and rocks are rapidly being exhausted. Sandstones are silica rich rocks cemented together with a wide range of materials. As silica is chemically inert and a very hard material, when sandstones break down much of the cementing material becomes removed naturally but the remaining grains can be treated industrially to remove non-quartz particles by froth flotation, white acid washing and by specialised milling processes.

Rocks and minerals

The geologist will tend to classify a mineral as being a single substance with a precisely defined chemical content whereas rocks can take a wide range of forms and be either composed of one particular material or can be aggregates of many different minerals. Most potters and glassmakers tend to accept a rather wider interpretation and usually describe such materials as the feldspars and clays which have a varied content as being "minerals" whereas they should, more correctly, be described as "rocks."

Rocks are usually classified under three headings:-

Igneous, which includes rocks which have been molten or partly molten such as the basalts, granites, etc.

Metamorphic, which refers to rocks which have been recrystallised, usually as a result of pressure combined with heat

Sedimentary, which refers to materials which have been deposited in various places as a result of being transported by water, ice or wind. Most of the sands, clays and limestones are sedimentary

Much of the sand currently used for making clear glass in Britain is imported from Belgium. There are a few good deposits, however, and those mined at Loch Aline are considered to be of high quality. A typical analysis of this sand shows 99·75 to 99·85% silica, 0·05 to 0·10% alumina, 0·009 to 0·013% iron oxide and the remainder of very small amounts of calcia, magnesia, sodium oxide, potassium oxide, titanium oxide and chromium oxide.

Many of the batch materials used for making glass occur as natural minerals, though there are a few synthetic chemicals which are also available. A few of these materials can be mined with sufficiently close tolerances in their con-

Illustration of rose quartz

tent of impurities to be used directly but most of them are now chemically and physically treated in order to achieve a consistency suitable for them to be used safely in both glass melting and glaze formation. It is important both for the glassmaker and the potter, particularly when melting batch or preparing glaze, to obtain good details from suppliers before making the necessary calculations as there can be considerable variations in content which may not conform strictly to those which are expressed in a particular batch or glaze formula.

Terms that are often met in relation to the description of rocks or minerals are those of "acid", "intermediate" or "basic." Most of the igneous rocks are composed of various silicate minerals. The amount of silica in them, however, varies considerably and it is the proportion of silica which is normally used to indicate whether one falls into one category or another. In a so-called acid rock the silica content is usually greater than that required for basic chemical requirements and a certain amount of free quartz is often found. Orthoclase feldspars and micas are characteristic of acid rocks.

Basic rocks tend to be heavier than acid rocks, contain rather less silica and are often likely to be rich in iron. Many of the plagiolistic feldspars and the various feldspathoids are said to be basic. Intermediate rock tends to have no quartz or feldspathoids but can be composed of various plagioclase materials. The fluxes for clay bodies are usually composed of alkali or alkaline earths and are often likely to be feldspathic materials. These will form a glass if heated to a sufficiently high temperature and in a clay body they gradually soften and melt. In the process they tend to reduce the firing temperature of the body and help to fill the pores. They are not used to a great extent in glassmaking because of the high alumina content but are popular ingredients of most glazes. They all contain some silica and alumina in addition to alkaline flux material. They are igneous in origin and often have some quartz and mica in association. The two principal feldspars are Orthoclase which is predominantly a potash feldspar with a theoretical composition of $K_2O.Al_2O_3.6SiO_2$ and Albite

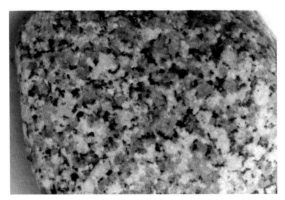

*A piece of granite showing various grains. The darkest spots are mica,
the white areas are feldspar and the grey areas are quartz*

which is predominantly a soda feldspar with a theoretical composition of $Na_2O.Al_2O_3.6SiO_2$. In fact they tend to vary considerably and most orthoclase will have some soda and most albite will have some potash.

There are many rocks which contain feldspars and are used in clay bodies and glazes. Occasionally, they may also be used in glassmaking. The most common of these are:-

Nepheline syenite This contains both potash and soda feldspars and is found in Canada, the United States and Norway. It is very popular because it has a greater fluxing power than either orthoclase or albite.

Anorthite This is a mixture of soda and lime feldspars which is sometimes used in the production of porcelain bodies.

Pegmatite A mixture of potash feldspar and quartz with considerable variations in content it is increasing in use as supplies of mined feldspars become exhausted.

Cornish stone (China stone) This was used considerably in England as it is the only suitable native feldspathic rock available. It contains both albite and orthoclase but tends to have small quantities of mica and fluorine minerals. The fluorine presented hazards in the firing so chemically prepared material without fluorine has been substituted and is available if required.

Mica This is not a feldspar but is chemically similar. It is available in quantity from the waste of china clay workings and often tends to be used to replace up to 25% of the feldspar in a prepared body

Lepidolite and spodumene Two lithium based feldspars which are used in small quantities when specially high fluxing qualities or low expansion bodies are required. They are also used in glassmaking as sources of lithium to produce a low expansion flux or as a seed material for the production of glass ceramics.

III.
Clay—a general classification

Clay is found and used in several forms and many of these have been given names which relate either to their nature or to their usage. It is one of the most abundant materials on earth and has been used by man for a variety of purposes over the centuries. It would have soon become obvious to primitive people that it was easily formed into decorative or useful shapes, became temporarily hard when it had been dried in the sun and became permanently hard when subjected to the heat of a fire. Its plasticity is such that it is an amazingly versatile natural material. It can be pushed or manipulated into shapes that will then retain this shape, apart from some shrinkage as it dries or, before it is fired, can be returned to a plastic mass by simply adding water. The use of clay by various civilisations has made its shards into something of a major element for archaeologists in the dating, distinguishing and chronology of the different cultures. It is found in a wide variety of forms and is almost always contaminated by other minerals. Some cultures also added various materials such as straw, sand, broken and ground pottery and many different minerals. All of these have served to affect colour and firing characteristics to the extent that another identification possibility has become readily available to the archaeologists in their researches.

The various types of clays are often described either by their location or by their characteristics. The first of these, the primary clays, often rich in kaolinite, are known as residual clays, china clay or kaolin (the Chinese name for a high ridge and now often spelt "gaolin") and are usually found in very large deposits, often several hundreds of metres thick. They usually have a high content of large grains of quartz, mica and feldspar and lack plasticity. This lack of plasticity means that they inevitably need to be mixed with more plastic clay for the purposes of making pottery. They tend to fire white because they are of virtually free from colouring oxides. This makes them particularly suitable for inclusion in porcelain and bone china bodies. They can withstand high temperatures and also have low shrinkage, particularly in drying.

The large and excellent deposits found in Cornwall were first given the name "China clay" and this seems to have been adopted as a general name to describe similar deposits in many parts of the world. In America the term "Kaolin" seems to be used for similar material. The English China Clay Company markets several refined versions of so-called china clay including some specially prepared for incorporating into porcelain.

Refractory clays are often considered to be those which will withstand very high temperatures (usually over 1300°C) without deforming and can be either primary clays or secondary clays. They often retain considerable physical strength after firing.

The secondary or sedimentary clays tend to have fine particles by virtue of the fact that very fine materials are more easily transported for considerable distances by rivers whilst coarse material tends to be deposited in the early stages. Also, the longer the journey, the greater the amount of grinding received by the particles. They are much more plastic than the primary clays.

Other very fine minerals become transported or picked up on the journey and these become very difficult to separate These clays vary enormously both in content and character and as a result can rarely be defined precisely. Many of them are called plastic, long or fat clays and are usually very strong throughout most of the forming and firing processes. They are often contaminated by various impurities, particularly iron, which affect colour and fusing qualities. Many of them also tend to have high shrinkage. Some of them are also contaminated by organic matter which before firing gives them a grey or blue colour and a strong characteristic smell.

The decay of this organic matter is said to contribute to the plasticity of these clays though it has little or no effect on the final colour as it burns out early in the firing.

Those clays which, because they have accumulated quantities of sand or similar non-plastic material, lack plasticity become known as short clays. They can also tend to lack some strength in the forming processes but may or may not be strong after firing. Fireclays are usually "short". Those which have been transported by glaciers and tend to contain a high proportion of pebbles and gravel and are known as boulder clays. Some clays are carried along by fast rivers and are deposited near to the mouth or where the river suddenly widens or deepens and loses its force. They usually contain large quantities of sand, are mostly used for brickmaking and are known as brick clays.

Shales

Shales are largely composed of clays which after being deposited have been compressed. When they have been subjected to heat and further pressure where they have been deposited they harden considerably and become slate. Shales are often ground down into small particles and used as additions to other clays in brickmaking.

Ball clays

These are usually described as fine secondary clays, though some of them may well be tertiaries. They are usually grey or blue in colour, and very plastic. They are called ball clays because it used to be the practice when the material was mined in Devon and Dorset to roll the clay into large balls weighing about 35 lbs which could then be easily loaded on to whatever form of transport that was being used. Ball clay is not normally suitable for use on its own because of its high shrinkage. This can be as high as 17% so in prepared clay bodies it is usually mixed with china clay. The two materials are complementary. They both tend to fire to a white or near white state. China clay has low plasticity, is very refractory and has low shrinkage whereas ball clay is very plastic, fuses relatively easily and has high shrinkage. As a result most manufactured clay bodies for the making of white ware are composed largely of mixtures of china

China clay pit in Cornwall, Geological Survey Photograph No. MN2770. From Geology and Ceramics, HM Stationary Office

clay and ball clay together with other minerals to suit the particular type of ware required. Ball clay is often also introduced to give greater density to a fired body.

Fireclays

Most so-called fireclays are highly refractory but cannot be easily defined. As a general rule, clays that will withstand firing to temperatures of 1500°C and above tend to be called fireclays.

They can be plastic but are more usually short. Most of them are relatively free from impurities but some have a considerable organic content. They mostly fire to a white or cream colour but some contain iron bearing minerals which produce patches of colour. Fireclays usually have a very coarse texture and are sometimes introduced into stoneware bodies to produce open qualities. The iron bearing fireclays are also introduced so that the iron, usually in the form of iron pyrites, can break through a glaze to produce decorative effects, particularly in reduction firings.

The fireclays are often found in conjunction with coal seams and there is a body of opinion which suggests that as the coal resulted from rotted and compressed vegetation, the same plant life was responsible for removing much of the fluxing material from the original clay deposits, so producing the refractory nature of the fireclay. It is often used together with aluminous cement for making large sculptural forms. It is the basis of most of the common refractories used in furnace building and of the clay bodies used for producing sanitary ware and firebricks.

Primary clay

Secondary clay

Illustration to show the usual location of primary and secondary clays

Earthenware clay

Natural earthenware clay is perhaps the most variable clay to describe. When used largely as it is found it is often called "common" clay and constitutes most of the clay used for making pottery, tiles, bricks and roof tiles throughout the world. Its colour when fired can range from white to cream, grey and pink to brick red. It usually contains sufficient impurities to make it hard when fired to temperatures between about 950°C to about 1100°C. but often begins to deform when fired to temperatures higher than this.

Many potters still use clay that, apart from cleaning and maturing, is virtually as it was dug from the ground. Others, and much of industry, use prepared clay bodies from specialist suppliers.

A typical prepared clay body for throwing would be made from approximately:-

China clay	25%
Ball clay	25%
Feldspar	20%
Calcined flint	30%

Other materials such as wollastonite, talc, cornish stone, lime, etc, can also be included. The plastic ball clay is crucial to the throwing characteristics of the clay body and amounts of this can be reduced considerably if the prepared clay body is not to be used for throwing. This reduces shrinkages so for making tiles, an earthenware body could be modified to be approximately:-

China clay	30%
Ball clay	10%
Talc	30%
Calcined flint	30%

Sometimes as much as 8% calcia (lime) could be included in place of some of the talc.

Many of the clay bodies used for producing earthenware in modern factories and studios are prepared commercially from a mixture of china clay, ball clay, feldspar or cornish stone and calcined flint, though some factories and some potters still dig and use the natural clay from their own clay pits, modifying them as necessary to fit their particular type of production. Perhaps the most common type of natural earthenware is known as "terracotta". Usually this is simply iron bearing clay which fires to a strong red colour and is used for making for such things as plant pots, roof tiles and tin-glazed earthenware. It is often used without modification after digging except for cleaning, pugging and storing. Whilst the term "terracotta" is almost always reserved for this red clay it can also refer to other natural clays which may be grey or near white in colour.

Stoneware clay

Stoneware clay is a term that is not precise. It refers generally to clays which will fire to temperatures between 1100 and 1300°C allowing the pores to become filled with glassy material which makes the ware impervious to water. They do not occur naturally to the same extent as other clays and are usually made up by manufacturers from mixtures of various clays which will provide sufficient glassy particles whilst retaining sufficient capacity to resist the higher firing temperatures required. It can include fireclays or mixtures of various primary and secondary clays. The term is mostly used in reference to the kind of ware which it produces rather than to any geological origins.

Marls

These are the red clays containing iron oxide and used for low fired iron stained earthenware. The term used to refer solely to clays containing iron oxide and a high proportion of calcium products which softened the effect of the iron and created a range of ochres, buffs and pinks. Marls tend to be very friable and need a lot of preparation and weathering to make them sufficiently plastic to enable them to be used without modification for making pottery.

Bentonite

This is often described as a clay but is in fact, a montmorillonite and is formed by the decomposition of volcanic ash or lava. It is similar to kaolinite but has a different molecular structure which contains none of the weak hydroxyl bonds on the outside of the layers which hold the clay layers together. As a result, the bentonite layers slide easily against one another to produce a slippery greasy material which acts as an excellent lubricant, particularly for rock drilling operations. If bentonite is introduced into water there are no bonds between the layers to restrict entry, so considerable amounts of water can be absorbed. Its use in ceramics is largely as a plasticiser. Amounts up to 2% calculated on a dry weight basis, are commonly added to clay bodies to improve plasticity. It is also particularly useful as an additive to raw glazes in place of some or all of the china clay, in which case amounts up to 10% can be used. Porcelain bodies

Removing brick clay from a pit in Surrey. Geological Survey Photograph No A.8937 Geology and Ceramics. H.M. Stationery Office

that are low in plastic clay and are required for throwing are often plasticised with about 5% bentonite.

Firing clay. When clay is fired to temperatures above 900°C the fluxing materials begin to create small pockets of glass in the pores, sealing some of them and bonding the clay particles together. At this stage the clay is still porous but is relatively strong and hard and cannot be returned to a plastic state by introducing water. As the temperature rises more glass is formed and seals the pores to the extent that the clay is no longer porous. Eventually a situation can be reached in which so much glassy material is formed that the clay bloats and begins to sag. There is, therefore, a range of temperatures, relating to the chemical composition of each clay, to which it can safely be fired. This is known as the firing range of the material. The firing ranges vary considerably and several terms have evolved which refer to the type of ware for which clay is used. Unfortunately, many of these terms cannot be precisely defined.

Clay is usually given the theoretical formula of $Al_2O_3.2SiO_2.2H_2O$. For purposes of calculation of the active ingredients the H_2O is disregarded. This formula refers to the mineral kaolinite but the clay which is deposited naturally and then retrieved for turning into ceramic material will have acquired a wide range of other materials which may or may not be bonded by ion exchange and which establish much of its behaviour and character.

Clay formulae
The theoretical formula for clay as shown translates to 39·5% alumina, 46·5% silica and 14% water. For comparison, Hamer & Hamer in their Potters' Dictionary, A & C Black Ltd. give analyses of various sample clays which

show by weight as percentages:-

	China clay	Fireclay	Ball clay	Stoneware	True marl
Alumina	44	41	37·5	32	15
Silica	53	55·5	56·5	63	64
Iron oxide	1	2·3	2	2·2	4
Calcia/magnesia	1	0·7	0·5	0·6	14
Potash/soda	1	0·5	3·5	2·2	3

The clays which are prepared for making into the various types of ceramic ware usually contain amounts of feldspar to provide some fluxing action and quartz to provide extra silica The same feldspars are also used as major components of ceramic glazes.

The common feldspars in use are also given theoretical formulae and these are:-

Albite (soda feldspar)	$Na_2O.Al_2O_3.6SiO_2$
Orthoclase (potash feldspar)	$K_2O.Al_2O_3.6SiO_2$
Anorthite (lime feldspar)	$CaO.Al_2O_3.2SiO_2$
Spodumene (lithium feldspar)	$Li_2O.Al_2O_3.4SiO_2$

These are most unlikely to be found as minerals corresponding to the above formulae. For instance each of them is likely to contain something of another. For example, potash feldspar will almost certainly prove to contain some Na_2O and CaO. They are all also likely to have a small iron content. There are also some feldspars that lie somewhere between those indicated and these are known as the plagioclase feldspars.

Actual analysis of three typical potash feldspars are:-

	(a)	(b)	(c)
SiO_2	68	65	68
Al_2O_3	17·5	18	18
Fe_2O_3	0·2	trace	trace
CaO	0·5	1	1
MgO	0·25	trace	trace
K_2O	10	16	10
Na_2O	3	-	3

There are also various feldspathoids used in clay bodies and glazes for which theoretical formulae have been established. The most common of these are:-
(1) Cornish stone This is often presented as having equal parts of Na_2O, K_2O, and CaO together with 1·7 parts of alumina and 8 parts of silica but is likely to have even greater variation in content than the feldspars noted above. Nevertheless, it has been a very popular glaze material in Britain over the years and at one time was considered to be the only viable native feldspathoid to be used. It had the disadvantage of often containing calcium fluoride which caused problems from toxic volatiles released in the firing. Latterly this has been removed chemically but now it seems that it has become more economic to use the greater fluxing qualities of imported feldspars.

A typical analysis shows:- 72·9% SiO_2, 14% Al_2O_3, 4% Na_2O and 3·8% K_2O.

(2) Nepheline Syenite This material is usually given the theoretical formula of $K_2O.3Na_2O.4Al_2O_3.9SiO_2$. It has a low melting temperature and because of this has become a popular ingredient in glazes. It is the feldspathic material most likely to be used in glassmaking. Large deposits are readily available in America.

A typical analysis shows:- 56·3% SiO_2, 24·9% Al_2O_3, 9·1% K_2O, 7% Na_2O.

(3) Petalite This is often used in small quantities in glazes to introduce lithia. It has a fluorine content which can cause some bubbling of the glaze if used in quantity. There are various theoretical formulae one of the most popular being $Li_2O.Al_2O_3.8SiO_2$. It is also used as a source of lithia in glassmaking.

A typical analysis is:- 74% SiO_2, 16·4% Al_2O_3, 3·4% Li_2O, 1·2% Na_2O, 0·7% K_2O, 0·6% MgO, 0·5% CaO.

There are many other materials that are used as batch materials for both glass and glazes. Those used for producing opacity and crystals are described under that heading. Those used for producing colour are also described under a separate heading.

Frit

Another sort of batch material is frit. This refers to glaze or glass materials that have been melted together and then ground to an appropriate particle size before being mixed into batch. This offers the possibility of reducing the handling of toxic materials such as lead oxide by first converting them into a silicate. In addition, frits are often created to enable water soluble materials to be converted into a form in which they can be introduced into a glaze slop. Many of the important batch materials, particularly the carbonates, and the various source materials for providing boric oxides are soluble in water and would create all sorts of problems if used in solution. Converting materials into frits is also a useful method of removing volatiles which could give rise to problems in firing. As they are prepared commercially they tend to have a consistent formula and because of this produce predictable and reliable results. They are also relatively simple to incorporate into any necessary batch calculations.

Some popular frits are:-

	SiO_2	Al_2O_3	PbO	K_2O	Na_2O	CaO	B_2O_3
Lead bisilicate	1·86	0·086	1				
Borax	1·98	0·18		0·3	0·35	0·62	0·63
Calcium borate	0·61	0·097				1	1·5
High alkali	2·59	0·01			0·5	0·5	0·62

Slip

Slip is often considered to be a simple straightforward mixture of clay and water which forms a thick liquid suspension. Until comparatively recent times it was rarely little more than that. Nowadays it is subject to additions of a wide

Figure, *glass and ceramic, by the author*

range of extra materials to render it suitable for particular purposes. Traditional English slipware was usually based on common red clay re-reinforced with additions of fine quartz and occasionally with china clay but today even the slips used for decoration are usually strengthened by including some feldspar, some fine quartz or flint to make the slip more dense and various fluxes and frits to help to produce glassy particles in the pores when it is fired.

Clay particles suspended in water tend to gather together in larger particles or aggregates called flocks. Other materials, if they are fine enough, behave in a similar manner. The degree to which these flocks are allowed to form is often regulated in slip to suit particular purposes. For example, in a casting slip, the tendency is deliberately much reduced by what is known as deflocculation in order to allow a slip to become fluid without the necessity of adding further water. For most decorative and coating purposes however, there is rarely any need to attempt to alter a slip but occasionally this may be deemed necessary and can usually be achieved by simply adding very small amounts of calcium

Thrown and turned stoneware with spray applied vitreous slips using lithium and calcium fluxes to produce the desired colour from cobalt, iron and manganese. Mary Burrows. Courtesy of Cumbria College of Art and Design

chloride, hydrochloric acid or vinegar. When the particles are encouraged to gather together, the process is known as flocculation. It is a normal phenomenon for fine particles to be attracted to each other more strongly as the distance between the particles decreases The process is not confined to slips. It can also be used by the potter for glazes and in general to settle any fine suspensions, to thicken both slips and glazes or to maintain in suspension coarser particles which would normally settle out of a liquid. Another use is to strengthen stored clay.

Deflocculation processes involve electrostatic charges. When these have been modified to the extent that the particles repel each other they then lose the tendency to settle out of suspension and remain in place. This forms what is known as a colloidal suspension and in reference to slips and glazes the process of inducing this state deliberately is known as deflocculation. On the other hand, if the electrostatic charge is sufficiently reduced, the particles can revert to being attracted to each other in a similar manner to that produced by the effect of polarity in a magnetic field. The reason for this is that clay has a flat crystal form with positive charges at the edges and less dominant negative charges on the faces. When the electrostatic charges are increased the effect is to cause the crystals, normally layered together like a pack of cards, to repel each other and to form a completely loose arrangement which enables the slip to become more fluid without the addition of extra water.

The most common additions to slip are colouring oxides. In general, the proportion of these oxides is greater in a slip than it would be in a coloured glaze. Whilst 1% cobalt oxide would be give a very strong blue in a glaze, as much as 4% might be necessary to give a strong blue in a slip. Just as in a glaze, cobalt on its own tends to produce a bright garish blue if introduced into a white firing clay but beautiful subdued blue colours can be achieved by including either some red clay or a little iron oxide. Additions of iron oxide to a white firing body will produce a range of cream colours with additions up to 4%, a range of browns with additions up 12% and black with additions around 15%. As common red clay can contain up to 8% iron oxide, this can often be substituted or modified to suit.

In fact, many potters make cream and brown slip by mixing red and white clay in suitable proportions. Common red clay into which feldspar has been introduced gives some rich browns whilst, if the clay is calcareous or has had calcia added to it, the colour from the iron will tend to be bleached. Just as the intense blue of cobalt oxide could be subdued by including some iron oxide, the black resulting from high additions of iron oxide can be made richer by adding a little cobalt oxide.

Other common colouring oxides are:-

chromium oxide	up to 5% producing a range of grey greens in a white clay
copper oxide	up to 6% producing a range of strong greens which may not be apparent until the pot has been glazed. Any more than this amount can produce areas of metallic black, particularly if the oxide is not finely ground and not well mixed into the slip
manganese dioxide	up to 12% will produce a range of browns. These are often modified by including some iron oxide
nickel oxide	this not a popular colouring oxide but in additions of between 2 and 6% produces another range of grey browns

Ideally a slip should be sieved through a fine lawn to remove any sand, etc. to produce a smooth liquid. This tends to have the effect of giving the slip a slightly higher shrinkage than that of the body it is to cover. Colouring oxides also need to be ground finely and mixed into the slip thoroughly before it is sieved.

Another use of slip is to produce a type of glaze applied to the pot when it is at the leather hard stage and called a slip glaze. This is usually a simple mixture of approximately 50% glaze and 50% slip but there are clays around, particularly estuary deposits, which have sufficient fluxing materials in them to be used without modification. Sometimes a little more flux may be required and wood ash is often added to produce the sort of character found in tenmoko glazes. Slip glaze is also used as a buffer to provide a better interface between the clay body and a glaze. This is usually applied when there is a sufficient difference in the expansion of the body and the glaze to cause flaking or shivering (see Glaze faults) in which case it becomes necessary to produce a slip with an expansion approximately midway between those of the glaze and those of the clay body to reduce stress. This can be calculated but most potters simply produce a few test tiles to find a suitable mixture. Buffer layers can also be applied in the form of a white slip glaze on stoneware bodies to help with the production of good colour response in iron rich glazes.

In normal clay plate particles become attracted to each other like cards

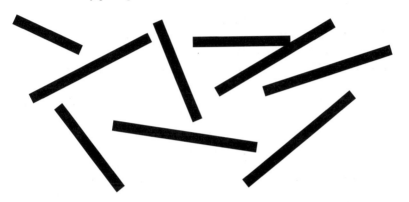

When deflocculated the negatively charged particles become loose and fluid

Flocculants are generally soluble materials used to increase viscosity. They tend to be either acids or salts which act as acids and usually only need to be added in proportions as low as 1% of the weight of the solid matter. There is no tendency to a reversal of the action with an increase in the proportion as happens with deflocculants.

Deflocculants tend to be alkaline and are used to increase fluidity by separating the particles. Increasing the proportion of deflocculant to clay material increases the fluidity until a point is reached when with further additions the action becomes reversed and the slip begins to thicken.

Casting slip

Casting slip is also a suspension of clay in water which must be able to flow readily into a mould without settling and to pour out again after leaving an even layer on the sides of the mould. To produce a smooth surface it should not have excessive shrinkage yet should have just sufficient to release the cast easily from the mould and should not wet the mould so much that there is difficulty in drying. A simple mixture of water and clay which will pour well will inevitably contain too much water to satisfy the criteria outlined above so it becomes necessary to produce a liquid which is sufficiently fluid to pour but has a much reduced water content.

Clay particles tend to gather together because of electrical attraction and this creates a tendency to form globules, called "flocks" in a slip. If this attraction is modified correctly then the clay can separate into individual particles so that they float separately instead of gathering into groups. The common method of achieving this situation is to introduce a small amount of alkali, often sodium silicate and/or soda ash, usually in equal parts of each. The ratio of the alkali to clay varies considerably from one type of clay to another but it often lies between one third and one half of one percent of the weight of the dry clay. The alkali is known as an electrolyte or a deflocculant and has the property of causing the particles to repel one another with the effect of reducing by about a half the amount of water needed to make a suitable slip. In other words, a casting slip of about the right consistency without an electrolyte would be about equal parts by weight of water and clay whereas with a suitable addition of electrolyte the proportion would be more likely to be something in the region of 35 to 50% of water to clay. As there is less water present, the density of the deflocculated slip will also be increased. A litre of untreated slip would weigh less than 1·5 kg whilst a deflocculated slip of similar fluidity could weigh up to 1·9 kg. Whilst such a slip might be used in industry, in small workshops it would be more likely to weigh about 1·75 kg. A well prepared casting slip needs to be sufficiently fluid to pour well, to be able to fill all the crevices in the mould and to take a good impression of the detail.

Some clays, particularly surface clays, will not deflocculate or will prove so difficult that they are unsuitable for making into casting slip. As there is no need for a clay to be used as a casting slip to be malleable, the basic dry material is often made up from a mixture of clays including just enough ball clay to give some strength, some feldspar to add flux, together with some flint and

A stoneware pot by Melanie Staniforth sprayed with three distinct layers of vitreous slip. The inner layer based on vanadium pentoxide has broken through the outer layers. Courtesy of Cumbria College of Art

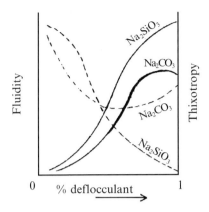

Graph to show fluidity/thixotropy versus % deflocculation

some fine grog to increase the hardness and the permeability. When mixed into a slip, it should be able to pass through a 120 sieve. The result should be sufficiently permeable to allow the plaster to absorb the water and should be able to produce a good ceramic body when it is fired.

In his book on ceramic faults, (A & C Black Ltd) a suitable starting recipe suggested by Harry Fraser, which works for many casting slips is to take:-
   10 kg of plastic clay
   10 to 25 grams of sodium silicate (140 Tweddle)
   10 grams of soda ash and
   850 cc of water.

If making up a slip using powdered clay then the recipe would be:-
   10 kg of powdered clay
   12 to 38 grams of sodium silicate (140 Tweddle)
   12 grams of soda ash and
   4 litres of water.

In industry the various materials and the amount of commercially prepared deflocculant required is calculated carefully.

In a small workshop it is still common practice to mix up a litre of thick slip without deflocculants and then to add small progressive quantities of deflocculant made up of 30 cc of sodium silicate (140 Tweddle), 30 grams of sodium carbonate and 60 cc of hot water, stirring well after each addition. The experienced potter will able to assess when the slip is right simply by testing it by dipping in a finger. The inexperienced person will almost inevitably add too much which rapidly reverses the effect and cause the slip to thicken quite quickly.

Hamer & Hamer in their excellent potter's dictionary suggest a simple method of finding the ideal quantities. They suggest that after each addition of the deflocculant, the litre of slip should be poured into a large funnel and allowed to run through into a suitable container. The time for the slip to clear the

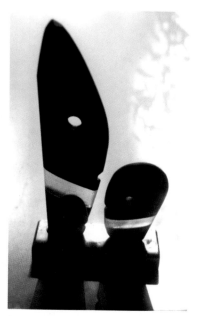

Family group, ceramics and glass, by the author

funnel is recorded each time. The times become shorter as the slip reaches its maximum fluidity and then begin to increase again as the action becomes reversed. The amount of deflocculant corresponding to the shortest time is usually the most suitable.

Many potters use the traditional deflocculant made from a mixture of sodium silicate and sodium carbonate and find it perfectly adequate. Occasionally there are clays, particularly those rich in calcium in which this mixture does not work very well and it then becomes necessary to change to sodium carbonate, to sodium tannate or to use one of the commercial polyacrylate deflocculants based upon sodium and ammonium which can be obtained readily prepared from specialist pottery suppliers. These commercial deflocculants offer other advantages. They do not attack the surface of the plaster moulds. There is much less tendency for the casts to distort and the prepared slip remains stable for a much longer time. Most casting slips, particularly those which have been deflocculated with sodium silicate and sodium carbonate will tend to thicken if left standing for more than a few days. The attraction of the particles seems to be successful in gradually resisting the action of the deflocculants and as a result they begin to move together again to form flocks. It then becomes necessary to stir them vigorously and to resist the temptation to add water. This action of changing the viscosity of a slip by leaving it to stand or by stirring it vigorously is known as "thixotropy". If the slip is left standing for a further length of time it will gradually form a gel but is still recoverable to the right consistency by applying some hard stirring action.

IV.
Fired clay

For many years the most common of the fired ceramic materials was "terra-cotta" which normally referred to the unglazed red-brown or grey ware, often coarse in texture, comprising flower pots, roof tiles, field drain tiles, etc. The porous nature of some low fired clays is often used to advantage in hot countries where the evaporation of moisture from the outer surfaces of vessels tends to keep the water or wine in the containers very cool.

If such bodies are intended to be used for the production of earthenware they are normally fired to temperatures of or just above 1100°C so that sufficient cristobalite is formed to exert a beneficial squeeze on the glaze as it cools down. This type of firing is known as bisque or bisc. If the bisque is to be used for stoneware, then it is usual to fire it to a lower temperature, about 1060°C, as the cristobalite is not needed and the extra porosity at this stage is useful as stoneware glazes tend to be applied thickly.

The names given to various types of fired clay may result from the temperature to which they are taken rather than the actual constituent materials. Most clay bodies contain amounts of alkali, alumina and silica in the form of clay, feldspar and quartz. During a firing, these materials change and interact considerably. The first of these changes occurs when the feldspar begins to melt and dissolve much of the quartz and some of the cristobalite formed during the initial break up of the kaolinite lattice. When the body has been fired until it becomes dense the formation of glassy particles gradually fills the pores. The clay particles also begin to shrink together.

The formation of small crystals of mullite also formed during the break up of the kaolinite lattice is enhanced by the various alkali oxides present. At this stage, the molten materials would only be sufficient to cement the solid materials together and if cooled, the resulting ware would be classified as earthenware.

If the materials are used to produce white ware, increasing the temperature of the firing to 1200–1250°C will result in the amount of molten materials being sufficient to fill the pores and make an impervious, dense form of pottery known as "vitrified hotelware" in Britain and as "vitreous china" in the United States and is a form of porcelain. Increasing the temperature even further causes the molten material to become more fluid and active to the extent that it dissolves most of the crystals of free silica. Clusters of needle shaped mullite crystals develop by growing into a glassy phase and if cooled at this stage a completely dense material is formed which is known as hard porcelain.

Terms tend to be interpreted rather widely and earthenware is a term used by studio potters to describe most glazed ware which has been fired to a temperature at which the clay body remains partly porous but is sealed with a glaze. This meaning is similar to that accepted in many countries but in indus-

Clay particles after low biscuit firing. They are held together by sintering where they touch each other and as a result the joint area is small and the ware is weak and easily broken. Biscuit ware usually refers to the clay bodies which have been fired to a condition in which they are hard but still sufficiently porous to accept a layer of wet glaze

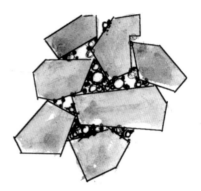

Biscuit in which there is sufficient cementing of the particles to give strength whilst retaining sufficient porosity to take a glaze

When the body has been fired until it becomes dense the formation of glassy particles gradually fills the pores. The clay particles also begin to shrink and fuse together After Hamer & Hamer, The Potters Dictionary, *A & C Black*

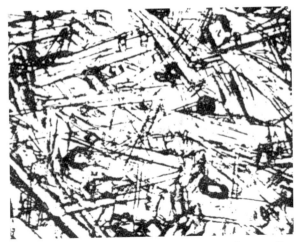

Micrograph of fused china clay, showing mullite needles
(The Effect of Heat on Ceramics, *W. F. Ford. P. Maclaren and Sons Ltd. 1967*)

try, particularly in Britain, it is a term more traditionally used to describe low fired white or cream ware which has a transparent glaze.

Red or grey clay which has been coated with a white opaque tin glaze, whilst it seems to fall into the general European description of earthenware, is usually called Majolica or Faience. These terms originate from the island of Majorca and the Italian town of Faenza where this type of ware started to be made towards the end of the fifteenth century. It tends to have a red porous body but occasionally can be covered with a white slip and a transparent glaze instead of the traditional opaque tin glaze.

The meaning of the term faience has been extended in Europe and now seems to embrace all the glazed porous bodied ware whether it be coloured or white. It is often a very popular base for potters to exploit their decorative skills as the white tin glaze is highly supportive of many kinds of on-glaze and lustre painting. The Dutch blue decorated tin glazed ware known as "Delft" has many similarities to Majolica but its basic body is much lighter in colour and so it tends to be categorised as earthenware. It is reputed to have resulted from early Dutch attempts to imitate Chinese porcelain.

The following are examples of prepared earthenware bodies taken from various sources (proportions by weight and as a percentage of the body):-

	(1)	*(2)*	*(3)*	*(4)*	*(5)*	*(6)*
Ball clay	48	25	26	30	25	60
China clay or Kaolin	24	25	26	25	25	
Cornish stone	24	20	18			
Flint	4	30	30	10		
Feldspar				25	30	10
Talc				10	20	30

It must be obvious from the table that there is a wide range of proportions used in the formulation of prepared bodies. Much of this depends on whether the resultant clay is intended for throwing, for production jiggering and jolleying processes or for casting. Some variation will also result from the nature of the materials used. English china clay tends to have little plasticity whereas some of the kaolins from the US are reasonably plastic. The cornish stone which features in many British recipes provides more silica than the common feldspars. Numbers (1) and (6) have a high content of ball clay which make them very plastic and are probably intended for throwing. They will, however, be subject to high shrinkage. The others are all fairly standard formulations, would not throw as easily as Nos (1) and (6) but could probably be used quite reasonably in this context and also for industrial-type production.

Stoneware

By far the most popular form of ceramic ware produced by studio potters is stoneware. Whilst earthenware has become almost wholly the prerogative of industry very little stoneware is produced industrially. This again is a term which is loosely interpreted. Some refer to it simply as ware which has been fired above temperatures of about 1200°C but this is an over-simplification as some stoneware is fired at temperatures little more than 1100°C, some of the red stonewares in particular being fired to temperatures lower than 1200°C. It tends to be ware which has most of its pores filled with glassy particles to the

White Ovoid Form *in stoneware by Hans Coper. From The Eagle Collection, The Shipley Art Gallery Gateshead, Tyne and Wear Museums. Private loan*

CERAMICS AND GLASS: A BASIC TECHNOLOGY

extent that it is either non porous or nearly so and in which the glaze and body have become sufficiently integrated for some of the character of the glaze to be produced by materials which have migrated from the body. The stoneware glazes tend to be hard and resistant to scratching. Stoneware is also often used as ovenware because it has a reasonably good resistance to thermal shock, has a strong impervious body, and because the glaze is not easily chipped. Basically it is a rather like a type of ball clay which has accumulated sufficient fluxing materials to produce glassy phases which fill or nearly fill the pores.

Many potters use suitable clay as found in particular localities to produce their stoneware and this accounts for much of the considerable variation in character which can be found in this kind of ware.

Another variation much exploited by studio potters lies in the possibility that unlike earthenware it can benefit considerably from firing in a reducing atmosphere.

The fact that it is not as porous as most other ware means that it tends to be heavy, often has a somewhat coarse body and is rarely delicate in form but offers the advantage of having greater mechanical strength than most other kinds of pottery and of offering the potter plenty of scope to introduce an element of individuality.

The following are examples of prepared stoneware bodies from various sources (proportions by weight):-

	(1)	(2)	(3)	(4)	(5)	(6)
Ball clay	32	40	38	15	30	30
China clay	32	10			40	
Cornish stone	32	50				
Quartz	4		4			
Fireclay			35			30
Silica sand			4			
Feldspar			5	10	15	
Red clay			14		5	10
Stoneware clay				75		30
Flint					10	

There is an even greater apparent disparity in the nature of prepared stoneware bodies than there is for earthenware bodies. Natural stoneware clay is often used as a basis for prepared bodies and this can vary substantially in both its nature and content. Again, ball clay is often added to improve plasticity, red clay added to give colour, coarse fireclay, sand and grog, etc, to give open textures and strength, particularly for making sculptural forms, and sometimes to increase the refractory qualities.

Feldspar and cornish stone provide the fluxes necessary to react with the silica to provide the glassy material which fills the pores.

Stoneware pot by Robin Welch, The Eagle Collection, Shipley Art Gallery, Gateshead, Tyne and Wear Museums. Private Loan

Porcelain

Porcelain is sometimes described as being a white translucent form of stoneware. It has similarities in that its pores become filled with glassy particles but both the composition of the body and the firing needs to be much more precise as it is very easy to produce a material which will slump and even melt if overfired. There are again differences in terminology in various countries which can cause some confusion. In Britain, the term "porcelain" usually refers to hard porcelain and the term "china" to bone china whereas in the United States "porcelain" tends to be used to describe vitreous technical ware and "china" is used to describe vitreous ware produced for domestic purposes.

In Europe, the position is not clarified and "porcelain" is often used to describe any white, vitreous and translucent ware.

Soft porcelain, sometimes known as soft paste porcelain is rarely made now. It had a lower firing temperature which tended to make the ware very brittle and the essentially high proportion of fluxing material in the body made production difficult.

Porcelain was developed by the Chinese, possibly in the ninth or tenth centuries BC and their success is often attributed to access to a particular white high firing clay which was also sufficiently plastic to be used for throwing purposes. There is, however, a body of opinion that the plasticity of the clay resulted from careful preparation and considerable ageing rather than from a

Translucent porcelain vessels with sandblasted decoration. Lorraine Wheatley
Courtesy of Cumbria College of Art and Design

natural plasticity. Another theory is that the plasticity resulted from the fine particle size of the local feldspar.

None of the European clays, such as the English china clays proved to be sufficiently plastic for throwing, so white or near white firing ball clays were mixed with them. The classical recipe for hard porcelain is 50% clay, 25% feldspar and 25% quartz but there are now many variations in these proportions.

Porcelain made for cooking tends to have more clay and less quartz whilst porcelain with a high degree of translucency usually has a greater emphasis on feldspar and quartz. In recent years small percentages of bentonite have often been introduced to increase plasticity.

Some feldspar and some quartz is usually part of a porcelain body, the feldspar melting early in the firing and dissolving some other materials to help to produce a white translucent ceramic form consisting of crystals of mullite, quartz and a little cristobalite, bonded together with glassy particles.

It has been described as being composed largely of masses of glass supported by crystals of mullite. Hard porcelain bodies which contain little or no free silica are now often deliberately produced to achieve a much stronger body. Similarly, crystalline fillers such as alumina and zircon have been introduced to improve the strength of modern porcelain bodies.

In the sixteenth century, the Medici managed to produce a form of porcelain from a mixture of glass frit and pottery It was sometimes known as milk glass and was difficult to fire successfully because it became so soft at its maturing tempera-

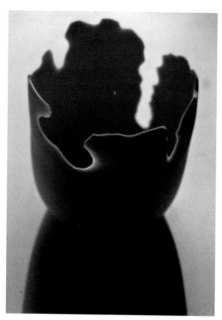

*Sandblasted porcelain vessel by the author showing a marked
degree of translucency on thin sections*

ture that it tended to sag or collapse. When China clay became readily available this type of frit porcelain soon faded out of the picture.

The following are examples of prepared porcelain bodies from various sources (parts by weight):-

	(1)	(2)	(3)	(4)	(5)	(6)
China clay or Kaolin	55	53	25	4	45	25
Ball clay			25	15	10	30
Feldspar	25	25	25	20	25	28
Quartz	15	17	25	20	20	17
Bentonite	5	5				

The proportions of materials used for porcelain are much more similar than those used for stoneware.

Plasticity is often introduced by including bentonite rather than ball clay. If the resulting colour is not critical, then ball clay, which will usually turn the porcelain a slightly cream colour, is often used. It is noticeable that the quantities of feldspar and quartz in these examples are reasonably similar.

One of the qualities most sought for in porcelain is translucency. This is generally considered to relate to the amount of incident light which is transmitted through the material but the amount of light reflected from the surface is also of considerable importance. There are wide variations of both these

Porcelain forms by Jasmine Jones. Courtesy of Cumbria College of Art and Design

qualities in types of porcelain but bone china tends to remain within close proportions of high transmission and high reflection and as a result is much more constant in its translucency.

The reason for the translucency of porcelain and bone china is that they are composed of crystals, glass and porosity all of which have different refractive indices. The smaller these differences are, the greater the translucency. The glassy phase is most important and a high glass content has a beneficial effect in porcelain. In order to achieve this, the ware is sometimes overfired about 150°C above its vitrification temperature or the proportions of feldspar and quartz are increased.

Perhaps surprisingly, bone china has a greater proportion of crystals and less glass than porcelain yet is consistently translucent. This is because of the smaller difference in refractive indices in bone china.

Paul Rado in his *Introduction to the Technology of Ceramics* gives a table which amply illustrates this. It shows the refractive indices of the constituents as:-

	Bone china	*Hard porcelain*
Glass	1·5	1·48
Quartz	-	1·52
Mullite	-	1·64
Anorthite	1·58	-
Beta-tricalcium-phosphate	1·62	-

This shows that the differences in the refractive indices of hard porcelain come to 1·6 whilst those in bone china are only 1·2.

*Bavarian porcelain body showing a nest of mullite needles
on the site of a feldspar grain surrounded by rounded quartz grains
and unresolved clay masses oriented in a flow structure (1000 ×)
(V. D. Frechette in Characteristics of Ceramics,
Eds L. L. Hench and R. W. Gould, Marcel Dekker Inc, 1971)*

Porcelain is famous for its whiteness and its translucency but it has other qualities which have proved to be extremely useful. It has a high resistance to chemical attack and this, togther with its fine surface and its ability to withstand high temperatures has made it a popular material for much laboratory ware. Its electrical qualities together with its inherent strength has also made it into a material in considerable use for insulators.

Mullite needles fulfil an important role in many ceramic bodies. They act as reinforcing bars in a similar manner to the carbon fibres used in making up racing car bodies or the steel rods used to reinforce concrete. They also act as a useful bonding agent between ceramic and glazes by penetrating both areas.

Bone china

This was developed by Josiah Spode (1754–1825) in order to produce a white translucent ware to satisfy the demand for something approaching the quality of Chinese porcelain. After considerable experiment he produced a body consisting of approximately 50% bone ash, 25% china clay and 25% feldspar.

This body when fired produced crystals of calcium phosphate, anorthite and calcium silicate. In contrast to most other ware bone china is first fired to a high temperature of 1250–1280°C. and then glazed at a much lower temperature of approximately 1060°C. The bone ash, which is produced from calcined cattle bones, is milled into fine particles containing much colloidal material. This colloidal material contributes some plasticity which despite the low clay content helps to produce a body which can be thrown relatively easily. A common myth about bone china is that it is a fragile material. This is not so and bone china is really considerably stronger than hard porcelain, having a chipping resistance about four times higher and a breakage resistance about twice that of porcelain.

The myth probably arises because bone china is often made in very delicate forms and because of its low clay content is certainly very fragile in the green, unfired state. It also suffers from the disadvantage of having a very narrow firing range which places critical demands on the kiln operations. When the ware is approaching 1260°C reactions take place very quickly and softening and distortion can soon occur. In order to counter this, ware is often packed for its biscuit firing onto powdered alumina. If on the other hand, the potter becomes too cautious to the extent that the ware is underfired, then there is an immediate loss both in translucency and strength.

Despite its considerable mechanical strength, bone china is not suitable for cooking. It has a high thermal expansion and its glaze is relatively soft. The reasons for its considerable fired strength are that bone china has a high proportion of crystals (about 70%) and because these crystals are substantially smaller than those in porcelain.

The following are examples of prepared bone china bodies:-

	(1)	(2)	(3)
Bone ash	40	52	49
China clay or Kaolin	32	24	25
Cornish stone	28	24	25
Ball clay			1

It is noticeable that in this case there is very little difference in the proportions. As bone ash provides some plasticity, ball clay is not often used. The small amount included in example (3) would hardly seem to be sufficient to be significant.

Parian ware
Parian ware was developed at the Spode factory in Stoke on Trent in 1844 and is basically a porcelain to which ground bone china and feldspar has been added to produce a soft paste, unglazed body much used for producing sculptural forms. It often contained small amounts of iron oxide to give the ware a creamy colour.

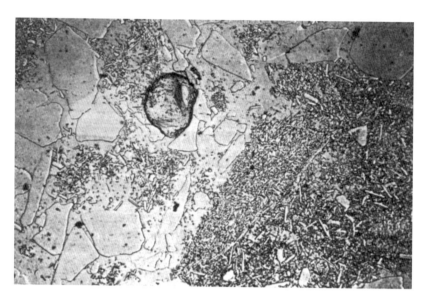

Electron photomicrograph of a porcelain body showing little quartz solution. The fine scaly material is primary mullite from the clay whilst the needles are secondary mullite, (×4000)
(Fine Ceramics, Technology and Applications, F. H. Norton, McGraw Hill, 1970)

Cooking ware

There have been several attempts at producing ware which will stand the thermal shock of being used in ovens for cooking and, generally speaking, despite being very near the edge, stoneware or porcelain will often suffice. Ware that will withstand the direct contact with a heat source is, however, a little more complex. Ware designed to withstand use in ovens has necessitated the production of porous bodies with low thermal expansion, often marketed as ovenware. This is not particularly difficult to achieve in industrial situations but one considerable difficulty lies in finding a suitable glaze of similar low expansion. Lithia based bodies made by mixing clay and petalite have a sufficiently low expansion to be used as ovenware. A suitable glaze needs careful consideration and application. A lithia/zinc oxide/alumina/silica glaze can be sprayed directly on to the green unfired ware as a very thin coat. This meets with some success but the firing temperature is critical and the subsequent heat management needs to be similar to that required for the production of a glass/ceramic material.

Another type of ware which is intended to be flameproof is cordierite porcelain. Unlike the lithia based ware, this is a nonporous body which is fired to temperatures around 1380°C and is made from a mixture of clay, alumina and MgO containing minerals such as talc. Cordierite has a formula of $2MgO.2Al_2O_3.5SiO_2$ and produces bodies with expansions of approximately 20×10^{-7}.

Again there is a difficult problem of finding a suitable matching glaze and in most cases it is necessary to resort to finding a solution in the range of glass/ceramic materials. For the craftsman, the production of this type of ware has particular difficulties in that the firing temperature is critical and slumping and melting can occur quite suddenly. A formula for this type of body is:-

Talc	24·4%
China clay	36·7%
Calcined china clay	36·7%
Barium carbonate	6·2%

The types of ware described above have been overtaken by developments in glass ceramics in which cooking ware can be made by normal glass production methods but then treated appropriately to change the glass into a glass ceramic.

The process is described further under "Glass ceramics" but it is relatively simple to produce ware with a very low expansion which does not need a glaze and will be able to withstand direct contact with a source of heat. The so-called ceramic hobs on cookers are an obvious example. Flame proof ware has been produced in this way for several years making the production of so-called flame proof ware in ceramic material less viable.

Salt or vapour glazed ware

This is a somewhat unusual technique and whilst it was once used considerably for the production of drain pipes and some domestic ware it is now only used by a few potters who specialise in this type of production. The body used is usually high in silica and often rich in iron oxide which acts as a flux and helps to develop a vitrified body. The technique works because of the action produced when damp salt, sometimes mixed with a small quantity of borax (up to 10%) and occasionally with some sodium nitrate is thrown onto the fire at particular stages in a firing, usually at temperatures between 1100°C and 1250°C. The soda vapour reacts with the silica and alumina on the exposed surfaces of the ware and forms a layer of soda–alumina–silica glaze. At the same time, chlorine and water vapour forms dilute hydrochloric acid fumes which are released into the atmosphere through the flues. The initial reaction is described as:-

$2NaCl$ (salt) $+ H_2O$ (water) $\rightarrow Na_2O$ (sodium oxide) $+ 2HCl$ (hydrogen chloride)

Three or four saltings per firing are usually required. When borax is used together with the salt it is often recommended to use salt alone for the first saltings, followed by a mixture of salt and borax or boric acid and completed with boron compounds alone 1100°C is considered the minimum temperature at which salt glazing can commence because steam does not react with salt vapour below this temperature.

The technique was popularly used for the production of domestic ware such as wine bottles and various storage jars in Germany in the 12th, 13th and 14th centuries. In areas where there was suitable fireclay such as along the Tyne

Typical salt glaze pot production at a former drainpipe factory at Bardon Mill

valley there was a considerable industry for the production of salt glazed drain-pipes, chimneys, etc. Some of the former drainpipe making factories such as that at Bardon Mill in Northumbria turned successfully to the production of salt glazed garden pots, bread crocks, etc, using local fire clay which contained some iron oxide to give a warm mottled brown colour to the ware when salt glazed drain pipes were overtaken by the production of plastic pipes. Tradi-tional brown or grey orange peel effects are not the only possibilities in salt glaze. Porcelain slips are often effective. Colours can be applied to the body in the form of oxides or as slips. Some individual potters have experimented with the technique and introduced various slips and silica rich materials such as rice ash to produce some very interesting ware. Fireclays rich in silica are the pre-ferred clays for salt glazing but other clays can often be modified to suit the technique. It is essential that there is sufficient free silica and some alumina so sometimes fine sand is added to a low silica clay to help to make it suitable for this process. Insufficient salt produces poor glazes whilst excessive amounts or a firing temperature which is too low often leads to white scum on the ware. Whilst salt glaze is much thinner than most other forms of glaze, when prop-erly formed it has excellent resistance to acid, alkalis and to crazing, making it ideal for drain pipes. As a process it offers the advantage of only needing one firing as the forms do not need to be biscuit fired.

The interior surfaces of ware other than those of shallow dishes need to be glazed as the salt rarely reaches these sufficiently to produce a glassy sur-face, though if the vapour does penetrate these applied glazes they will tend to become crazed because of the high expansion of the extra sodium oxide.

     Ceramics and Glass: a Basic Technology

Salt glazed jug in medieval style

They may also be sufficiently fluid that they run down vertical or near vertical surfaces.

Borax Consolidated in their book on Ceramic Glazes give the following details about the effect of iron in the clay body on to salt glazed ware:-

    0 to 2 percent iron oxide produces white to tan colours

    3·5 to 4·75 percent iron oxide gives browns

They also say that lime produces a greenish yellow glaze on high iron content clays. High lime clays may refuse to take a bright glaze at low temperatures and are best salted at high temperatures. High lime content in the clay tends to give a thicker glaze.

Up to 1·5 percent magnesia improves the glaze but when the content exceeds 3 percent there is dullness and a tendency to crystallise. Soluble calcium and magnesium salts tend to give dull, thin straw coloured glazes and the clay should be treated with barium carbonate to counter this effect.

Up to 5 percent titania improves the brilliance of the glaze. Addition of 2% zinc chloride to the salt is often effective in improving the glaze quality. Potassium chloride or lithium chloride is sometimes introduced in a similar manner.

Zelda Mowat who produced a lot of salt glazed ware at Harrow gives suggested some basic recommendations in an early edition of *Pottery Quarterly*:-

Tight packing offers the advantage of heat retention and slow cooling to give richer colour.

If the firing is helped by adding wood to the fuel the fly ash gives interesting emphasis when it settles on to some surfaces.

She estimated that 1 lb of salt per cubic foot of kiln capacity was about the correct amount.

Her firing strategy was:- Long slow firing
Long soak at high temperature
Long period of oxidation at the end of the firing whilst the temperature was still rising
Long slow cooling

The firing cycle was:- Oxidising up to 960°C
Light reduction to 980° C
Moderate reduction to 1100°C
Heavy reduction to 1140°C
Moderate reduction to 1250°C

Other potters recommend a quick cooling to 1080°C to avoid an excessive production of cristobalite.

Hamer & Hamer in their *Potter's Dictionary*, suggest experimental mixtures of 50% salt and 50% sawdust. They also suggest possible additions of small quantities of sugar or baking flour to aid reduction.

As the interior of the kiln tends to become completely covered by an ever thickening layer of set glaze, ware can be affected by blobs of molten glaze material dropping from the roof. To counter this it is normal practice to use high alumina firebricks or to coat the interior with alumina and to use high alumina kiln shelves where possible. Pots can also be seated on to coils of a mixture of high firing clay and alumina, dusted well with alumina on the surface to prevent pots sticking to the shelves.

When salt glazing is carried out on a relatively small scale as would probably happen in a studio or workshop there is always a potential danger from the fumes so it is essential that suitable precautions are taken to ensure that they disappear safely or are processed through a scrubbing system so that the fume is absorbed by water and then neutralised by being passed through some suitable alkaline material. On a larger scale, the fume seems to flow through tall chimneys into the atmosphere and seems to have no visible effect on either the surrounding vegetation or the people who work and live in the vicinity. Certainly the complex at Bardon Mill which operated for many years seems to have had no adverse effect and both population and the local plants seem to be

A blob of glaze material (called a "dropper") which has fallen from the roof of a kiln and settled on the side of a salt glazed pot

remarkably healthy. Despite this, and possibly because of concern about the acidic vapour release, an alternative process was developed in which sodium carbonate or sodium bicarbonate was substituted for the common salt. This became known as "soda glazing" and has become very popular, particularly in some areas of the US. There is still some release of volatile materials but as this consists mostly of small quantities of carbon dioxide it is insufficient to attract the attention of the environmentalists.

Again, an addition of about 10% borax is beneficial in reducing the temperature at which the soda can be used by about 80°C and also has the effect of enhancing some of the colour response and producing a smoother surface. The action of sodium carbonate is far less vigorous than that of salt which is very aggressive so spacing and placing of pots becomes important. Salt glaze and soda glaze are both colourless but a fine range of colours can be obtained by coating the pots with an appropriate coloured slip and by varying the reducing/oxidising atmosphere in the kiln. Whilst the danger from volatiles is comparatively small there is one feature which could have drastic consequences. The soda is often mixed with water and sprayed into the kiln through bung holes. If too much water is introduced at one time then the sudden production of large amounts of steam could result in a potential explosion from the rapid expansion. Some potters wrap up the soda in wet paper towels and feed these into the kiln at appropriate temperatures. There is obviously a great many possible variations in the method of introducing the soda. Another simple method is to place small fired pots containing the soda at strategic places in the kiln during the initial packing.

A salt glazed pot showing the typical orange peel effect

Potters interested in trying this system of glazing should read the very informative handbook on soda glazing by Ruthanne Tudball published by A & C Black and the University of Pennsylvania Press.

An interesting alternative to salt or soda glazing is suggested by W. G. Lawrence in his book *Ceramic Science for the Potter*. The introduction of zinc dust or flakes into the firebox towards the end of a firing will volatilize the metal to produce a yellow glaze over a blue body which results in a dark, greyish blue green colour.

Raku

Raku is a process for producing pottery which defies much of the normal established criteria. In its simplest form as practised originally by the Japanese it was a method of producing earthenware pots, especially bowls, for the tea ceremony. These pots were first biscuit fired, glaze was applied and dried. They were then plunged directly into a small, red hot updraught kiln. When the glaze was melted and the bubbles smoothed out into a glossy surface the pots were removed with tongs and cooled quickly, often by plunging them directly into water. The results had a lot of spontaneity and individual character because of the immediacy of the process. The Japanese tea bowls were made very simply by hand, had a quiet modesty and were very often endowed with a humble but dignified character which amply suited the occasions for which they were made.

The Raku process has been developed considerably in the west and the rapid achievement of the results has made it ideal as an activity which lends itself to social gatherings of potters. Almost any kind of clay can be used but it is essential to open the body by adding suitable materials.

These often include up to 40% of grog but fireclay, vermiculite and sand are also popular. Some potters prefer to introduce materials such as sawdust or ground vegetable matter which will burn out in the firing. Feldspar is also sometimes introduced to strengthen the body. Coarse fireclays are popular because they produce a strong texture yet in contrast some potters have been remarkably successful in using a fine porcelain body.

The initial biscuit firing is usually to about 900°C which produces a soft but open biscuit which will have a reasonable resistance to thermal shock, will accept a glaze but has allowed any volatiles which might have caused trouble in the glaze to be removed. Whilst such bodies are rather fragile they offer a great opportunity to develop oxidation, reduction, the possibilities of the effects of smoky fume and considerable variation in colour.

Virtually any studio type kiln will suffice but the most common is a simple cylindrical model, easily knocked together for the occasion out of part of an old oil drum and its lid, lined with ceramic fibre, and fired with a basic venturi gas burner. A popular alternative is to stand the pots to be fired on an insulation brick base but to then arrange the lined oil drum so that it can be lowered over the pots for firing and then lifted off easily when access to the pots is required.

The colour possibilities are very wide. Coloured slips, coloured bodies, colouring oxides and coloured glazes can all be used successfully. The glazes need to be low firing, ranging from 750°C to 1000°C and this helps to provide wide colour responses.

Lead, leadless and alkaline glazes are all in common use though in most countries it is necessary to use lead frits rather than raw oxides. It is also unwise to use lead based glazes if the firing is to be reduced. There is also an increased possibility of exposure to toxic fume if lead based glazes are used. It should also be remembered that low fired lead glazes, particularly if they are decorated with copper may not reach the required standards of lead release demanded by current legislation.

Some of the colour responses are:-

Iron	In a lead based glaze - yellow to brown
	In a borax frit glaze - greens and browns
	In a an alkaline frit glaze - blues and blacks
Cobalt	Blue in most glazes but a tends towards purple in alkaline glaze
Copper	Green in most glazes but moves towards turquoise in alkaline glaze Can produce reds in reduction
Manganese	Purple brown in most glazes but moves towards mauve in alkaline glaze
Tin	Opaque white in most glazes but reduction can produce lustred effects

Coiled earthenware pot with incised decoration. Raku fired at 770°C using low temperature frits. Dawn Campbell. Courtesy of Cumbria College of Art

The Japanese technique of allowing the glaze to settle and then dipping the pot into cold water produces very interesting crackled surfaces. Reduction is often achieved by allowing the glaze to settle, placing the pots in a shallow bowl containing sawdust or similar material, covering the pot with more sawdust and then taking out the pot and dipping it into water. The pots can just be left to cool in the sawdust and this produces rich black and blue-black areas on the unglazed surfaces.

Some potters produce lustred surfaces on raku pots. Whilst these can be very attractive, most of the materials used to produce this type of lustre release toxic fume so appropriate precautions must be taken. Alkaline glazes with additions of appropriate metal salts and heavy reduction also tends to produce rich lustred surfaces.

The salts used are:-

Silver nitrate	Yellows
Potassium dichromate	Greens
Copper chloride	Turquoise
Iron chloride	Ochres
Bismuth subnitrate	Mother of pearl

Raw glazed ware

Another type of pottery which at one time filled virtually the whole of small workshop production in Europe but is not so common now is raw glazed ware, sometimes known as "once fired" or "slip glazed" ware. Many common clays will melt if taken up to a sufficiently high temperature and some iron bearing clays were used to excellent effect in China to make slip glazes on a stoneware body. It was relatively easy to reduce the melting temperature of the iron bearing clays when necessary by introducing small quantities of fluxing material such as feldspar or wood ash. The colour of these glazes ranged from tan to black because of the iron and other metallic oxides present and many of the famous Chinese glazes such as tenmoku, oil spot, partridge feather and mirror black provided fine examples of raw glazing. As the name implies the glaze is usually applied to the ware before the clay has become dry, though in some instances, frit glazes with a low clay content are applied to a dry body. There is no separate glaze firing, the body and the glaze maturing together in the one firing and normally producing a matt or semi-matt surface. There are obviously considerable economic advantages in only firing once and in often being able to use cheap common clay as a glaze. There is also some technical benefit in that the body and glaze become well integrated.

The low clay glazes comprised mostly of frits together with some bentonite to help the glaze to stick to the pot are applied to dry ware. In contrast, the glazes applied to pots which are still drying have a high proportion of clay in them, which may be anything between 40 and 100%. It is possible to apply the glaze successfully by the usual means of pouring, dipping or brushing at almost any stage between the pot being strong enough not to collapse as the wet glaze is applied to one which is already leather hard but different clays respond differently and it is essential to run a test to find the right glaze consistency and the stage at which a particular clay can best be slip glazed. The slip can easily be applied too thinly or too thickly and as a result may flake off as it dries, may crawl, simply may not stick or may cause the pot to crack. These glazes usually have a wide firing range though some particular effects may need critical temperature control. They rarely form cracks or pits but may have a tendency to crawl.

Typical raw glaze recipes are:-

(1)	Common fusible clay	80%
	Iron oxide	5%
	Spodumene	15%
(2)	Common fusible clay	75%
	Iron oxide	5%
	Feldspar	10%
	Wood ash	10%

Raw glazing is most often carried out with stoneware or at least with ware which is to be fired over 1100°C. The rate of firing can also be critical in that work fired too quickly can easily result in work exploding and scattering broken pieces of glazed pot around the kiln where it can stick to the shelves or to other pots. Some slip glazes can be very fluid and form thick layers at the base of bowls, may tend to run on vertical surfaces and become thin on rims.

Egyptian paste

Materials for glazes tend to be those which are insoluble in water but there is one particular instance in which soluble fluxes are used. This is in making what is commonly known as Egyptian paste. It was used in ancient Egypt for producing beads, amulets and similar small objects.

A typical modern recipe for this material is by weight:-
20% ball clay (or china clay with some 2% bentonite)
35% feldspar (usually soda feldspar but potash feldspar is suitable)
35 % flint
10% soda ash

This material is a mixture of clay, soluble alkaline salts and small amounts of copper oxide or other suitable colouring oxide. It is mixed with water to form a modelling material and made into various forms. On drying the salts and metallic oxides migrate to the surface. When the forms are fired they flux the silica to produce a thin coloured glassy surface layer in the nature of a ceramic glaze.

The proportions can be varied. An open texture can be achieved by including some coarse sand. When too much flux is added or if the mixture is over-tired, this can lead to a complete collapse of the forms leaving a bubbly mess in the kiln.

As the fluxing material only migrates to the surfaces from which clay dries, the underside of objects resting on a kiln shelf or other flat surface will not develop a glaze but some form of separator is still advisable so the models are normally placed in a kiln on refractory powder, placing sand or a thin sheet of ceramic fibre for firing.

Firing is usually to between 850 and 950°C.

The technique became very popular a few years ago as a method of producing modelled objects which did not need a second firing to produce a glazed surface. This produced an advantage in saving kiln space. Beads are easily made and can be fired by being suspended on a suitable length of nichrome wire.

The traditional Egyptian rich turquoise colour results from an addition of about 2% to 4% copper oxide but other colouring oxides and stains can be used successfully. For example:-
0·5% to 2% of cobalt oxide will give a range of blues
2% to 4% manganese dioxide will give browns and purples
1% chrome oxide will give a pale yellow-green

The soda ash content can be reduced if the application of further glaze is preferred.

V.
The glass melting process

If sand, which is simply a form of granular quartz, is heated to a sufficiently high temperature it will melt and form a glass known as vitrified silica or silica glass. This is produced commercially for a variety of specific technical purposes, particularly for those which require a high resistance to thermal shock. In order to reduce this melting temperature to one that becomes commercially viable for glass or glaze making, a flux (network modifier) is added to the sand. This means that if soda ash is melted together with the sand to a temperature of about 1400°C in an inert refractory container it will form a molten glass. This happens because early in the process of heating the two materials, the soda ash (Na_2CO_3) melts and coats the grains of sand with hot liquid. At the same time carbon dioxide gas (CO_2) is given off leaving the alkali, sodium oxide (Na_2O) to attack the silica.

As a result, the solid silica surfaces provided by the hot sand are in contact with highly active soda. The reaction between the two causes some of the silica bonds to be broken, allowing some of them to react further with the soda. As two silica tetrahedra separate, the O_2 from the dissociated Na_2O very quickly occupies the vacant space between them and prevents the re-establishment of the silica–oxygen–silica bridge. Any adjacent oxygen atoms are then described as being "non-bridging".

Exactly the same process exists in glaze making except that the silica is likely to be introduced in the form of flint or quartz powder or together with some alumina and fluxing materials as part of one of the felspathic rocks.

In this manner there is a continuous process of opening up and loosening of the silica grains, allowing the alkali to have access to the underlying silica network and repeating the attack until all of the crystalline silica structure is destroyed. In its place is a fluid random network which is molten glass. The inclusion of the soda ash has resulted in a lowering of the melting temperature. It also means that in general, the more alkali that is included, the lower the melting temperature. It also means that some of the spaces in the glass become occupied by sodium atoms which restrict the possibility for the silica to vibrate freely. When the molten SiO_2–Na_2O is cooled fairly rapidly the random network does not have time to redevelop into organised crystal formations and retains its random nature to form a glass.

Potassium oxide (K_2O), usually introduced as potash, (K_2CO_3) has a fluxing action similar to that of soda ash and is often used as a total or partial replacement for the soda. Potassium has a similar electron configuration structure to that of sodium and the oxides produce similar chemical and physical properties, a similar fluxing action and similar effects on the finished glass. It is often introduced to a glass because it has the ability to enhance the refractive and reflective qualities.

A mixture of potash and soda in a glass batch also produces a material that is more resistant to corrosion than a glass containing just one of them. A glass which is just formed from a mixture of soda or potash and silica however, would not prove to be satisfactory in practice and would need to be stabilised.

In order to do this a stabilising element such as calcia which is also a modifier is usually introduced. As a result the glass becomes, (usually with a few additions), the soda–lime–silica glass from which most bottles, containers and windows, etc, are made. If calcia (CaO), often described as lime, is added to the soda in a batch, the atoms attach themselves to any detached silica atom which happens to become temporarily available. Calcium ions form non directional Ca–O bonds and the effect is to break down the continuous Si–O network. This has the effect of opening up the network further and as a result the lime acts as a flux in a similar manner to the soda. It also makes the resulting network much more stable. An excess of lime however, makes the molten glass very fluid but decreases the time available for working before it begins to harden. Unfortunately, it also gives the glass a tendency to devitrify. This is because the crystals which form $Na_2O.CaO.6SiO_2$, and called devitrite have a bond energy which is low in relation to the molten glass from which they separate. In the case of a glaze however, the extra calcia can be readily accommodated as the crystal formations which develop are of considerable importance in forming various opaque glazes. The glaze also has a considerable physical advantage in being bonded to a ceramic form.

Other fluxing materials such as lead oxide, magnesium oxide and barium oxide operate in a similar manner to calcium oxide in that they also act as stabilisers but also introduce their own particular qualities. For instance, magnesium oxide is often introduced into a glaze because of the smooth, buttery quality it produces. In window glass production where it is introduced, usually in the form of dolomite which also introduces some calcia, it is considered to improve weathering qualities.

VI.
Glass constituents

It has already been established that the various minerals needed to make glass fall into the categories of glass formers and glass modifiers.

Glass formers need to be able to enter a tetrahedral arrangement with oxygen similar to that described for silica or are like boron which enters into a triangular co-ordination with three oxygen atoms. They must be able to form a very strong element–oxygen bond and must also be able to enter into a situation in which the oxygen atoms link to no more than two glass forming elements (cations) but can link glass forming elements to other elements. This property becomes important in the matter of linking the glass formers to the modifying materials in the glass and also in linking glass either in the form of a glaze to the surface of a pot or when forming vitrified areas within stoneware and porcelain. Silica is the major glass former in almost all commercial glass and is used in large quantities around the world particularly for making the soda–lime–silica glass which is used for bottles and windows, etc. It is also the major glass former used in making glazes and in the glassy material which fills the pores of fired pottery.

Another glass former is boric oxide (B_2O_3) which is often used to replace some of the silica in a type of glass known as borosilicate. Boric oxide is specially introduced to facilitate melting operations and to develop properties such as resistance to chemical attack and to both thermal and physical shock. It helps to produce scratch resistant surfaces but tends to attack furnace refractories It is also used in glazes to help the melting and in achieving a glaze which will fit a particular ceramic. The glass formers are now more commonly described as "network formers" because they are capable of linking their atoms together very strongly to form a continuous three dimensional network.

Other minerals which form part of a glass batch are generally known as network modifiers and their function is either to help the melting process by acting as fluxes or to produce some beneficial effect on the finished glass. They are unable in the absence of a glass former, to make a glass. Other minerals, called intermediates, also cannot form a glass independently, but their atoms enter into a network and become part of it. They can also have a network modifying role. The chief network modifiers acting as fluxes are soda (Na_2O), potassium oxide or potash (K_2O) and occasionally lithia (Li_2O). These are alkalies and are usually used in conjunction with the alkaline earths, the most common of these being calcia (CaO) and magnesia (MgO). Zinc oxide is also used occasionally. The calcia, magnesia and zinc oxide also act to improve the chemical stability of the glass.

The chief intermediates are alumina and lead oxide. The lead oxide acts both as a flux and opens up the network. It enhances the optical properties, particularly the refractivity and reflectivity of the glass. Alumina has the effect of suppressing devitrification, increasing the working temperature range, raising the viscosity of the glass and produces glass of high durability. In a glaze this becomes particularly useful in helping to prevent the glaze from running on vertical or near vertical surfaces. It has an important role in the manufacture of many refractories.

The crystalline forms of silica and the silicates, in common with other crystalline materials have specific melting points but when they have been used in the manufacture of a glass they change into a material which softens over a range of temperatures because varying amounts of energy are required to break down parts of the random network at different stages. The silica does not recrystallise on cooling because its viscosity becomes too great to allow the necessary movement within the network for ordering to take place. Whilst a glass retains the random network and some of the character of a liquid it assumes a solid form which is often far more rigid than that of many other solids These network modifiers tend to occupy the voids in the random silica network forming non-directional bonds. This has an important impact on the resulting physical properties of the glass.

Network modifiers

The extent to which the modifiers fill the voids also has considerable effect on the ability of the glass to resist thermal shock. If a material is heated, the atoms vibrate increasingly violently according to the amount of heat energy which they absorb. In the case of vitrified silica which has no other elements to fill the gaps in its network the atoms can vibrate merrily with little necessity to expand to accommodate the amount of movement. On the other hand when the voids are cluttered with modifiers, these, dependent on their size, have very little space in which to vibrate and it becomes necessary for the glass to expand to allow this to happen. This accounts for the fact that glass with a high proportion of soda to silica tends to have a high coefficient of expansion whilst a glass with boric oxide filling the role of a flux and needing comparatively little soda or potash will tend to have a low coefficient of expansion.

These qualities become very important when considering the suitability of a glass for a particular purpose and when calculating the batch contents of a glaze to ensure that it will fit the ceramic body to which it is to be applied. The viscosity of types of glass varies greatly with temperature so the achievement and awareness of this quality affects much of the making and forming activity.

Viscosity of a glass at a particular temperature is strongly dependent on its composition and this allows considerable latitude in the possibility of designing a glass for a specific purpose. For example, fused silica is melted at a high temperature, has excellent resistance to thermal shock but because of its high melting point cannot be worked by hand. In contrast, lead glass tends to have a high density, melts and can be worked easily by hand at comparatively low temperatures and has a high refractive index making it eminently suitable for high quality decorative ware and some optical glasses.

The viscosity of glasses are very temperature dependent and are greatly affected by composition. Some of the points on a temperature/viscosity scale are often quoted so the following table will give some indication of the meaning of the various terms:-

Melting point	The temperature at which the glass is sufficiently fluid to be considered a liquid.
Working point	The temperature at which a glass is easily deformed.
Softening point	The temperature at which a glass can be handled without causing significant changes in dimension.
Annealing point	The temperature at which atomic diffusion is sufficiently rapid for residual stresses to be removed.
Strain point	At temperatures below this point fracture will tend to occur before there is any plastic flow. The transition point will be above the strain point.

VII.
Raw materials for glass and glaze

A noted technologist once made an interesting comment to the effect that the six elements most used in glassmaking and ceramics namely, O, Si, Al, Ca, Mg, Na are amongst the eight most commonly occurring in the earth's crust, oxygen being by far the most common. When these elements occur together in various rocks, silica and alumina become the most prolific of the solid materials.

Mixtures of various mineral oxides are used to form glass and glazes and when prepared for founding or for application to a ceramic body they become known as "batch".

At least one of these oxides must be what is known as a "glass former" or "network former" which when heated sufficiently will become molten and then retain its properties as it sets into a glass.

Many of the batch materials also fulfil a dual role in the process of making a glass or a glaze and can often act as a network former as well as acting as a network modifier.

As previously stated the glass formers enter a tetrahedral arrangement with oxygen atoms as described for silica with the exception of boron which enters a triangular co-ordination with three oxygen atoms. They must be able to form a very strong element–oxygen bond and must also be able to enter into a situation in which the oxygen atoms cannot bond to more than two glass forming elements but can link glass forming elements to other elements. This property becomes important in the matter of linking the glass formers to modifying materials in the glass and also in linking glass in the form of a glaze to the surface of a pot or when forming vitrified areas within various ceramics.

There are few minerals which have the property of forming a glass and the best known and most used of these is silica. Others commonly used in glassmaking are boric oxide, arsenic trioxide, antimony trioxide and phosphorous pentoxide but these are rarely used for their glass forming ability and are introduced for their other properties. For instance, boric oxide also acts as a strong flux and is introduced mainly because of its potential for creating a glass with a low coefficient of expansion and a good resistance to both thermal and physical shock. Arsenic trioxide and antimony oxide are used in small quantities as refining agents, helping to clear the glass of small bubbles (seeds).

Arsenic trioxide and phosphorous pentoxide when dispersed in a molten glass tend to separate into discrete particles which scatter the incident light to produce a white opalescent effect. Arsenic trioxide is most unlikely to be used in a glaze because of its toxicity. Other glass formers which may be introduced for other reasons are antimony oxide, germanium oxide and selenium oxide.

There are some differences in the minerals used to make glass and those used for producing a glaze.

As those used in making a glaze slip must be materials which can be suspended in water without becoming dissolved several materials such as sodium carbonate, potassium carbonate and many of the minerals supplying boric oxide which are commonly used in glassmaking but are introduced as dry powders are unsuitable for glazes because they are soluble in water.

When the oxides from these materials are required for a glaze they are usually introduced in an insoluble form such as one of the many feldspars or as one of the specially prepared frits (see page 27).

A glaze is simply a layer of glass bonded to a ceramic substrate but whilst the silica in a glass is almost always introduced as sand. In a glaze it is much more likely to come from silica containing materials such as clay, feldspar, calcined flint or occasionally, wood ash. This tendency runs throughout the range of materials used for glass or glaze batch. Those introduced for making glass are likely to be straightforward oxides or carbonates of particular elements whereas those used for making glazes, whilst providing similar oxides, are likely to be part of much more complex natural materials. This difference in approach lies very much in the dictates of the practicalities involved but there is also a certain amount of background philosophy. The major concern over the centuries has been for glassmakers to produce glass which exploits the qualities of transparency, light, colour and refractivity. In order to do this successfully with any consistency the materials used have needed to be as simple and pure as possible.

In contrast to this, in ceramics, particularly in small scale production there has developed a tradition which originated in China, Korea and Japan of exploiting the subtlety and the possibilities offered by the considerable mix of elements in the raw materials available, particularly when considering colour and surface quality. Glassmakers on the other hand have sought to use iron free materials wherever possible in order to produce a clear brilliant and colourless glass whereas in ceramics, particularly in the Far East and in much modern stoneware and porcelain, iron, either by migrating from the clay body, by being part of the glaze raw materials or even by deliberate application as decoration has played a major part in ceramic glazes. The celadon glazes all relied on iron modified by small quantities of so-called impurities such as titanium dioxide, manganese dioxide and phosphorous pentoxide to provide the subtle colour associated with this type of glaze. The black/brown glazes known as Tenmoko and Chien all relied heavily on natural iron bearing materials.

Silica

Silica is the major glassformer in almost all glass and is used in large quantities around the world, particularly for making soda–lime–silica glass which is used for bottles and windows. It is also the major glassformer used in making glazes.

It is normally used in proportions of between 50% and 80% of a glass or glaze batch and in glassmaking is usually introduced in the form of sand. This sand is usually subject to tight specifications because it is essential to ensure in most production that it is as free from iron or chrome oxides as is possible. Both of these oxides have a considerable effect on the colour of the resulting glass so much of the sand which is used today has to be treated chemically in a hot acid leach process in order to ensure that it is of a suitable standard.

Boric oxide

The other common glassformer, boric oxide was used in glazes by the Romans, probably derived from some form of borax, but was not used to any extent in glassmaking until the mid-Eighteenth century when large deposits were discovered in California. There is a two fold advantage in that as well as acting as a glassformer, boric oxide also functions to some extent as a flux by reacting with the silica and with the other batch materials to lower the overall melting temperature. The most common source of boric oxide are: borax (hydrated borax), borax (anhydrous), boric acid and fused boric oxide.

Hydrated borax contains approximately 36·5% boric oxide, 16·25% sodium oxide and 47·25% water.

On heating this rapidly turns into anhydrous borax which will melt on its own to form a clear glass at 740°C (1365°F). These materials are usually turned into a frit whenever boric oxide is needed for a glaze as most of the minerals used to supply boric oxide tend to be soluble in water. They may, however, be used successfully in glassmaking where the release of considerable amounts of steam can be an advantage as it helps to provide a stirring action in the melting process. In a glaze it would probably cause glaze material to be thrown from the surface of the ceramic body. Such material arriving on to a kiln shelf would create pockets of glass.

This is particularly common when a sufficiently high proportion of colemanite which is a naturally occurring form of calcium borate $(2CaO.3B_2O_3.5H_2O)$, is introduced into a glaze batch to provide boric oxide. This material is varied in its composition but usually has a high water content and has become noted for its tendency to cause spitting of glaze material from the ceramic body on to kiln shelves or on to adjacent forms so it would be prudent to use this in small quantities or to replace it with a calcium borate frit.

Anhydrous borax (also known as dehybor, sodium biborate or sodium tetra-borate) is generally preferred for glassmaking because of its reduced bulk. Both forms of borax contribute some sodium oxide in addition to the boric oxide. If the sodium oxide is not required, boric oxide can be introduced in glassmaking in the form of boric acid or as fused boric oxide. In modern ceramic glazes it has become normal practice to introduce boric oxide as part of a commer-cially prepared frit, some examples of which are described later.

Network modifiers

The other minerals which form part of a glass or glaze batch are generally known as network modifiers and their function is either to help the melting process by acting as fluxes or to produce some beneficial effect on the finished glass. They are unable, in the absence of a glassformer, to make a glass. Other minerals, called intermediates, also cannot form a glass independently, but their atoms enter into a network and become a crucial part of it. The chief network modifiers acting as fluxes for both glass and glazes are sodium oxide, potassium oxide, lead oxide and occasionally, lithia. Lithia is a strong flux but additions to a batch need to be kept as low as 1% because of a tendency to attack the furnace refractories. These are all classified as being alkalies and are used in conjunction with the alkaline earths, calcia and magnesia to improve the chemical stability of the glass. Zinc oxide is also used for the same purpose but not to the same extent. It is often introduced to a studio glass batch to replace some of the calcia in order to make the glass long working and into glazes as a matting agent.

The chief intermediates are lead oxide and alumina and whilst titania, zirconia and stannic oxide can be technically classed as intermediates they are unlikely to be used simply in this context.

Lead oxide acts both as a flux and as a material which opens up the network. It enhances the optical properties, particularly the refractivity and reflectivity of the glass and provides a soft brilliant material which is conducive to the processes of cutting and engraving.

Alumina has the effect of suppressing devitrification. In small quantities it reduces the melting point of a soda–lime–silica glass and also has the property of increasing its viscosity. In a glaze this proves particularly useful in helping to prevent the glaze from running off vertical or near vertical surfaces. Alumina is a major constituent of most glazes because of this quality whereas in a glass it is usually restricted to less than 2% of a batch. When more alumina than this is introduced into a normal type of glass batch for hand working the increased viscosity tends to make the glass difficult to form without resource to constant reheating.

There are glasses, however, which have been specially formulated to accept a very much greater percentage of alumina. These are the so-called "alumina glasses" made for specific purposes which require a very high resistance to thermal shock. These are unlikely to come within the scope of the small studio or workshop glassmaker because of the high founding temperatures required.

It can be introduced into a glass as hydrated or calcined alumina, as part of one of the many feldspathic rocks or as part of the blast furnace slag, prepared and sold commercially as "Calumite" which is usually introduced as a refining agent. Nepheline syenite is the feldspathic material most likely to be used to introduce alumina into a glass batch as many of the others tend to be contaminated with iron. In glazes alumina is also introduced as a constituent of feldspar or similar material but it is often added simply and conveniently as a constituent part of clay.

Sodium oxide is by far the most common flux used in making glass but probably takes second place to potassium oxide in glazes. In glass, sodium oxide is usually introduced as sodium carbonate (soda ash) and has been the major fluxing material from the earliest glassmaking activities when it was introduced as the natural mineral natron and as the ash from burnt seaweed and marsh plants. It is now produced chemically, mostly from common salt and is a powerful flux which generally produces a glass with a high coefficient of expansion. A once popular source of sodium oxide was saltcake (sodium sulphate) which was available cheaply from the manufacturers of sulphuric acid. Its major use in glassmaking, however, was as a refining agent which was used to remove the silica scum from the surface of molten glass.

In glazes, sodium oxide is normally introduced as part of soda feldspar or similar materials such as cornish stone. The sodium carbonate used in glass-making would be unsuitable as it is soluble in water.

Potassium oxide is the second most popular glass flux and is often used in conjunction with lead oxide in the crystal industry as it improves the brilliance of the glass and gives higher electrical resistance than soda ash. It is normally introduced into glass as potash (potassium carbonate) but in glazes it is usually introduced as potash feldspar or as wood ash. Much of its early use in glassmaking was also in the form of wood ash as it was convenient to use this material which became available in quantity from the firing of the furnaces and accounted for much of the colour and character of the so-called waldglas or forest glass which was produced throughout Europe. Unfortunately, the ashes from some trees were not as good as others and produced forms of glass which over the years have proved to be somewhat unstable. Potassium carbonate is now manufactured from potassium chloride which can be found naturally in large quantities.

Lead oxide has a long been an important and strong, high quality flux in glazes but perhaps surprisingly it never reached any real consequence in glassmaking until George Ravenscroft developed its potential in the early part of the 17th century. Since then it has become highly regarded as being an essential component of most high quality glassware and much optical glass. Recently, however, it has suffered some notoriety both as a glaze and as a glass material because of the on-going concern with toxic metal release and as a result of this there has been much research into possible replacements that will offer similar qualities. Barium carbonate became a popular replacement until it was realised that this material was equally toxic. In glaze making, lead oxide is not generally permitted in its raw or in its carbonate form and must be introduced as part of a suitable low solubility frit. In the latter part of this century lead oxide has found a new role by being introduced in high proportions into glass to absorb radiation in the nuclear industry.

Lithium oxide is not used to anything like the same extent as soda and potash because of its apparent expense and its tendency to attack furnace refractories but it does have special qualities of reducing melting and working temperatures and provides some interesting colour responses. Its strength as a flux is sufficient to mean that the quantities required are somewhat lower and this can go some way in negating its apparent high cost.

It is a common material in many glass-ceramic batches where it supports the formation of crystalline material. It can be introduced as lithium carbonate, but particularly in glazes, is more likely to be introduced as part of one of the lithium feldspars such as lepidolite or petalite.

Stabilisers

Other materials have a role as stabilisers. In the right proportions, they help to increase the resistance of the glass to the actions of decay and devitrification. They often help with the fluxing action and, particularly in glazes, they are often introduced in quantity to provide a useful range of matt and crystalline effects. The most common of these stabilising network modifiers is calcium oxide. This is produced mainly from limestone and limespar and is normally introduced into a batch in the form of calcium carbonate. It is in plentiful supply though many of the mineral deposits tend to be contaminated by iron oxide and need to be chemically treated before use. In commercial glass production it can be included in amounts up to 10% but as quantities over about 5% start to shorten the working life of the glass it is often replaced in part in studios and workshops by zinc oxide. In amounts over 10% it starts to reverse its stabilising properties and starts to encourage devitrification.

This can be devastating in commercial glass production but is turned to advantage in some glazes where amounts of up to 25% are often deliberately introduced so that the crystalline properties can be developed to form a range of what have become known as lime matt glazes. In both glass and glazes it is often introduced in the form of dolomite, a material which produces a mixture of calcium and magnesium carbonates.

Magnesium oxide is also a stabiliser and helps to prevent devitrification but as with calcia, when introduced into a glaze in quantity either as dolomite or as magnesium carbonate, matt glazes can result. In a glass it is said to improve the weathering qualities. It is usually used particularly in the flat glass industry together with lime, often in the form of dolomite.

Another stabilising oxide is that of barium. Similarly it is normally introduced in the carbonate form which can be found as the natural mineral witherite but is more often produced commercially from barytes (barium sulphate) which is much more readily available. It is being used increasingly as a replacement for lead oxide in optical and other glasses in which a high refractive index is required and started to become very popular as a glaze material because of the interesting and unusual colour responses it generated, particularly in matt glazes, but as its toxicity has now become recognised, it has been banned from use in some areas such as schools and colleges.

Cast sculpture in lead crystal

Refining agents

Some materials are introduced as refining agents. They provide a stirring action in the molten glass by producing large bubbles which collect small ones on the way to the surface. This removes seed and helps to form a homogenous glass. These materials also often provide dual roles in acting as accelerators and decolourisers.

Arsenic trioxide has been the accepted refining agent for many years but is now being replaced to some extent by antimony oxide. Both materials are very toxic and must be handled accordingly. They are both used in conjunction with nitre. Sodium sulphate (saltcake) and barium sulphate have also been used as refining agents from time to time and the slag from blast furnaces marketed as Calumite is now proving to be a popular refining agent, used together with anhydrite in commercial production in situations in which the iron content does not prove to be a problem.

Glaze materials

The various minerals used for making glazes are rarely simple and as a result are often given a theoretical formula on which the glaze recipe is based. It is common practice amongst potters touse remarkably simple basic glaze recipes and because of the considerable variety in the content of the materials designated, results based on the same recipe can easily be found to be vastly different from one studio to another. For example, a glaze recipe could be as bland as being quoted as one part of clay, one part of feldspar, one part of wood ash and one part of limestone.

Blown form with sandblasted decoration

Whilst limestone could safely be considered to be calcium carbonate with traces of metal oxides, all the others are materials of considerable variation and even theoretical formulae often given for clay and feldspar are likely to be very different from the actual material. At least a theoretical formula will give sufficient of an approximation to produce something vaguely in common to that described which an experienced potter can then modify as necessary.

Wood ash on the other hand is even more wildly varied and a change of type of ash can change the character of a glaze completely. One type of ash for instance, contains approximately 80% silica whilst there are others that have practically no silica at all. Another complication in acquiring and using wood ash is that like clay or some of the minerals, there are differences in materials from different sources. Plants of the same species will inevitably show some differences in the ashes they produce when grown on different soils but despite this there is a considerable amount of similarity which would suggest that a plant uses a considerable degree of selectivity in what it uses to form its individual structure. Wood ashes have always played a prominent part in oriental glazes and this tradition has been maintained and cultivated by many contemporary potters. The fact that they usually contain a rich and complex variety of fluxes together with some alumina and silica, colouring oxides and opacifying material such as phosphorous pentoxide and titanium dioxide means that many of them contain all that is necessary to make a form of glass or glaze.

This wide variety of fluxes means that wood ash helps to produce a continuous melting process as bonds are being broken and realigned over a wide range of temperatures. When the plant material is burned to form ash it leaves a mixture of carbonates, sulphates and oxides together with some residual carbon. This is usually washed, sieved and dried to form a glaze batch material. The amount of washing can have a crucial effect on the nature of the ash as several of the salts, particularly potash, are soluble in water and tend to disappear or be substantially reduced in the washing process. This is just what is required for a glaze material but when being used for a glass, it is the potash

Stoneware pot with wood ash glaze

that is the most important part so it is essential that this is retained or even recovered from a washing process. As glass batch is concerned with dry or nearly dry materials the presence of soluble materials is not so important.

Another complication in acquiring and using wood ash is that like clay or some of the minerals, there are differences in materials from different sources. Plants of the same species will inevitable show some differences in the ashes that they produce when grown on different soil but despite this there is a considerable amount of similarity which suggest that a plant uses a considerable amount of selectivity in what it chooses to form its individual structure.

An analysis of the oxide provided by two different plant ashes is shown below:-

	(1)	*(2)*
Silica	33	78
Alumina	22	9
Iron oxide	2	3
Calcia	11	4
Magnesia	5	2
Potash	9	2
Soda ash	5	1
Phosphorous pentoxide	13	1
Titania	trace	

It must be obvious that a glaze made from a recipe which simply gives a bald statement such as "wood ash - 3 parts" can easily bear little resemblance to its description. The experienced potter can overcome this as a fund of awareness of the behaviour of his materials will have been built up and from a few simple tests will be able to modify the glaze to satisfy the necessary criteria.

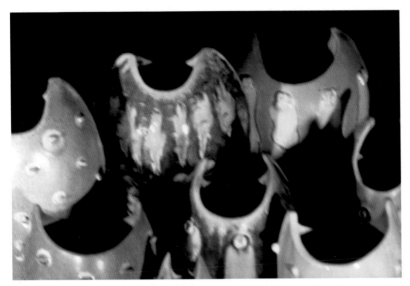

Coiled porcelain forms with glass incorporated into the clay structure. Sabrina Ramsay.
Courtesy of Cumbria College of Art and Design

Somebody with little experience will almost certainly find some difficulty but may be lucky and may even find something better than that expected. At least the potter can make up small quantities of glaze and produce a range of test tiles without much trouble. The glassmaker, whilst if he has sufficient crucibles can melt tests of glass batches, does not have access to such a simple procedure as that available to the potter.

Wood ash played a significant part in medieval glassmaking and the colour, usually greens or ambers and occasionally brownish purples resulted from the types of wood and the firing. Unfortunately, the high lime and potash content of the wood ash often created glass which was far from durable.

Glaze frits

Some glaze materials for various reasons cannot be incorporated into a basic glaze slop. In this case two or more materials are melted together and then reground to a suitable particle size. For instance, lead oxide, cadmium salts and barium carbonate, because of their toxicity, are not permitted to be used in many countries'so it becomes necessary to buy commercially prepared frits which incorporate such materials. They are usually combined with sufficient silica to make the resulting material have a very low solubility. Further major advantages with this process are that there is a much reduced problem with siliceous dust.The resulting frit would be likely to be of more consistent quality than would be the case when using raw materials, the glaze would melt and fuse more readily, potentially dangerous and difficult volatiles would have been removed in the fritting and the likelihood of blistering of the glaze would be reduced.

Working temperature ranges of glaze oxides

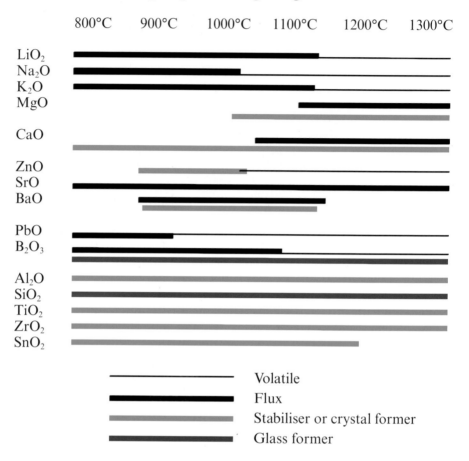

| | 800°C | 900°C | 1000°C | 1100°C | 1200°C | 1300°C |

LiO_2
Na_2O
K_2O
MgO

CaO

ZnO
SrO
BaO

PbO
B_2O_3

Al_2O
SiO_2
TiO_2
ZrO_2
SnO_2

———————————— Volatile

———————————— Flux

———————————— Stabiliser or crystal former

———————————— Glass former

Another major reason for fritting is to make soluble minerals into materials which are insoluble in water. There are several of these soluble minerals. The most important are the various soluble forms of soda and the materials supplying boric oxide. There is one common mineral which is insoluble and which will provide boric oxide. This is colemanite and this cannot be used in quantity without being calcined because in its raw state it contains a very high proportion of water. Glazes incorporating both lead oxide and boric oxide are quite common and very often this means that a glaze could contain a mixture of two frits, thus simplifying the glaze recipe considerably.

VIII.
Glass—a general classification

There are three common types of glass in general use. They are:-
Soda–lime–silica glass
Lead glass or lead crystal
Borosilicate glass
None of these are likely to consist solely of the materials implied in the names. They are all likely to have various important, but probably minor quantities, of other materials in their constitution. For example, they will all contain small quantities of alumina. Lead silica glass will also be almost certain to contain some potash. Soda–lime–silica glass used for windows will probably contain some magnesia.

Soda–lime–silica glass forms by far the greatest proportion of the glass used today and includes in particular window glass, bottle and container glass, and the cheaper types of table and decorative ware. A typical recipe for a soda–lime–silica batch for bottles and containers would be:-

SiO_2	70%
Na_2O	23%
CaO	5%
Al_2O_3	2%

Lead silica glass this includes all the varieties of lead crystal and is mostly used for more expensive table ware, cut and engraved glass, much of the work made by studio glassmakers, some types of optical glass and the high lead glass with

A typical lead crystal drinking glass, cut and polished

*A block of full lead crystal with inclusions by
Oiva Toikka ground and polished*

a high resistance to radiation used in the nuclear industry to provide viewing possibilities.

A typical recipe for lead crystal would be:-

SiO_2	56·6
Al_2O_3	1·4
PbO	29·0
Na_2O	4·25
K_2O	8·25

Borosilicate glass this is used mostly for the manufacture of laboratory equipment, the chemical industry, heat resistant cooking and table ware, and for pieces produced by studio lampworkers and individual craftsmen.

A typical recipe for a low melting borosilicate glass suitable for handworking would be:-

SiO_2	66
B_2O_3	22·7
Al_2O_3	4·5
Na_2O	6·8

The necessary calculations for turning the recipes into batch quantities are given in the next Chapter under the heading of "Batch calculations."

There are many other types of glass made for specific purposes which form only a tiny proportion of world production. They include optical glass, solder glass which is designed to fuse to metals, armour glass, infrared and ultraviolet control architectural glass and the coloured glass used for stained glass windows.

The raw materials for making glass when mixed together to be introduced into a furnace are known as batch. In common with ceramic products these raw materials in earlier times all consisted of minerals used largely as they were found and mixed with ashes from the burning of various plants. Nowadays, similar minerals tend to be used but they are commercially prepared to acceptable standards of content and consistency. Some batch materials are also manufactured rather than found.

Plant ashes are very rarely used commercially and are now only likely to be used experimentally by a few individual craftsmen in glassmaking. They are, however, a common constituent of ceramic glazes. Where, by virtue of the wide range of oxides and salts contained, they provide much of the character of a glaze, some of the necessary fluxing action and the promotion and growth of crystalline effects.

Glass is also classified according to its optical properties. It is broadly divided into two categories "Crown glass" and "Flint glass." Unfortunately, these two terms also mean different things to various people To the artist and the historian the crown glass refers to sheets of glass made by spinning out bullions and then cutting them into panels. Flint glass is a term which originated with the early experiments by George Ravenscroft to reproduce the Venetian Cristallo. In the early attempts he used calcined flint pebbles and this created the name. He later introduced lead oxide and substituted sand for the pebbles but the name "flint glass" remained.

Vitreous silica
Silica is melted without the addition of glass modifiers to produce a product called vitreous silica.

Sculpture made from extruded vitreous silica

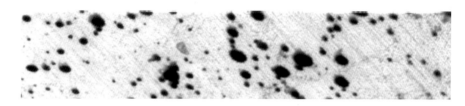

*Enlarged photograph of the end of a piece of vitreous silica tubing
showing the porous nature of the material*

It is very porous and has a very low coefficient of expansion which makes it highly resistant to thermal shock. Because of this it is often used to cover electrical heating elements.

IX.
Batch calculations

The calculations necessary for compiling batch for glazes and for glass are basically the same. The ingredients tend to differ slightly as in glassmaking the materials used are mostly oxides, carbonates, etc, of particular elements whereas in glaze batch much greater use is made of complex minerals such as the feldspars and clays. It will be evident from the notes on batch materials that whilst it is the various oxides that affect the nature of the glass or glaze melting those that are introduced in the form of carbonates, nitrates, sulphates, etc, create a considerable release of gas, mostly of carbon dioxide, nitrous oxides or sulphurous oxides during the melting process. In order to arrive at a weight of raw material to provide a particular amount of oxide it is, therefore, necessary to refer to appropriate conversion factors. These are listed in the appendix on tables.

Materials such as silica are a straightforward conversion as one kg (2·2 lb) of sand provides one kg (2·2 lb) of silica whereas many of the other materials are rather more complex. Feldspar is an obvious example. For convenience it is often presented as containing one part of alumina, one part of sodium oxide and or potassium oxide and six parts of silica. In fact, the material varies considerably from these approximations. Small quantities of other materials are often involved and the iron content can be crucial if colour is an important factor.

It is often necessary in dealing with such materials to establish the molecular weight of the mineral. These are listed in the tables on page 242.

A theoretical potash feldspar would have the following molecular weight:-

$$K_2O = (2 \times 39 \cdot 1) + 16 \qquad = \ 94 \cdot 2$$
$$Al_2O_3 = (27 \times 2) + (3 \times 16) \ = 102$$
$$6SiO_2 = 6 \times (28 \cdot 1 + 16 \times 2) \ = 360 \cdot 6$$

The total molecular weight for a theoretical potash feldspar would therefore be 456.

For the purpose of calculation a potash feldspar would be seen from the conversion tables in the index as requiring 5·91 kg of raw material to provide 1 kg of K_2O, 5·46 kg of material to provide 1 kg of alumina and 1·544 kg of material to provide 1 kg of silica. Using the alternative conversion factors, i.e. material to oxide, it can be seen that 1 kg of potash feldspar would provide 0·169 kg of K_2O, 0·183 kg of alumina and 0·648 kg of silica.

The calculations for glass batch are relatively straightforward but take a little practice and care.

To use a simple example, a glass requiring 70% SiO_2, 23% Na_2O, 5% CaO and 2% Al_2O_3 could be converted to a batch recipe as follows:-

70% of SiO_2 × conversion factor of 1	= 70 kg of sand
23% of Na_2O × conversion factor of 1·71	= 39·33 kg of soda ash
5% of CaO × conversion factor of 1·785	= 8·925 kg of limestone
2% of Al_2O_3 × conversion factor of 1	= 2 kg calcined alumina

This means that to produce 100 kg of glass it is necessary to use 120·255 kg of batch.

To reverse the process, a glass batch composition would be converted to the oxide percentage by using the other conversion factor (batch to oxide):-

70 kg of sand × conversion factor of 1   = 70% SiO_2
39·33 kg of soda ash × conversion factor of 0·585   = 23% Na_2O
8·925 kg of limestone × conversion factor of 0·56   = 5% CaO
2 kg of calcined alumina × conversion factor of 1   = 2% Al_2O_3

Unfortunately, most glass compositions are not as simple as those examples so an example of calculations relating to a current glass recipe is as follows:-

Batch for full crystal

Sand	57 kg × conversion factor of 1	= 57 SiO_2
Soda ash	6 kg × conversion factor 0·585	= 3·51 Na_2O
Potash	14·8 kg × conversion factor 0·682	= 6·82 K_2O
Pot.nitrate	4 kg × conversion factor 0·466	= 1·68 K_2O
Litharge	31 kg × conversion factor of 1	= 31 PbO

It can be seen from the previous example that in the simple soda–lime–silica batch much of the soda ash has been replaced by potash which is the normal practice in lead glass. There is no calcia as the lead oxide acts as both flux and stabiliser.

In all the calculations given above kilograms are used as examples but as all the amounts are proportional they could just as easily be calculated as referring to pounds, cwt or tons.

The calculations for glazes tend to be slightly more complex as a weight of material such as feldspar or clay will supply various weights of oxides to the batch. For example, if it is assumed that the first of the glass batch recipes shown was intended as a glaze, then instead of providing Al_2O_3 as calcined alumina it would be more convenient to provide this as clay, in which case some of the requirement for silica would be provided at the same time. Alternatively, there is also a requirement for Na_2O so part of this could be provided by including some soda feldspar, in which case the alumina requirement and part of the silica requirement could also be satisfied. In fact this formula would be unlikely to be used for a glaze as there would almost certainly be a requirement for more alumina than that described.

There are many ways of calculating glaze requirements including computer programs and various charts but one of the simplest methods of carrying out this process is that described by Dora Billington in her book "*The Techniques of Pottery*" published by Batsford. The following is an adapted from her description.

Formulae for glazes are usually described as being split into three components:-

  1. The base or flux, i.e. Na_2O, PbO, etc.
  2. The amphoteric, usually alumina
  3. The acid, usually silica, sometimes together with boric oxide

She uses a commonly quoted but old lead glaze as an example. The use of lead oxides or lead carbonates in glazes is now illegal in many countries but for simplicity this would be shown as:-

Base	Amphoteric	Acid
1 PbO	$0.3\ Al_2O_3$	$2.5\ SiO_2$

In order to establish the weights of material required it is usual to plot a chart. For example:-

PbO	Al_2O_3	SiO_2	Raw material	Mol. wt.	Parts by weight
1	-	-	litharge	223	223
-	0.3	0.6	clay	258	$258 \times 0.3 =$ 77.4
		1.9	flint	60	$60 \times 1.9 =$ 27

From the chart it will be obvious that by calculating the amount of clay to provide the 0.3 of alumina there is an automatic inclusion of 0.6 silica. This leaves a requirement of 1.9 flint on the bottom line to bring the amount of silica up to the required 2.5. In order to bring the parts by weight to a percentage statement it is necessary to total the amounts which in this case this would be $223 + 77.4 + 27 = 327.4$. The amounts are then expressed as a proportion of this by dividing each amount by this total, for example:-

223 divided by 327.4 = 0.68 or 68%
77.4 divided by 327.4 = 0.24 or 24%
27 divided by 327.4 = 0.08 or 8%

A more complex formula introducing extra fluxes would be 0.6 lead oxide, 0.2 potassium oxide and 0.2 calcia making up the usual figure of 1, 0.3 for the alumina and 2.4 for the silica. Expressing this in a chart as before and then using the standard theoretical formulae for feldspar and china clay this would read:-

PbO	K_2O	CaO	Al_2O_3	SiO_2	Raw material	Mol. wt.	Parts by wt.	%
0.6	-	-	-		Litharge	223	$0.6 \times 223 = 133.8$	44
-	0.2	0.2	1.2		Feldspar	556	$0.2 \times 556 = 111$	37
-	0.2	-	-		Whiting	100	$0.2 \times 100 = 20$	6.5
-	-	-	0.1	0.2	China clay	258	$0.1 \times 258 = 25.8$	8.5
-	-	-	-	0.2	Flint	60	$0.2 \times 60 = 12$	4

As lead oxide and lead carbonate are not allowed to be used for glaze making in most countries, lead is commonly introduced in the form of a low solubility frit, the most popular being lead bisilicate ($PbO.2SiO_2$).

This can be accommodated in the formulae as described above with the lead content being similar but automatically including two parts of silica for each part of lead oxide.

Reference. *A Dictionary of Glass*, C. Bray, A & C Black Ltd.

X.
Structure and basic chemistry
Structure

The studio glassmakers who melt batch tend to stick to well tried formulae, gradually modifying the batch as necessary until it become one which provides consistent results. Studio potters often use their materials and processes in a similar manner. This is obviously a sound approach which will work well until something goes wrong, or for some reason there is a major cause for change. Unless there is a good understanding of the underlying structure of both materials the procedure on either account can be difficult. Glass is obviously different from most other solids in both its chemical and physical nature. Because of its unusual behaviour and characteristics it is often very difficult to find meaningful explanations without a basic understanding of the reactions of the various elements concerned. Clay and the making of ceramics also involve an underlying structure which is equally complex, yet using what are largely similar materials the results may be different but strongly related. Difficulties do arise, however, and the necessary corrective measures can often be just as obscure. Much of the concern relates to the structure of crystalline materials and their changes to and from a non-crystalline glassy state.

An important consequence of the fact that only outer electrons take part in bonding is that there is a limit to the valency that an atom can have. Low valency numbers mean low numbers of bonds per atom. This, together with size restrictions in packing atoms close to each other, limits the number of nearest neighbours a particular atom can have in a solid where atomic positions are localised. The majority of atoms in a solid do not move around freely as they do in gases and liquids. X-ray diffraction experiments show that atoms in crystals are arranged in a very regular pattern or network, each atom of a particular type having a well defined position in the network. Crystalline sodium chloride for example consists of alternating Na^+ ions and Cl^- ions in a network of cubic symmetry.

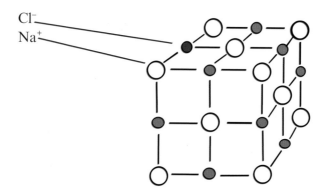

This network in a grain of stable salt stretches for billions of atoms in the three directions but the repeating unit or unit cell is simply that shown in the figure.

One requirement for a unit cell is that it must tessellate in space, i.e. when unit cells of the same shape are stacked together they completely fill space. There are only seven basic shapes which fulfil this requirement. Together with variations which allow for different types of atoms in a unit cell there are only fourteen types of unit cell and all crystal structures fit into one of these fourteen types, called Bravais lattices.

That being the case, why do we see so many varied and wonderful crystal shapes such as frost on a window pane, snowflakes, patterns on galvanised steel and surface crystals on ceramic glazes? The reason is that crystals grow from the liquid phase and not in the stacking of atoms in a unit cell. Crystals only show their basic shape if they are allowed to grow uninhibited without contact with other foreign particles such as dust, bubbles or other crystals.

Silica is the material which is most common to both glass and clay. It forms the largest proportion of a theoretical chemical formula for clay and is also by far the major material used in glass making.

It seems reasonable in the light of this to use silica and its response to heating and cooling processes to introduce the chemical and physical changes which take place.

The chemical formula for silica is SiO_2 and this simply means that there are twice as many oxygen atoms as there are silicon atoms in each silica molecule when it is in association with other molecules and that silica can be described as a compound of silicon and oxygen. This is useful information but it gives no real indication of the way that these atoms are placed in relation to each other. A grain of sand could contain millions of atoms and each atom of silicon would be bonded to four oxygen atoms whilst each oxygen atom would be bonded to two silicon atoms. A single molecule of silica would therefore be best described as SiO_4^{4-} but as it assumes a different ratio when forming various compounds, it is commonly described as SiO_2. It might help to visualise the arrangement in each molecule if we consider three balls all of the same size placed together on a flat table so that they touch each other. Another similar ball is then placed on top so that it touches all of the others. These balls would represent the oxygen atoms and the basic pyramid so formed is called a tetrahedron. There would however be a space in the centre where a much smaller ball could sit.

The term "tetrahedron" is one which keeps cropping up in texts on ceramics and glass. It would be reasonable to assume that most people would not have an instant image of what a tetrahedron looks like.

As an extension of the visual image of the four balls already described, it might help to think of a pyramid with a triangular base and

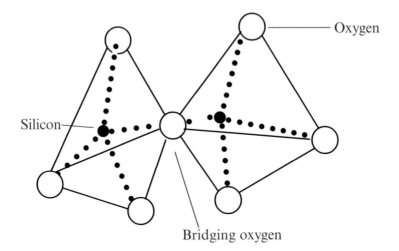

Oxygen

Silicon

Bridging oxygen

three sides, the base and the sides all being exactly the same. This is the most common illustration of a silica tetrahedron. It would have an atom of oxygen at each corner and an atom of silicon sitting in the centre.

To return to the image of the four large balls and one small one sitting on a table. If a straight line is drawn from the centre of the small ball and outwards through a large ball this builds up the tetrahedra but as each "O" is bonded to a second "Si". The line pierces another small ball which is itself connected to more of the large balls and illustrates the way in which the lattice is built up.

Each Si–O bond is represented by a straight line from the centre of the Si atom to the centre of the O atom. This line then continues outwards to indicate that each O is bonded to a second Si. As each Si is in turn bonded to four O's an arrangement emerges in which each O becomes located at a corner of a tetrahedra and serves as a bond to adjacent tetrahedra. This connecting role of the O's is called bridging.

The silica tetrahedra, joined to other tetrahedra by the oxygen atoms at each corner builds into a regular network. (The silicon element is said to be 4-valent whilst the bivalent O's link the individual tetrahedra together.) When the material is heated the structure becomes mobile in the sense that the bonds break and rejoin allowing the tetrahedra to rotate relative to one another but always keep enough bridging O's to maintain the network. This is the reason that it is possible to draw very fine fibres in hot glass and the reason why the viscosity of hot glass changes gradually with temperature.

There are three possible formations in which two silica tetrahedra can join together with a common oxygen bond. When these formations are common to both (or further) tetrahedra to form a regular lattice the resulting structures are either quartz, cristobalite or tridymite.

The manner in which the various tetrahedra are bonded affects the various phases or conversions that can take place whilst maintaining the same SiO_2

CERAMICS AND GLASS: A BASIC TECHNOLOGY

formula. If the arrangement is regular then the material will be crystalline but if the arrangement is random then the result will be a glass.

Some of these phases are known as alpha-quartz, beta-quartz, alpha-cristobalite, beta-cristobalite, alpha-tridymite, beta-tridymite, silica gel and silica glass, etc. The crystalline forms will have little significance to the studio glassmaker but will be of considerable importance to the potter, the glass pot maker and to the maker of furnace refractories as each phase has a different thermal expansion and density.

Many of the changes occur as a result of heat. For example, as materials are heated, alpha forms change to beta forms and these, after reaching higher temperatures turn eventually into an amorphous molten glass. It is the resulting changes in behaviour which are of greatest significance to the potter or furnace builder.

Clay containing cristobalite is used by the potter for making glazed earthenware because the conversion from beta forms to alpha forms during the cooling exerts a beneficial squeeze on the glaze. (See compatibility and glaze fit, page 130.) On the other hand, the sudden reduction in volume at this point, which may be as much as 3%, in stoneware or in refractories, can cause dunting. Because of this the potter tends to introduce finely powdered flint into an earthenware body as this converts readily and beneficially to cristobalite whereas in a stoneware or refractory body where amounts of cristobalite are not required he or she would tend to introduce sand or coarse particles of quartz as this would be less likely to convert into cristobalite in the time available during a firing.

The time element is important. Many conversions would normally take several days to complete but this time can be reduced to a matter of hours in the presence of suitable catalysts. For example, conversion to the cristobalite phase calcia and magnesia are effective catalysts.

For conversions to the tridymite phase, in addition to the calcia and magnesia, potash, soda, alumina and feldspar are also effective catalysts. Because of the time element it is possible that in some firings no conversion to cristobalite will take place so it is the normal practice when carrying out a biscuit firing for earthenware to soak the kiln at a temperature at or above 1100°C in order for the conversion to develop. Once cristobalite is present in a body then the inverse conversion, beta to alpha, cannot be ignored and the reduction in volume at or below 280°C is unavoidable. In glass furnace refractories this would be only be of major concern if for some reason the furnace was cooled down to a temperature below 280°C (540°F) before reheating it again to melt more glass. In this case there could be a possibility of particles of refractory material breaking away and finding their way into the glass to create problems of stones or cords.

Quartz converts to tridymite at temperatures above 870°C (1598°F) but at normal atmospheric pressure does not revert to quartz on cooling. It is used to make the type of silica bricks used for the construction of glass furnace crowns. When it is maintained at temperatures above 1470°C (2678°F) it gradually turns into cristobalite. The various arrangements of the tetrahedra can produce material with a relatively wide range of densities. Silica with an open structure can have a density as low as 1·98 whilst the more compact structure of quartz can have a density as high as 2·7.

When the earth was cooling, quartz was formed because the transition from molten material to solids was very slow and there was plenty of time for the silicon and oxygen atoms to produce a strong regular structure in the form of quartz.

The silica used in glaze or glassmaking is normally in the form of sand which is largely composed of small grains of quartz. If this material is heated to a temperature exceeding 1713°C (3115°F), the bonds which keep it as a hard crystal material are broken and it melts to form a glass. If it is then cooled at a fairly rapid rate its behaviour is completely different to that which occurred during the cooling of the earth and the development of quartz. Each of the transition temperatures is passed too quickly for any of the crystal networks to be formed. The silicon and oxygen bonds simply do not have time to reunite in a denser and more orderly arrangement. Eventually, as the material approaches room temperature the viscosity is so high that it behaves as the rigid solid known as vitreous silica, or as silica glass.

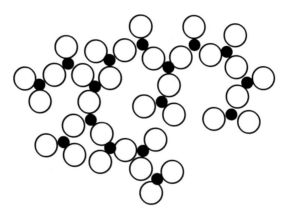

A two dimensional sketch of the structure of vitreous silica. Another oxygen would be immediately above each silica atom (shown in black). Below, the modifiers take up positions in the available spaces

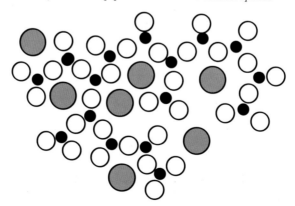

During its formation the vitreous silica retains the density of the molten liquid and there is no regular repetition of tetrahedra as there is in the crystalline form. The cold solid glass keeps a random structure similar to that of the molten liquid except that in the latter case the fluidity results from a process in which the bonds continually break and reunite. The spaces in the random network of vitreous silica vary considerably in size but the average is much greater than that in quartz. It is this which produces the low density of vitreous silica and is also the reason for its low coefficient of expansion.

In the case of the vitreous silica, vibrations can take place without forcing the material to expand because the atoms can simply vibrate into the adjacent empty spaces. When fluxes are added to silica to reduce the melting temperature they fill these spaces and, as a result, the glass must then expand to accommodate vibrations as the temperature increases. This creates a higher coefficient of expansion.

In a crystalline silica network the bonds form a tight regular structure. In vitreous silica the bonds form a random network. In commercial glass and glazes, this random network contains molecules of modifiers, stabilisers, colouring oxides, opacifiers, etc.

It has already been established that glass has a random network of molecules. In contrast, clay is a material of infinite variations which relies on a layered crystalline structure to form the basis of all possible differences in its constituent parts and in its characteristics. The building block of all the different clays is the kaolinite crystal which is formed by the breakdown of feldspathic rock or similar minerals by water containing carbon dioxide. In some cases the rock first decomposes to mica whilst in others it results from a slow action of percolating water followed by decay and weathering. In the process, amounts of clay, silica and various salts are produced according to the composition of the feldspar from which they are derived.

Feldspar is the name for a variety of aluminosilicates. The most common of these is potash feldspar ($K_2O.Al_2O_3.6SiO_2$) and the next being soda feldspar ($Na_2O.Al_2O_3.6SiO_2$). These are theoretical formula and the feldspars usually contain a wide range of minerals. They are also usually found as mixtures of the two feldspars rather than as single minerals. The development of hydroxyl ions in the feldspar results in the formation of alumina in a sheet form. By virtue of further development and substitution a laminated crystalline structure of kaolinite is formed. At the same time particles of other minerals become part of the clay and are responsible for much of the nature and behaviour of the final product.

The process can be assessed approximately as:-

$K_2O.Al_2O_3.6SiO_2$ (potash feldspar) $+ 2H_2O + CO_2$
$\rightarrow Al_2O_3.SiO_2.2H_2O + 4SiO_2 + K_2CO_3$ (potassium carbonate)

Potassium carbonate is soluble and as it gradually washes out it leaves kaolinite.

Kaolinite is the name given to the pure mineral and is often given the formula of $Al_2O_3.2SiO_2.2H_2O$ but should more correctly be given the formula of $Al_2Si_2O_5(OH)_4$. Kaolin is the name more commonly given to the primary clay

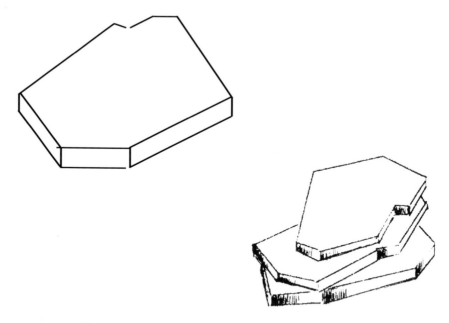

The approximately hexagonal layers of aluminium silicate

often known as china clay and is a material which is much more difficult to define though the formula for kaolinite is often used for calculation purposes.

The clay particles are in the form of flat plates. Each plate has negative charges on its faces but carries positive charges on its edges. In normal neutral conditions these particles are attracted to each other to form loose groups.

The clay crystal is very tiny and several million atoms are necessary to form a single sheet of aluminium silicate. Many thousand of these are required to

An electron micrograph of kaolinite showing the typical hexagonal crystals (× 16,000)
(Fine Ceramics, *Norton, McGraw Hill, 1970*)

make a single crystal. There is still scope for some variation in the size of the crystals. Those in china clay and fireclays are generally large in comparison to those of plastic ball clays which are extremely fine.

Many thousands of these sheets are required to make a single crystal.

Many hundreds of such crystals would be necessary to make a grain of clay dust. In primary clay these layers tend to be largely symmetrical in their stacking arrangement with one lying directly above the other, whereas in secondary clays they tend to be somewhat irregular as shown in the diagram.

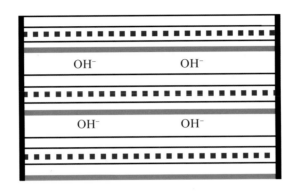

| Gibbsite |
| Linking oxygen |
| Silica |
| Hydroxyl bonds |
| Gibbsite |
| Linking oxygen |
| Silica |
| Hydroxyl bonds |
| Gibbsite |
| Linking oxygen |

Sheets of gibbsite–silica are joined to other layers by hydroxyl ions

In glass and in crystalline silica the linking atoms are of oxygen and the same situation exists in clay where the crystal is formed by alternate layers of gibbsite (aluminium) and silica linked together with oxygen. The sheets of gibbsite–silica are joined to other gibbsite–silica layers with hydroxyl ions.

The diagram above is a simplified version of the layers and in fact, other ions may be present in a clay structure which affect both its characteristics and behaviour.

The silica tetrahedral layer as shown can occasionally be penetrated by an aluminium atom which replaces one of the silicon atoms. Similarly, there is sometimes a replacement of some of the aluminium in the gibbsite layer with magnesium and iron.

There are many minerals similar to clay in that they have a layered structure. Mica is an obvious example but in this case the bonding of the mica layers is by potassium. Whilst it is possible to split mica this bonding is stronger than that of clay and as a result there is no sliding action as there is with clay and the mica particles which are often present in clay tend to reduce its plasticity.

Sericite on the other hand is a similar mineral which, whilst it does not help the plasticity of clay, sits comfortably with the clay particles and does not reduce the plasticity to any degree.

The 14% water in the kaolinite structure is tied into it chemically and is called "bound water" or water of crystallisation. There is usually more water, particularly in plastic clay, which is contained between the particles. This separates the crystal layers and relates to the OH⁻ ions attached to the surface. In addition, there is a third amount of water which makes the clay plastic and workable by lubricating the particles so that they can slide against each other to a greater or lesser degree according to the amount of water. This is called the water of plasticity. As the clays dry this water evaporates out and the clay becomes progressively more sticky. As it dries out completely the clay becomes hard though some of the water may remain trapped in the pores.

The plasticity of a clay is very important to the potter as it defines many of the working possibilities. If a clay will not slide easily under pressure, it becomes known as a "short" clay and is difficult to work but may still be totally suitable for some processes. A plastic clay on the other hand will move easily and can be manipulated readily into various forms but may have the disadvantage of having high shrinkage which is sufficient to produce distortion or cracking in the drying process.

It is of course possible to find a clay that is too plastic and which as a result will not really be workable by virtue of the fact that it has little mechanical strength and anything of any size will tend to collapse. Much depends on the ability of the plate like particles to slide against each other. Small plates will slide more easily than large ones. The strength of the attraction between the plates and the amount of lubrication which can be induced is also vital.

There are several factors which affect plasticity. The most important of these being:-

> moisture content
> size and variation of the particles
> the strength of the bonds
> the proportion of actual clay material present
> the presence of plasticisers.

To some extent these factors are intermingled. For instance the amount of water which the clay can hold before becoming seriously weakened depends largely on the proportion of fine clay particles present. China clay, which is found near to the rocks from which it was formed, will have large crystals regularly stacked and as a result will have little plasticity but if it has been transported it will usually have abraded sufficiently to reduce the particle size and as a result its plasticity is enhanced. There is a body of opinion that china clay similar to this was the reason that the Chinese had a porcelain body which was sufficiently plastic for thowing. Ball clays which are mostly composed of fine particles are much more plastic than clays which have coarser particles. This explains why ball clays are often added to clay bodies to make them workable. The fine particles such as those found in ball clay are likely to average about 3 microns across whilst those of china and coarse clays can be approximately ten times this size. Another factor which greatly influences the proportion of fine particles is that of the presence of non-clay materials. These are unlikely to have qualities of plasticity in themselves and are often of such a size that they can be removed or reduced considerably by introducing sufficient

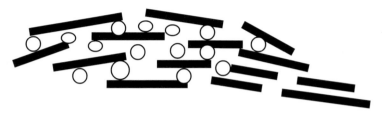

*Water between the particles of clay acts as a lubricant
and allows them to slide against each other*

water to make the clay into a fine slip and then running it through a sieve. Ideally, clay which has been reduced to a slip and blunged should be aged or stored before use to allow the development of action by bacteria on remnants of organic matter. It is also normal practice to add a small quantity of weak acid and/or some Jeyes fluid to such clay before storage as the physical attraction between particles is affected considerably by the acidity and the souring which results from the Jeyes fluid.

Both the increased acidity and the souring promoted by the Jeyes fluid work together. In such an atmosphere the storage, or in the longer process of weathering, both in damp conditions, the minute particles are allowed to develop their maximum attraction and thixotropic strength. The soluble material which can be found in some water, in particular in sea water, can make it unsuitable for adding to clay. It tends to migrate to the surface during drying and form a scum.

Sometimes it becomes necessary to add materials known as plasticizers to a clay. The most common of these is a clay like material called bentonite. This is a montmorillonite produced by the decay of volcanic rock and has very fine particles averaging about 0·05 microns across. When it contains water it is an extremely slippery and greasy material in considerable demand as a lubricant in the oil drilling industry. It is usual to add between 1 and 2% to a clay body calculated on the dry weight of both materials. In some clays, particularly porcelain bodies which may not have a high clay content, it may be necessary to extend the proportion to something approaching 5%. Unfortunately, this brings the disadvantage of increasing the shrinkage of the resulting material.

In practical terms it is not easy to add it to a clay body and the dry powder needs to be mixed with double its weight in water. Once this has resulted in a greasy mass, fingers or suitable tools can be pushed into the clay, and the resultant holes filled with the prepared bentonite. The clay then needs to be kneaded well before being left to stand before further kneading. The process is not as simple as it sounds because the slipperiness of the bentonite makes kneading quite difficult. It is often also necessary to push the mixture through a de-airing pugmill before the final kneading takes place.

There are commercial plasticizing materials available which work by increasing lubrication. These are polymerised carbohydrate pastes, bacterial colloidal gels and synthetic inorganic colloids. They are often preferred for use in porcelain bodies because they are colourless and improve green strength.

For some purposes, particularly those which involve large sculptural forms or some types of stoneware it is normal practice to sacrifice some plasticity in order to gain mechanical strength and/or texture.

In this case, materials such as sand or grog are added to the clay. It is often something of a dilemma for the potter when it becomes necessary to modify a clay to suit a particular operation. For example, it becomes much easier to pull a handle if the clay is plastic so there is a temptation to increase the plasticity of the material to stop it from breaking whilst it is being manipulated. Unfortunately, it is then all too common to find that a beautifully made handle can shrink so much in the drying that it will either crack or come away from the pot.

If large and heavy sculptural forms are being made from reasonably flat slabs joined together the clay can be short and contain fairly large amounts of grog and/or coarse sand which reduces the shrinkage considerably and increases fired strength. If the slabs have to be bent, however, the amount of grog and/or sand may need to be reduced considerably.

When clay is fired it is transformed into a hard material which cannot be reconstituted into its original plastic form. The nature of that hard material depends largely on the type of clay, its various fluxing materials, the various fillers and the temperature to which it is fired. The necessary fluxes may be present as a natural part of the clay body as tends to happen with stoneware clays but more often than not, particularly in industrial production, they are added separately to provide suitable body formulations for the type of ware required.

Reduction

This is a process scientifically described as when an electron is added to an atom or an ion. The result of this, which is of greatest concern to glassmakers and potters, is that of removing oxygen from molecules, particularly those of the metal oxides. Other common effects are the addition of hydrogen to a molecule and the diminution of the positive valency of an atom or ion, i.e. variable valency forms of oxides producing differing colouring effects.

It is something which can be used positively in producing metallic or iridescent surface effects on glass or glazes, in the attainment of particular colours in a clay body a glaze or a glass. It can also prove to be a disadvantage because if a furnace or kiln atmosphere is not sufficiently well monitored a founding or firing can go disastrously wrong. A common example in glassmaking is that of a furnace containing lead crystal which because of the accidental provision of a reducing atmosphere can cause the greying of the glass or even the creation of visible metallic lead particles. Another common occurrence is when a green or turquoise glass containing copper oxide is being reheated in a glory hole, the incidence of a reducing flame can produce a thin copper layer on the surface. It is used deliberately in the founding process to produce colours such as copper ruby and some carbon ambers.

The deliberate creation of a reducing atmosphere in a kiln is also used by potters to affect the clay during a firing for example, a clay which normally

Garden sculpture in reduced stoneware

fires to a terracotta colour because of the iron content can reduce to black. In high temperature firing such as that for stoneware and porcelain a reducing atmosphere can help to flux the body and can produce interesting effects by promoting the migration of colour from the body into the glaze. The colour of ware such as the celadons depends considerably on controlled reduction. Raku tends to be reduced by the action of the sawdust and shavings in appropriating any available oxygen as they burn. The development of the so-called smoky lustres relied heavily upon the provision of a reducing atmosphere to produce the metallic surfaces.

The bonds affecting the various oxides involved in both ceramics and glass making vary considerably. Some are extremely strong and others are relatively weak. This means that there is almost a kind of league table of those oxides which will give up their oxygen most readily in a state of reduction.

There are also a few which reduce without showing any marked effect and some which can only be reduced in very special conditions which are not met in the normal studio glassmaking or pot making processes.

Basic chemistry

Much of the development and behavioural characteristics of the basic materials, the effects of firing or founding and the resulting ceramics or glass forms can only be explained satisfactorily through an understanding of the fundamentals of chemistry relating to them.

As yet science cannot predict or explain everything, for example, the path of a lightning strike or the position in a liquid where a crystal will start to grow, nevertheless it is remarkable how much can be explained using simple ideas as to how materials are composed and how modern theory of structure of matter can be used with great precision to determine many fundamental properties. Such detail may not be necessary for practical ceramic or glass makers to obtain a working knowledge of their craft but it is essential that they understand some of the basic science so that expensive mistakes are not made, that glass and ceramics can be prepared with the required properties and that materials are handled safely.

From the eighteenth century to date, studies of the way materials react together has shown there are a limited number of fundamental types of matter. These are the elements. Eighty nine elements are known to occur naturally and a further seventeen have been prepared artificially in particle accelerators. Elements can be grouped together according to their chemical nature, and more importantly, to

IA	IIA	IIIB	IVB	VB	VIB	VIIB	VIII	VIII	VIII	IB	IIB	IIIA	IVA	VA	VIA	VIIA	0
1																	2
H																	He
1.0079		Key:															4.0026
3	4		Atomic number									5	6	7	8	9	10
Li	Be		Element symbol: Metal Nonmetal Intermediate									B	C	N	O	F	Ne
6.94	9.012		Atomic weight									10.81	12.01	14.01	15.99	18.98	20.19
11	12											13	14	15	16	17	18
Na	Mg											Al	Si	P	S	Cl	Ar
22.99	24.31											26.98	28.09	30.97	32.07	35.45	39.95
19	20	21	22	23	24	25	26	27	28	29	30	31	32	33	34	35	36
K	Ca	Sc	Ti	V	Cr	Mn	Fe	Co	Ni	Cu	Zn	Ga	Ge	As	Se	Br	Kr
39.10	40.08	44.96	47.87	50.94	51.99	54.94	55.85	58.93	58.69	63.55	65.39	69.72	72.61	74.92	78.96	79.90	83.80
37	38	39	40	41	42	43	44	45	46	47	48	49	50	51	52	53	54
Rb	Sr	Y	Zr	Nb	Mo	Tc	Ru	Rh	Pd	Ag	Cd	In	Sn	Sb	Te	I	Xe
85.47	87.62	88.91	91.22	92.91	95.94	[99]	101.1	102.9	106.4	107.9	112.4	114.8	118.7	121.8	127.6	126.9	131.3
55	56	71	72	73	74	75	76	77	78	79	80	81	82	83	84	85	86
Cs	Ba	Lu	Hf	Ta	W	Re	Os	Ir	Pt	Au	Hg	Tl	Pb	Bi	Po	At	Rn
132.9	137.3	174.9	178.5	180.9	183.8	186.2	190.2	192.2	195.1	196.9	200.6	204.4	207.2	208.9	[209]	[210]	[222]
87	88	103	104	105	106	107	108	109	110	111	112	114	116	118			
Fr	Ra	Lr	Rf	Db	Sg	Bh	Hs	Mt	Uun	Uuu	Uub	Uuq	Uuh	Uuo			
[223]	[226]	[262]	[261]	[262]	[263]	[264]	[265]	[268]	[269]	[272]	[277]	[289]	[289]	[293]			

57-70 lanthanides

57	58	59	60	61	62	63	64	65	66	67	68	69	70
La	Ce	Pr	Nd	Pm	Sm	Eu	Gd	Tb	Dy	Ho	Er	Tm	Yb
138.9	140.1	140.9	144.2	[145]	150.4	151.9	157.3	158.9	162.5	164.9	167.3	168.9	173.0

89-102 actinides

89	90	91	92	93	94	95	96	97	98	99	100	101	102
Ac	Th	Pa	U	Np	Pu	Am	Cm	Bk	Cf	Es	Fm	Md	No
[227]	232.0	231.0	238.0	[237]	[244]	[243]	[247]	[247]	[251]	[252]	[257]	[258]	[259]

The standard periodic table

their atomic structure (as explained later), into the Periodic table. In the periodic table each element is denoted by its chemical symbol, e.g. hydrogen is H, oxygen O, silicon Si, etc, and elements in each group has similar properties. The alkali metals in group I all combine with oxygen to form oxides which act as fluxes in glasses. For example: sodium, (Na) combines with oxygen to form sodium oxide which is the most common flux in glass making. The combination results in Na_2O in which two units (atoms) of sodium are chemically bonded to one unit (one atom) of oxygen to give one unit (one molecule) of sodium oxide. When there is more than one atom of the same element in a compound it is numbered with a subscript as in Na_2O. An atom is simply the smallest unit of an element which can exist. Molecules are formed by atoms chemically combining together.

As a further example of the use of the subscript, silica is perhaps the logical example to use to illustrate this. It is an important constituent of most ceramics and glass and normally originates as a crystalline material described in formulae as SiO_2. This implies that a silica molecule is made up of one silicon atom in combination with two oxygen atoms. If we look at a theoretical formula for clay we find that it is usually described rather simplistically as $Al_2O_3.2SiO_2.2H_2O$. This means that it is a compound consisting of one molecule of alumina which has 2 aluminium atoms to three of oxygen, plus 2 molecules of silica, each of which has one silicon atom to 2 oxygen atoms and 2 molecules of water. Each molecule of water consists of two atoms of hydrogen and 1 of oxygen. From this it can be seen that a subscript figure as in Al_2 refers only to the element preceding it whilst a figure before a molecule as in $2SiO_2$ refers to all the elements in that molecule:-

    1 molecule of alumina provides
    2 aluminium atoms + 3 oxygen atoms.
    2 molecules of silica provides   2 silicon atoms + 4 oxygen atoms
    2 molecules of water provides 4 hydrogen atoms + 2 oxygen atoms

The various elements are listed in what is called the periodic table. This is a convenient arrangement of the elements in tabular form and indicates much of the nature and the possible relationships of the elements. The vertical columns in the table are numbered from 0 to VIII in Roman numerals and called "groups".

Much information can be gained from the periodic table and one of the most obvious is that the group of alkali metals lithium, sodium and potassium which form the strong fluxes in glass and glaze making are in group I on the left hand side of the table. Looking further at the table it becomes obvious that on the other side in group VII the elements there such as chlorine, bromine and iodine, known as the halogens, tend to form compounds which are strongly acidic. Moving towards the left from these halogens the tendency is for the elements to be less strongly acidic. From group III to group I the elements become more strongly alkaline.

The halogen gas fluorine from group VII together with nitrogen from group VI are all found in compounds used in ceramics and glass but are released as acidic volatiles during firing or founding and can cause considerable damage to kilns and furnaces, particularly around the flue areas. The solid materials carbon and sulphur often found in clay or introduced into batches as carbonates or sulphates also release acidic volatiles in a similar manner.

Another tendency evident in the table is that when moving from top to bottom of any group or from right to left along any period there is an increase in the atomic weight of the elements to the effect that the heaviest of those which may be used in ceramic or glass processes such as lead, gold and bismuth are all at the bottom of the table. The elements in group 0 are known as the inert gases because they do not react with other elements. Because of this they are often omitted from periodic tables which have been specially formulated to relate only to ceramics and/or glass.

Elements in the remaining groups have the capacity to form compounds with other elements and their position in the groups up to group VII indicates their valency (the extent to which they can combine with other elements). Those in group VIII are called transition elements and have various valences.

Group I contains alkali metals and these are important fluxes in both ceramic and glass processes. They are said to be monovalent and all bond with oxygen, which is in group VI and divalent, in a ratio of two atoms of alkali metal to one of oxygen in order to achieve a balance They are:-

Lithia	Li_2O	(Lithium oxide)
Soda	Na_2O	(Sodium oxide)
Potassa	K_2O	(Potassium oxide)

Group II contains alkaline earth metals that are also used considerably in ceramic and glass processes and these bond with oxygen in the ratio of one alkaline earth to one of oxygen as they are both in the same valency group. Their bonding tends to be stronger than that of the materials in group one and this quality affects various ceramic and glass processes. They are:-

Magnesia	MgO	(Magnesium oxide)
Calcia	CaO	(Calcium oxide)
Strontia	SrO	(Strontium oxide) - used mostly in lustres
Baria	BaO	(Barium oxide)

Whilst all the above have similar behaviour and characteristics there are two important materials in group III which share the bonding arrangement of two parts of the element to three of oxygen but play completely different roles in ceramics and glass. These are:-

| Alumina | Al_2O_3 | (Aluminium oxide) |
| | B_2O_3 | (Boric oxide) |

Usually listed with each element symbol is the Relative Atomic Weight (RAW).

In most lists relating to batch calculations, etc, these have been rounded up to whole numbers and as such are sufficiently accurate for this purpose. The need for greater precision in dealing with chemical reactions has led to the production of lists based on the weight of an atom compared to that of the carbon atom (isotope C^{12}, see later). As a result there are other lists presented which may show figures with various decimal place.

Atomic weights are extremely useful for calculating the precise weights of materials reacting together. For example, batch calculations rely on the use of atomic weights.

Virtually all of the raw materials used in the making of pottery and glass are, or have been, derived from minerals and most of these have some form of crystalline structure.

A crystalline material normally has a complex regular lattice whereas when it has been changed into a glass or a glaze the regular pattern ceases to exist and a random network is formed. The various changes which occur in these lattices and networks as crystalline material changes into glass, and, to a lesser extent when glass reverts to a crystalline material, affects many of the making processes.

Just as each element has an atomic weight so each molecule has an atomic weight which is found by adding up the atomic weights of all the atoms in the molecule. Looking up the atomic weights in the periodic table we find that hydrogen is 1 and chlorine is 35·45 so the molecular weight of hydrochloric acid is 1 + 35·45 = 36·45. For sodium carbonate we have to take into account the fact that there are several atoms of the same type involved.

Thus:-

$$Na_2 = 2 \times 23 \qquad = 46$$
$$C \ \ = 12 \qquad\quad = 12$$
$$O_3 \ = 3 \times 16 \qquad = \underline{48}$$

$$\text{Therefore, } Na_2CO_3 \quad = 106$$

We can also find the actual weights of materials reacting together. Sodium oxide has a molecular weight of 62 ($2 \times 23 + 16 = 62$) and carbon dioxide has a molecular weight of 44 ($12 + 2 \times 16 = 44$) so 106 parts by weight of sodium carbonate on heating gives 62 parts by weight of sodium oxide and 44 parts by weight of carbon dioxide. As long as the units are consistent throughout then parts by weight can be substituted by any system of weights, e.g. grams, pounds, tonnes, etc.

Ouch *by the author*

XI.
Chemical bonding

In the early 19th century physicists demonstrated that atoms of all elements were composed of three fundamental particles: electrons, protons and neutrons. Today we know that these are not the only atomic particles but these three still remain the most important and are the only ones needed to describe why atoms of different elements are different and how they combine to form the wide variety of solids, liquids and gases present in everyday life.

Experiments with cathode ray tubes and radioactive materials have shown that electrons carry a negative electrical charge and have almost no mass. Protons are much heavier and have a positive charge which is equal in magnitude to the negative electron charge. Neutrons which have no electrical charge are almost the same mass as protons.

Protons and neutrons form the nucleus of the atom and electrons are grouped in shells around the nucleus. Thus, the simplest element, hydrogen, which has one proton and one electron but no neutrons, and sodium which has eleven electrons, eleven protons and twelve neutrons can be represented pictorially in the diagrams below. In the diagram below, the electron is shown in a shell around the nucleus. This suggests the region of space which they probably occupy. Which shell they occupy is a measure of their energy. Strictly speaking electrons do not always occupy spherical shells but for most purposes it is convenient to regard atoms as spheres.

As we progress through the periodic table the number of electrons, protons and neutrons in atoms increases and the number of electrons in each shell is governed by strict rules.

The behaviour of an atom depends largely on the number of electrons in its outer shell.

The simplest and lightest atom is that of hydrogen which has one proton in its nucleus and one electron in its shell. This particular shell, the innermost, is

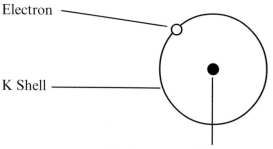

Nucleus containing one proton

Diagram of the hydrogen atom showing one electron in the K shell

known as the K shell and is capable of holding a maximum of two electrons so in this case there is a space available for another electron.

Helium is the next atom in the table and as this has two electrons in the K shell it completes the number of electrons which can possibly be accommodated. This makes that particular element very stable and as a result it cannot combine with its own or with the atoms of other elements.

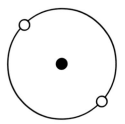

Diagram of the helium atom showing a complete K shell with two electrons

The electrons of the next element in the table (lithium) cannot be fully accommodated in the K shell as this is complete so it then needs the addition of an outer shell called the L shell to accommodate the extra electron. As an L shell will hold 8 electrons when it is complete but in this case only holds one electron, there is a considerable possibility for it to lose an electron to a combining element. These changes affect its electrical charge. It also means that lithium is in a position whereby it can react readily with other elements.

The next element in the table will have two electrons in its L shell and so on until the shell is complete and the element neon is reached.

If an atom loses or gains an electron as happens very often during the chemical changes which occur in the forming processes of most ceramics and glass, it is said to have been involved in a chemical reaction and is then called an ion. In the process the electrical charge is altered so the terms ion +1 or ion −1 (or two, etc) are created and relate to whether the atom has gained or lost electrons.

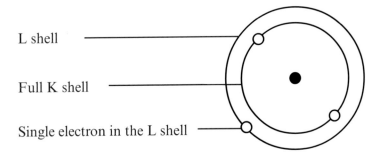

L shell

Full K shell

Single electron in the L shell

Diagram of the lithium atom showing a full K shell and just one electron in the outer L shell

CERAMICS AND GLASS: A BASIC TECHNOLOGY

By adding one electron after another, each of them having a negative charge of −1 whilst increasing the charge on the nucleus by +1 and by increasing the number of shells to accommodate them as necessary, the whole periodic table can be built up.

The position of an element in the periodic table can now be explained in terms of its atomic structure. The position is equal to the number of electrons in the atom, known as the atomic number of the element and elements in the same group have the same number of electrons in their outer shells.

For example:-

In group I there are the elements sodium (Na), potassium (K) and rubidium (Rb).

The table below shows this relationship

Group 1	Symbol	Atomic number	Electron configuration
Sodium	Na	11	2,8,1
Potassium	K	19	2,8,18,1
Rubidium	Rb	37	2,8,18,8,1

The single electron in the outer shell is easily removed in a reaction and this movement becomes easier as more shells are involved.

An isotope of an element has different numbers of neutrons but the same number of electrons and protons. Natural mixtures of isotopes lead to the Relative Atomic Weights of most elements not being whole numbers. For instance, natural hydrogen has a R.A.W. of 1·0079 because it contains a small quantity of deuterium (1 electron, 1 proton and 1 neutron) isotope. The increasing need for precision in the use of atomic weights in modern chemistry has led to the choice of the isotope C^{12} as the standard against which the remainder of the elements are compared.

Bonding

The fact that elements in the same group have similar properties and the same number of electrons in their outer shells shows that it is the shell electrons which take part in forming chemical bonds to give molecules. The formation of a chemical bond lowers the energy of the atoms taking part and thus the molecule formed is more stable than its constituent separate atoms. The number of chemical bonds an atom can form is called its valency. Hydrogen and the group one outer shell electron can only form one bond and, therefore, can only have a single valency.

Valency increases from the outer groups to the inner group elements. Water (H_2O) has two hydrogen atoms bonded to one oxygen, hence oxygen has a valency of two. Silica has two oxygen bonded to one silicon therefore silicon has a valency of four. Many atoms exhibit multiple valency, for example, iron forms two oxides, FeO (ferrous oxide) with a valency of two and Fe_2O_3 (ferric oxide) with a valency of three. A third oxide Fe_3O_4 (magnetite) can be described as a mixture of FeO + Fe_2O_3.

Looking at number of outer shell and valency combination of atoms forming a molecule shows that in chemical bonding an atom tries to make its outer electrons total eight, or two in the case of the first period elements. Thus in the case of sodium oxide, Na_2O, each sodium atom donates one electron to the oxygen with the formation of two sodium ions Na^+ with an electronic configuration of 2,8 and one oxygen ion O^{2-} with a similar configuration of 2,8. The balanced mutual attraction of the negative and positive charges of the ions holds the molecule Na_2O together. The donation and acceptance of electrons from one atom to another creates what is known as an ionic bond. Another way to fulfil the requirements of two or eight outer shell electrons is for the atoms to share electrons. This is called covalent bonding.

Carbon is the best known former of covalent bonding but silicon, which is in the same group, is similar. Covalently bonded carbon compounds form the basis of the study of organic chemistry. Carbon with four electrons in its outer shell has a valency of four but to gain or lose four electrons to make an outer shell of eight requires too large an energy change so carbon shares its electrons instead. Methane (CH_4) consists of a central carbon atom surrounded by four hydrogen atoms in a tetrahedral configuration with four covalent C–H bonds. Each hydrogen shares one electron from itself and one from the carbon to give an outer shell configuration of two. The carbon shares four electrons from its outer shell with four electrons from the hydrogens and so has an outer shell of eight electrons.

Not all bonds are purely ionic or covalent. In silica, the bonding between the silicon and the oxygens is about 50% ionic and 50% covalent in character which simply means that the bonding electronic charge is closer to the oxygen atom. An important property of the covalent bond is that it is highly directional. In silica the four bonds between the silicon and the four surrounding oxygens are all the same and the only way that the bonds can be evenly distributed in space is at 120° to each other, forming a tetrahedron with the silicon atom at the centre. This SiO_2 tetrahedron is the basic building unit of both crystalline and glassy silicates.

In general, elements in the middle groups of the periodic table (groups III, IV and V) tend to form covalent bonds and elements in the outer groups (groups I, II, VI and VII) tend to form compounds with ionic bond character.

It has already been established that chemical combination of atoms is brought about by the rearrangement of the electrons in their outer shells and that this is most easily achieved where there is the greatest possibility for movement and the greatest chance of moving towards a state of stability. Lithium is a case in point. As previously described it only has one electron in its outer shell, therefore, the most obvious way for it to move towards stability is to donate that electron to another element which can accommodate it in the process of forming a compound.

A table of the elements showing atomic weights and various valences is in the list of tables at the back of this book, page 251. It offers an alternative method of conveying the information in the periodic tables.

In this table hydrogen is shown as having an atomic weight of one whilst silicon is shown as having an atomic weight of 28. This indicates that silicon is 28 times as heavy as hydrogen. These atomic weights become important when calculating the proportions and weights of materials necessary to achieve a glaze mixture or a glass batch.

The valency indicates the possible states that an element can achieve in combining with other elements. This can be of considerable importance when considering the effects of colouring oxides. Iron can be used to illustrate this. It is shown as having a valency of 2 and 3. This means that when being introduced as an oxide into a batch for glaze or glass it can be in the form of compounds which will supply ferrous oxide (FeO) or ferric oxide (Fe_2O_3) and different colours will result. The atmosphere in the kiln or furnace (oxidising, neutral or reducing) will affect the amount of oxygen available to be taken up. Other materials in the glaze or batch can also affect the result by providing or accepting oxygen.

Ion exchange

Ion exchange is another term that seems to crop up regularly in books on both ceramics and glass and there appears to be an assumption that everybody knows exactly what it means. In fact there are numerous potters and studio glassmakers who have not studied even the most basic chemistry and physics. For them this expression will probably be meaningless. Perhaps the most common usage relates to glazes bonding to a body and to enamels bonding to a glaze, glass or metal. To understand this fully it is necessary to look at the process of chemical bonding.

This refers to the unit of force joining two or more atoms together to make a compound. The main types affecting glassmaking are: ionic bonds which are formed when ions of positive and negative charge attract each other to create a strong bond, and covalent bonds which are formed between atoms when they share a pair of electrons and often create a weak bond though they can be quite strong in a rigid network. The bonds of the various atoms which form molecules must result from a situation in which the process is favourable in terms of energy. The inert gases are the most stable of the elements because they have a complete outer shell of electrons. As a result they do not react with other elements because in their case, their energy cannot be improved by the process of forming compounds.

As shown earlier, the electrons in the outer shells of atoms are those most likely to be concerned with the formation of compounds. Molecules are only formed if in the process each atom moves towards a more stable configuration of electrons. They do this by either gaining, losing or sharing electrons. There are some electropositive elements with atoms which release one or more electrons easily. There are electronegative elements which gain electrons and there are also elements which tend neither to gain nor lose electrons. These variables produce a situation in which various types of bond are possible.

Firstly, that of an electropositive element with an electronegative element and called an ionic bond.

Secondly, that of an electronegative element with an electronegative element and called a covalent bond.

Lastly, that of an electropositive element with another electropositive element and called a metallic bond.

A good example of an ionic bond is that of sodium with chlorine. The sodium atom has only one electron in its outer shell. It can achieve stability by losing that electron. It then becomes known as a sodium ion and has a charge of +1 because it now has a positive nucleus charge of eleven and only ten negative electrons. On the other hand, a chlorine atom has an outer shell which only needs the addition of one electron to make it complete. In gaining this electron it becomes known as a chlorine ion and has a net charge of −1. When the sodium and chlorine react together, the outer electron of the sodium transfers to the chlorine to produce sodium and chlorine ions which are held together by the attraction of opposite charges. In this case both kinds of atoms become more stable, being more favourable in terms of energy, and sodium chloride is formed. Any concern with materials used to provide batch means having to deal with bonds which, though not all, are largely ionic.

There are some bonds which could be better considered as being covalent or metallic and become cations if they have lost electrons and as a result have gained a positive charge and anions if they have gained electrons and obtained a negative charge. The electronic charge, therefore, depends on the number of electrons that have been gained or lost in forming the ion.

Compounds with ionic bonding are made up of positive and negative ions arranged together in a lattice. The electrostatic attraction is uniform and extends in all directions equally.

This means that to break ionic bonds requires an input of considerable amounts of energy. Such compounds as these are usually very hard and have high melting points. As the size of the atom depends in part on the electrostatic attraction between the positive nucleus of the atom and the negative electron field around it, any change in the number of electrons changes the size of the particle. The size of an ion is important in relation to its ability to fit into a crystalline compound. The size of an ion is also important in its effects on a material when there is an ion exchange.

As a layer of glaze is being formed on a clay body or when an enamel is being formed on a glaze or glass the materials are heated until the atoms become sufficiently agitated for the bonds on various molecules to be "loosened" to the extent that the necessity for the best possible electrostatic attraction can be achieved by exchanges of ions. Strong bonds are formed in the process and as a result one material (glaze to body or enamel to glaze, glass or metal) becomes strongly linked to another.

The complex process of glass decay on ageing has long been considered to be one which involves ion exchange.

Weyl suggests that bonding at a glass surface is defective in itself because all the surface ions are in a state of incomplete co-ordination. This asymmetry of the surface produces abnormal interatomic distances and hence the space occupied by the surface ions is greater than usual, enabling replacement by ions of a larger or small radius to occur (*The Conservation of Glass*, by Roy Newton & Sandra Davison).

This subject is a very difficult one about which there is still a great deal of conjecture. It is described later under "Glass decay" on page 144. Those who need a deeper insight into this complex subject should read the book mentioned above which gives an excellent account of this area.

Ion exchange is involved in the chemical toughening of glass. The process is used mainly on thin glass and one method involves exchanging sodium ions on the surface with larger potassium ions which produce surface compression. Similarly, a glass containing lithium oxide can be toughened by immersing it in molten sodium chloride. Some lithium atoms on or near to the surface escape and are replaced by sodium ions. As these are considerably larger than the lithium atoms they cause considerable surface stress as the glass cools.

Eutectics

When reactions have taken place between elements, molecules of various materials are formed. These in turn become involved in further combination with other molecules in the formation of crystal lattices or in the random networks which form a glass. A comprehensive table of the molecules which may be met when considering the structure of a ceramic body, the make up of a glaze or the structure of a glass is shown on page 242 at the end of this book.

In this table molecular weights are also indicated as these are often used in calculations. As previously explained, they are made up from the sum of the atomic weights of the elements involved. For example, manganese has an atomic weight of 54·9 whilst oxygen has an atomic weight of 16. Manganese dioxide, therefore, has a molecular weight of 86·9 made up of the 54·9 from the manganese and 32 from the two lots of oxygen.

Most of the glassmaking processes and the making of ceramics involve heat and time. Many alloys and mixtures of compounds melt, i.e. change from a crystalline state to a liquid state over a range of temperatures. When a eutectic occurs the melting takes place at a single temperature. The way in which the atoms react with each other as a result of heat can be complex as they often tend to form and move in and out of bonding arrangements as various temperature stages are achieved. Similarly, there are changes which can also develop during the cooling cycle. The preference for particular molecules to bond together at certain temperatures creates a eutectic and the temperature at which the bonding takes place becomes known as a eutectic point. The achievement of suitable temperatures for these processes is generally well known and accepted but the importance of the time element is rarely given the same consideration. As heat is applied to the various minerals and/or prepared chemicals, atoms of the various elements involved start to become agitated and vibrate. Bonds which hold the molecules together tend to become less secure and as the heat progresses they loosen and seek other elements with which they can form bonds. As the temperature rises further, these new bonds can loosen and form different attachments. This rearrangement of bonds continues until the final temperature is reached.

Most of the minerals used have a regular crystalline structure. If heated sufficiently they eventually reach a temperature at which this regular structure ceases to exist and forms the random arrangement of atoms that is peculiar to a molten glass. At this stage, the time factor in cooling becomes all important. If the molten material is cooled slowly, the bonding arrangements reverse and a regular structure is formed again but if it is cooled quickly then the bonds do not have time to reorganise and, as a result, the random network of a glass remains. A common example of the importance of the time element can be found in many stoneware glazes. They often contain materials such as wood ashes which contain oxides which have a tendency to promote crystals. If these glazes are cooled quickly, as could happen in a small test kiln then the result could be considerably different from that of the same glaze fired in a kiln which cools slowly and so allows the crystals to form.

In the case of change from clay to a ceramic the action is not quite so straightforward. A sequence of changes takes place which first turn the clay into a porous but solid material which has lost its plasticity. Some of the constituent materials turn into glass which helps give the ceramic some strength. If the clay is fired to a sufficiently high temperature more glass is produced to the extent that the pores become filled and the resultant ceramic becomes non-porous.

This is not the whole picture because in the process of a glaze or a glass being formed materials do not melt at the same time. It is already established that the bonds break and reunite to form different compounds but there is another phenomenon which affects the melting sequence. This is the effect of eutectics. Most non-vitreous materials have a specific melting point yet there are many cases in which two materials, each with different melting points are heated in close association, then the melting point of each can be reduced considerably. The proportion of one material to another also has a strong bearing. Perhaps the most obvious and relevant example of this is that of silica and alumina. Both materials make up the major part of most ceramics and are both used in glazes and glassmaking. Silica has a melting point of 1710°C (3110°F) whilst alumina has a melting point of 2050°C (3720°F).

It would be easy to assume that the lowest eutectic melting point which could be achieved would relate to a mixture of equal parts of the two materials but this is not so and, in fact, the lowest melting temperature is reached with a proportion of 10% alumina to 90% silica. The lowest temperature at which the two materials will melt is known as the eutectic point.

The eutectic resulting from alumina and silica has its own relevance in the consideration of the making of refractories to withstand particular temperatures. For example, even a small quantity of alumina in a silica refractory could create a lower melting temperature than that required. It will be obvious from the graph that from the low point of a proportion of 10% alumina to 90% silica a firebrick would become increasingly refractory as the proportion of alumina to silica rises. This is a factor that is used as a specification in describing firebricks which are often sold as firebrick 30, firebrick 42, etc, to note the alumina content. This can be a little confusing because in some other refractories such a number can refer to the maximum hot face temperature in either centigrade or Fahrenheit.

These proportions are not common to all materials and the forming of eutectics is not necessarily confined to reactions between just two materials.

The melting together of alumina and silica would not appear to be particularly conducive to the making of glass or the melting of glazes as the resulting eutectic temperature is still too high for most normal production but when other oxides become involved this melting point can be reduced considerably. A eutectic which affects a high proportion of glassmaking is that of sodium oxide and silica. They react together at about 800°C. If a little sodium sulphate is introduced then this temperature is reduced. A good example of this is that of the early calcareous (clay–quartz–lime) stoneware glazes from China.

A typical sample analysis of one of these revealed the following % by weight:-

Silica (SiO_2)	62%
Alumina (Al_2O_3)	14·75%
Calcia (CaO)	23·5%

The resulting eutectic composition melts at 1170°C and makes a stoneware glaze at temperatures above 1200°C (*Details from Oriental glazes* by Nigel Wood) yet silica alone melts at 1710°C, alumina alone melts at 2030°C and calcia alone melts at 2570°C.

An excellent list of eutectic compositions and melting points is available in the book on ceramic glazes from Borax Consolidated. In glass making or glaze making considerable use is made of alkaline oxides and these introduce another dimension to the forming of eutectics because many of them melt before any eutectic can be established. They work by surrounding the silica grains with molten material which gradually attacks them to form silicates. Whilst there is no true eutectic in this case, many authorities suggest, for convenience, a figure to describe what might be considered as a eutectic point for batch melting. The resulting molten silicates react further with other batch materials in sequence, forming eutectics at various stages until the whole of the batch is melted and homogeneous. Some materials do not produce a simple graph to show one eutectic point. Lead and copper oxides for instance produce three eutectic points with a reverse trend between each.

Some of the minerals such as the feldspars and various wood ashes used for glaze or glass batch are already complex mixtures of various oxides so their behaviour in forming eutectics is not quite as predictable as it might seem. When other oxides are added, the plotting of a suitable simple graph to illustrate what is likely to be the forming of several eutectics becomes very difficult if not impossible. In a factory or in a research situation, three sided graphs would be produced to plot this behaviour but the individual potter or studio glassmaker is unlikely to feel inclined to become so involved. A compromise is often achieved by plotting a theoretical graph by assuming a mixture of oxides on one side and silica on the other. This offers the possibility of indicating the behaviour relative to particular temperatures in terms of a glaze being matt, glossy or crystalline in character.

Devitrification

The difficulties caused by devitrification in studio glass are exactly the same as those in the factory. Whilst it rarely occurs in a glassblowing studio it often occurs in kiln cast glass where the cooling of the material in a mould tends to be slow enough to allow nucleation to take place and for crystals to form. If the result is one in which there is uniform translucency or opacity then this may well be caused by some other factor such as glass to glass phase separation or simply the effect of dust on the pieces being fused or cast. The studio glass maker has always taken a rather wide, and often incorrect interpretation of devitrification and anything which in the process of creating cast or kiln formed work has become opaque or translucent tends to be labelled as being devitrified.

Glass will always try to regain a more regular crystalline lattice on cooling but it is restricted from doing so because of the viscosity of the material. If however, the glass is held at its liquidus temperature for any length of time, the network modifiers can help to form crystals of, for instance, devitrite. Typically. $Na_2O.CaO.6Si_2O$. These localised crystals have a changed composition from that of the glass resulting in a different coefficient of expansion. This creates areas of strain and tends to promote cracks. For those people responsible for industrial glass production, devitrification is something of that they hope will never happen so, as far as is reasonably possible, both glass founding, glass composition end the cooling rates are designed to reduce the possibility of it occurring. Because of this, the normal procedure is to cool the glass as quickly as is reasonably possible to a temperature at which it can be annealed. Unfortunately, some manufacturing processes need the glass to be in a malleable and working state for a long time and this enhances the possibility of the formation of devitrite.

The studio glassblower who wants a glass to stay workable for a long time may be tempted to reduce the amount of lime. In this case he runs the danger of producing a glass which is not very stable. The normal reaction would be to substitute another stabiliser for some of the calcia. Devitrification can occur in the molten glass while it is in the furnace, particularly if there are parts of the tank or pot that remain cool. This can cause the production of devitrification stones and/or cords and create a subsequent loss of production.

A manufacturer who wishes to produce a glass which hardens quickly to suit a particular forming process may decide to increase the amount of calcia in the batch as an increase in the calcia content of a glass reduces the time at which the glass remains malleable. If he overdoes this he increases the risk of producing crystals of devitrite as glass with a high calcia content tends to devitrify easily.

Experience would suggest that anything which has developed individual patches of what could possibly be crystalline material is likely to be suspect and should be discarded whilst glass which has become finely and evenly opaque or translucent throughout will probably be safe provided that there has been adequate annealing and if all the various pieces of glass involved are compatible with each other. Studio glassmakers producing kiln formed pieces need to be particularly careful when trying to remelt or fuse together glass that contains areas of devitrification with glass which is clear. The devitrified areas of glass will not melt as readily as the normal glass and as a result will resist moving into the intended form. Even if the two materials become successfully incorporated to any extent the result will inevitably be unstable and will either immediately or eventually probably crack or simply fall into pieces.

A clay body remains a largely crystalline material after firing but goes through a process of forming glassy phases which sinter the particles together or, as in the case of stoneware, fill the pores. Some of this glass can recrystallise during cooling and can also react with the glaze materials to form new crystals. In a glaze, however, the deliberate formation of crystals by the process of devitrification, is common practice and is responsible for a considerable number of different popular glazes (see Opaque and translucent glazes, 225). With these it is standard practice either to use a slow cooling cycle or to hold the firing at a specific temperature at some stage during the cooling. It is not strictly necessary, however, and a pot can be fired normally and then reheated to that temperature to allow crystals to grow. Crystalline and most matt and semi-matt glazes are the result of some form of devitrification. These glazes have been around for a long time and some of the famous oriental glazes such as the Chun (Jun) exist because of the formation of crystals within the glaze surface. A glass which has a high lime content tends to devitrify easily so calcia is usually kept below about 7% to provide an efficient stabiliser which will not produce problems. In a glaze with a high lime content, however, and an appropriate cooling cycle, this simply results in the formation of small crystals which give the glaze a fine matt or semi-matt surface.

In a glass, the random presence of seed materials such as titanium dioxide or zinc oxide can encourage crystal growth by acting as nucleating agents. Devitrification can occur in the furnace, particularly if there are parts of the tank or pot that remain cool. This can cause the production of devitrification stones and/or cords which often lead to a subsequent waste of material. The danger of devitrification in studio glass is exactly the same as that in the factory. It often occurs in kiln cast glass where the cooling of the material in a mould tends to be slow. Ideally glass should be cooled quickly through the critical stages after firing to minimise the risk of any undesirable devitrification.

If the result is one of random patches or single areas of devitrification then there is the same danger of the creation of strain. If the result is one which results in uniform opacity or translucency throughout the work then the procedure will probably have resulted in something resembling a glass ceramic, in which case the formation of strain is far less likely.

Cast sculpure by Professor Zora Palova. Photograph by D & D Studio, Bratislava, Slovakia

Glass ceramics

A controlled form of devitrification is currently being exploited in the manufacture of what have come to be called "glass ceramics". In this case glass has been specifically formulated with appropriate seed materials to produce fine, evenly distributed crystals throughout when reheated to a particular temperature, resulting in material with wide ranging properties. Types such as those based on lithium aluminium silicates usually have a particularly low coefficient of expansion, or even a negative coefficient of expansion thus creating a considerable resistance to thermal shock. They are produced largely for such things as cooker top surfaces and cooking ware in which the total resistance to thermal shock is very important. Many of these can be taken directly from a freezer to a red hot burner without damage.

In contrast, some glass ceramics have been created with a high coefficient of expansion in order to produce a material which by matching expansion and contraction will bond easily to particular metals.

Photograph of an unusual growth of crystals in a zircon/alumina based refractory at the bottom of a glass furnace

Others are made which have mica-like crystals, have a high physical strength and have such a low degree of brittleness that they can be machined in a similar manner to metals.

Some glass ceramics have found a ready application in rocketry and complex engineering.

There is no doubt that the range of uses that is developing for glass ceramics is increasing all the time. Even the scale of some projects is astounding. In recent years, Schott Glass of Germany made a huge glass ceramic astronomical mirror carrier over eight metres in diameter. The weight of the original glass casting was 44 tons and was 30 cm thick. It then had to be heat treated to turn it into a glass ceramic and after extensive machining had a final diameter of 8·2 metres, a thickness of 17·7 cm and a weight of 23 tons.

A great deal of research is being carried out into the considerable possibilities and potential of glass ceramics but as yet there is little sign of them being exploited in a studio. This is possibly because of the fact that whilst they could be of great value in structures requiring considerable strength there are few obvious aesthetic advantages over normal glass formed objects. Many glass ceramics also require rather higher melting conditions and more accurate controls than are likely to be found in the small studio or workshop.

The range of glass ceramics has increased enormously over recent years and they are now specially formulated to fit the needs of domestic, high tech engineering and many other processes. They can also be produced cheaply from such basic materials as basalt, furnace slag and fly ash from power stations. They are finding increased use in medical circles as materials for bone replacement and in dentistry for fillings to replace the mercury amalgam which is rapidly falling out of favour because of its growing reputation as a potential health risk.

The normal method of manufacture is to melt a glass from a suitably prepared batch, form it into the required shape as a glassy material and then to hold it at a suitable temperature to enable the polycrystalline structure of a glass ceramic to form. Alternatively, the product can be cooled and annealed normally and then reheated to follow the same procedure of being held at an appropriate temperature. The material is normally non-porous so it can be ground and polished without difficulty.

The process has not shown many signs of being exploited by artist craftsmen as yet, largely because it is seen as a highly technical process needing specially formulated glasses with suitable microfine nucleating agents evenly distributed throughout. In fact, whilst the glass industry has traditionally and, in the main, successfully tried to produce glass which is unlikely to devitrify, it is quite possible to find commercially produced glass which, with the right kind of encouragement, will produce a glass ceramic. The results will almost always be opaque and some of them can even resemble fine porcelain. Studio glassmakers who reheat industrial glass objects can often be surprised to find

Large standing form in devitrified borosilicate by the author

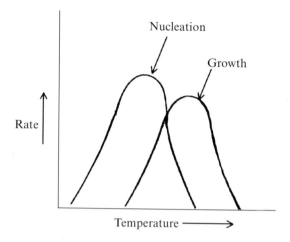

Rates of nucleation and growth.
Reproduced by kind permission of the Society of Glass Technology

unusual changes to both colour and opacity. These changes are often the result of devitrification and can occasionally produce a form of glass ceramic.

One glass ceramic manufacturing process which might be developed by the studio craftsman is that of sintering glass particles together before taking the resulting forms through the nucleating and devitrifying stages. Another interesting industrial approach which is attracting much attention is one of using the fly ash from power stations to produce glass ceramics.

It must be stressed that whilst a properly formed glass ceramic will tend to have considerable strength and stability, an unevenly devitrified glass will tend to have the opposite qualities. Pockets of devitrified material in a glassy material can create considerable weakness because of the strain which is likely to occur from the differing expansions and behaviour of the glassy and the crystalline parts.

Several materials have been introduced as nucleating agents in glasses to be turned into glass ceramics. The most common of these are lithia, titania, magnesia and zinc oxide. One of the interesting lithium based glass ceramics is that in which beta-eucryptite crystals have been developed. These are lithium aluminium silicate and are so small that the resulting glass ceramic is transparent. Eucryptite is unusual in that its atomic structure is such that it has a small negative expansion coefficient and as a result produces a glass ceramic which shrinks when it is heated. Because of this it can be used to toughen a sodium alumina titania silica glass. When the sodium ions at the surface are replaced by lithia ions, heat treatment can result in the formation of a beta-eucryptite glass ceramic skin. When cooled the surface tries to expand whilst the inside is shrinking and the resulting toughening stresses develop.

It is important for the successful production of glass ceramics that the nucleation and the crystal development phases overlap as shown in the diagram above.

An 8 metre diameter glass ceramic mirror blank for an astronomical telescope weighing 44 tons made by Schott Glass. By courtesy of Schott Information

Carbon and carbonates

There is one chemical which is heavily involved in ceramic and glass forming yet after firing and founding has been completed, rarely remains in either. This is carbon and can be found in group IV of the periodic table. It exists in a very hard pyramidical crystal form as a diamond and in a much softer sheet form as graphite, a material much used as a lubricant, and as a mould material for blown glass. It has the ability to combine with oxygen to form carbon monoxide (CO) which is a very insidious toxic gas, or to form CO_2 which is an extremely abundant gas produced by burning most fuels. It also forms CO_3 which can only remain stable when combined with other elements to form carbonates. These carbonates constitute a large proportion of the materials used in formulating a batch or a glaze. Potassium carbonate, sodium carbonate and calcium carbonate are the most common of these. As they become heated, carbon dioxide is driven off to leave the active oxide which forms part of the resulting material. It is important to take the loss of the carbon dioxide into account when calculating batch or glaze formula. By totalling the atomic weights of the elements in a formula we can find the molecular weight of the compound as described earlier and, if there is a release of gas or steam, we can calculate this to leave the weight of the active constituents. For example:-

calcium carbonate, $CaCO_3$ becomes:

calcium (40·1) + carbon (12) + oxygen (3 × 16) = 100·1

When the carbon dioxide has been released we are left with:

calcium (40·1) and oxygen (16) = 56·1

This means that if a certain amount of calcium carbonate is stated as part of a batch it becomes necessary to multiply that amount by 56·1 and divide by

Detail of a panel in devitrified borosilicate

100·1 to find the amount of calcium oxide which will become part of the glaze or glass. Conversely, if a glaze or glass formula requires a certain amount of calcium oxide then this figure needs to be multiplied by 100·1 and divided by 56·1 to find the amount of calcium carbonate which will supply this.

Moles

Atoms and molecules are very tiny particles and are almost impossible to visualise as quantities. To help with this particular difficulty a term has been devised to help with material calculations and is known as is the "mole". This is one of the accepted international terms of measurement and is often used to indicate a sufficient weight of a material to be viable in a practical sense. The mole is defined as having the same number of particles as are found in 12 grams of carbon-12. This calculates as being $6·022 \times 10^{23}$ (or 6,022 with 23 zero digits after the 6). In other words there are $6·022 \times 10^{23}$ atoms in a mole of a particular element or $6·022 \times 10^{23}$ molecules in a mole of a particular compound. For example, a mole of hydrogen will weigh 1 gram. As this is a standard reference point it means that a mole of an element such as aluminium with an atomic weight of 27 will weigh 27 grams. It also means that a mole of silica with a molecular weight of 60·1 will weigh 60·1 grams.

For the purposes of measuring reasonable quantities the mole is a very useful tool but when being used simply for comparative purposes it is probably just as convenient to use the atomic or molecular weight.

Taken from *A Dictionary of Glass*, C. Bray, A & C Black Ltd, London 1995.

Immiscibility and phase separation

Two other terms which often appear in technical literature relating to glass are "immiscibility" and "phase separation". In simple terms immiscibility refers to materials, particularly liquids, which under normal circumstances do not mix and which will separate readily into distinct layers. Oil and water provide

Electron micrographs showing the conversion of amorphous glass to crystalline glass ceramic

1. A flake of essentially amorphous glass containing dissolved nucleating agents

2. Heat treatment produces nuclei that initiate the growth of crystals shown as dark spots in the picture when they are 100 angstroms across

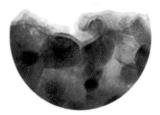

3. Crystallisation is almost complete with crystals now 600 angstroms across. Further treatment makes the crystals coalesce into larger ones

From Glass in the Modern World, *Terence Mahoney, Aldus Books, 1967*

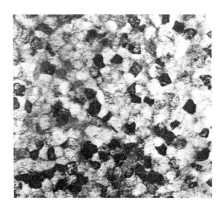

Sub microstructure in lithia–alumina–silica glass ceramic.
From Ceramic Microstructures, *John Wiley and Sons New York 1968*

an obvious example. When stirred together and depending on the proportions of the two liquids the oil will form into droplets suspended within the water or, alternatively, water can form into droplets suspended within the oil. When left to stand, according to the viscosity, they will soon separate into two different liquids and the oil will usually float on top of the water. In the case of liquids behaving in this manner the liquid with the greater density will sink to the bottom and the less dense liquid will float on top. These two liquids are said to be immiscible and when they have regained their identity as two distinctly different liquids they can be said to have been phase separated. This happens often in systems involving liquids so is not surprising that it can happen in molten glass. If the oil and water mixture is frozen quickly before it can separate, a solid material containing fine droplets of one material will be formed within the other. This often happens in most glasses, and particularly in commercial borosilicate glasses. The droplets are not visible to the naked eye and the glassware produced appears to be completely clear. However, if the glass is reheated, as would be the case if it was used for kiln casting or kiln forming, then the process of phase separation could continue to the extent that the glass becomes translucent or opaque. In the case of molten glass it is possible for two separate viscous liquids to form within the melt, particularly if it is left standing for some time. These can become quite different in character and create all sorts of problems if work recommences before the melt is made reasonably homogenous again. If however, particles of one glassy material form within another, the results can rarely be seen by the naked eye in completed forms but can be readily seen under a powerful microscope. This becomes known as glass to glass phase separation. Because of the length of time involved glasses usually become solid material on cooling before complete separation can take place. The transformation into a solid material is similar to the freezing of the oil and water mixture. Affected glass is said to be glass to glass phase separated because of the immiscibility. The viscosity of the melt can have a considerable effect. It is possible that melts of low viscosity can separate in time into distinct layers of glass, each with different compositions and behaviour to the extent that very fluid melts left to stand in the furnace may need considerable mechanical stirring to bring them back to a reasonably homogenous and useable glass. Melts of high viscosity will tend to have little separation to the extent that droplets can only rarely be found. In firing clay bodies and in the formation of various glazes, time is equally important in the development of phase separation. When a glass is melted properly, the resulting molten mass should be reasonably homogenous but in the course of cooling, phase separation can take place. The importance of the time element which has been stressed in the firing of clay can be just as important here. This is most evident when nucleation followed by crystallisation takes place as in the case of glass ceramics and in the formation of crystalline glazes. This is a form of phase separation.

Other forms of phase separation can occur. Some of these form matrices of droplets or complex connected microstructures within the glass. Sometimes they cause light scattering resulting in opalescence. They can be evenly distributed throughout the glass or can occur in pockets. Phase separation can develop when glass is remelted in the process of making cast forms in a kiln. There is a tendency among glass artists to ascribe any opacity which develops in glass to devitrification whereas it is often the result either of phase separation or, particularly in kiln forming, to the presence of dust particles.

XII.
Faults

Many of the problems which affect both potters and glassmakers are caused by contraction and to a lesser extent, expansion. These can easily lead to stresses which cause various types of cracks and breakages. Other problems involve the considered selection of suitable materials, their compatibility, the proportions in which they are used and the correct use of firing procedures.

The control of heat and time in the making of ceramics, the making of glass and successful glaze forming is also much more important than many people realise. In making pots, the removal of water is the cause of much of the initial shrinkage. Water in clay is lost in various stages. Much of it evaporates as the clay dries but the rest is lost as steam during the firing. A great deal of shrinkage can be involved and if this is not carefully controlled it can lead to distortion and cracking. This is often countered by the introduction of pre-fired materials such as grog. Sand can also be introduced into clay for similar reasons. It tends to open up the clay structure but can also create its own problems by allowing the possibility of creating more cristobalite than is needed or by simply making the clay too short for the required forming process.

Many potters are used to throwing their pots and putting them out in the sun to dry before firing. If the walls and bases of the pots are reasonably thin and even, this may cause no problem but it is always prudent to dry pots out slowly and thoroughly. To put this into perspective, consider a glassmakers pot which may have to hold over a ton of molten glass for several months. This will be likely to have clay walls over two inches thick. To reduce the possibility of it developing potential cracks or other weaknesses, it is customary to dry the pot very slowly and carefully over a period of several weeks before introducing it into the pot arch or the furnace.

Whilst there are no similar drying problems in dealing with glass, it is also easily affected by the stresses caused by shrinkage, to the extent that the coefficient of expansion of a glass needs to be considered very carefully, particularly when two or more different kinds of glass need to be fused together. The compatibility of these largely depends on them having the same, or very nearly the same, coefficient of expansion. It also means that glass needs to go through a careful process of annealing by being held at or near to particular temperatures for a period of time, followed by an appropriate cooling cycle depending on the thickness and nature of the glass involved. This will be described in greater depth under the heading of "Annealing".

A glaze also needs to have its constituents calculated to fit the type of ceramic being used. There is a considerable amount of leeway in this because there is a certain amount of elasticity involved but if the expansion of both materials is not sufficiently compatible, then the glaze can either flake away from the ceramic or it can craze.

Fused soda–lime–silica glass

There is another important consideration relating to ceramics, glazes and glass. If the resulting products are likely to have to withstand thermal shock the problems of expansion and compatibility will need particularly close attention. The problems encountered as a result of stress both in making ceramics and in glassmaking can easily result in a tremendous waste of materials, time and effort. Results can also have a devastating effect on customer relationship.

An understanding of the causes and effects of the forming processes and the behaviour of particular materials in various circumstances can reduce these difficulties considerably if they are given due consideration. Some materials may need to be removed from clay to avoid the possibility of causing defects such as bloating and cracking. Firing schedules must also be carefully considered in regard to the nature of the clay, the size of the articles being fired and the maturing temperature of the glazes being used.

Several measures are also available to reduce the possibility of the creation of seeds, cords and stones in glass and annealing schedules need to be suitable to the type and thickness of the glass.

Some of the problems and defects which may be encountered are:-

In ceramics	Distortion and cracking
	Dunting - stress cracks formed in the firing process
	Spalling - the breaking away of pieces of material from refractories in kilns and furnaces
	Bloating - blistering in the clay body caused by trapped gases
	Black core - a dark grey colour which occurs inside fired bodies

In slip	Uneven colour
	Slip shrinks away from the body
	Distortion of the form after slip has been applied
	Cracking of the form after the slip has been applied
In casting slip	Insufficient fluidity
	Insufficient permeability
	Cast not firm enough when released from the mould
	Slip materials too coarse
	Uneven interior surface in the cast
	Pinholes in the cast
	Cast too brittle
	Cast too flabby
In glazes	Crazing - often called crackle when deliberately induced
	Shivering - sharp long slivers of glaze breaking away from the pot
	Shelling, peeling - flakes of glaze falling from the pot
	Crawling - where the glaze rolls back upon itself to produce ridges or beads
	Flashing the result of volatile materials settling on the glaze
	Pitting and specking
	Matting, starved glaze, cut glaze - very thin or no glaze on some areas
	Pinholes and dimples - small craters or dimples caused by escaping gas
	Sulphuring - aired ware, sometimes known as starring and feathering
In glass	Seeds - small bubbles in glass
	Cords - lines of viscous material in molten glass
	Stones - solid matter trapped in molten glass
	Decay - crizzling, surface decomposition
	Incompatibility - when materials cannot be joined safely
	Annealing problems - usually cracks or breakage
	Devitrification - when part or all of a glass turns into a crystalline form

Ceramic faults

Many of the cracks which occur in the making of pottery need no explanation. They can be so obvious that the remedy is readily perceived. Most of those which arise before the ware is fired are caused by poor design, rapid or uneven drying, applying slip to clay which is too dry or too thin, uneven consistency or variation in the thickness of the clay. Those which occur during or after firing can also be obvious but there are others that are not so readily identified.

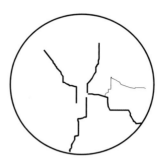

This type of crack develops on the base of a pot and is commonly known as a star crack. It often continues up the side of the pot.

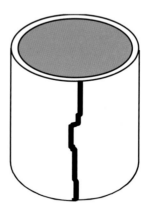

If the base of a pot is too thin for the sides a star crack can start at the base during drying and continue up the side of the pot. Similar cracks can also develop during a biscuit firing from those which started during drying but which might not have become visually evident at that stage. Such a crack can also be caused in a glaze firing by the layer of glaze on the inside being too thick for the body. The starting point of a crack is often a good clue, and this can be discerned by the fact that the widest part of a crack is often its starting point.

Rim crack showing the wide start point. Rim cracks are likely to have been started in the raw state by rapid drying or by the rim section being too thin but may not have developed until the ware had been fired. Firing in which the kiln was taken up quickly in the early stages would contribute to this type of crack. Another common cause of similar cracks in firing results from ware which after drying has been left standing in a damp atmosphere and as a result has re-adsorbed moisture.

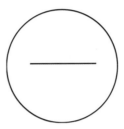

Straight cracks across the base of a thrown pot are usually due to uneven drying but can also result from the pot being left to dry on a non-absorbent surface such as a wheel head or a wheel bat.

An "S" crack across the inside of the base of a pot is usually caused by not removing any surplus water or slurry before leaving it to dry, or by fluidity problems with casting slip.

Cracks which have started by pieces being blown from the body are likely to have been caused by the ware still being somewhat damp on firing or by the inclusion of material such as pieces of limestone in the clay. These can absorb water and expand sufficiently to flake pieces of the body away and to start cracks.

Cracks which occur in the glaze firing often result from the application of a thick layer of glaze on to a thin body, or because the calculations to ensure a reasonably compatible glaze have not been adequate and the resulting glaze has resisted the squeeze which the pot has tried to put on to it. Another cause of cracking is simply that caused by thermal shock when a kiln door has been opened whilst the ware is still hot

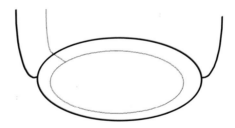

This type of circular crack around a base usually results from stress between glaze and body particularly when a thick layer of glaze has developed on the inside of the base. The circular piece will often drop out completely.

Many cracks are caused by dunting. This results from the fact that the clay body in the process of being biscuit fired turns some of the silica into cristobalite. In the cooling cycle there are two inversions which take place at 573°C (1063°F) for quartz and at 226°C (439°F) for cristobalite. There is a considerable shrinkage involved which in most cases exerts a beneficial squeeze on the glaze but if there is too much cristobalite or if the difference in the expansion rates of the body and the glaze is too great then the stresses become too much for the pot to stand and it cracks (see Silica phases and inversions, page 81).

There are also other possible causes in that expansion differences between a slip and the clay body can have a similar effect and there is a rare possibility that dunts can result from the inversion when a kiln is being taken up to temperature.

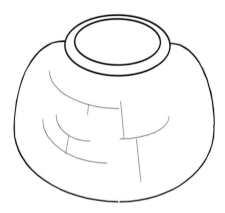

Dunts which occur during a biscuit firing are often very fine and as a result can easily be missed. They often only become really visible when a glaze is applied. If they happen to be missed at this stage it is virtually inevitable that the cracks will develop much further during the glaze firing.

It is standard practice in industry to ensure that the clay for ware that is to be glazed at earthenware temperatures contains sufficient fine silica particles and is fired sufficiently high to convert them into cristobalite during the biscuit firing and ensure the necessary squeeze on the glaze. On the other hand, if the clay is to be turned into stoneware, then it is normal practice to use large particle silica such as sand if this is considered necessary and to fire the biscuit to a rather lower temperature to ensure that less cristobalite is produced at this stage.

There are some rule of thumb remedies:-

(1) Sometimes taking a pot slowly through the inversion temperatures will appear to help and a pot may survive because of this but the stress is likely to be still there and may cause trouble later on

(2) The amount of free silica in the clay can be reduced

(3) The time that the pot is held at its top temperature in the biscuit firing can be reduced This allows sufficient glassy bonding materials to be formed without allowing time for too much of the silica to convert into cristobalite

(4) Extra fluxing materials other than calcia and magnesia can be added to the clay to turn some of the free silica into glassy bonding material which then leaves less of it available for inversion

A similar effect in porcelain is created by virtue of the fact that any free silica is likely to be very fine and turns readily into the glassy material which produces its translucency.

Conversely, in coarse stoneware, most free silica particles are likely to be large and whilst there will be sufficient conversion to glass particles there will be little conversion to cristobalite.

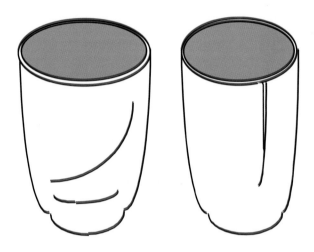

Dunts which develop in cooling after a glaze firing are the most common. They can be vertical, spiral or simply horizontal. The edges of the cracks tend to be very sharp but may still be so fine that they are not immediately discernible by sight but may be detected by touch. They may also only really develop some weeks after firing when the stress becomes just too much to be sustained and the pot falls or explodes apart. This behaviour is not confined to the stress caused by cristobalite but can also be caused by incompatibility of glaze and body.

Horizontal cracks often develop in tall pots simply because the top may cool more quickly than the bottom and when the sudden silica inversion takes place the top shrinks before the rest of the pot and causes the horizontal crack.

This irregular cooling can also occur in wide bowls and plates so it is important to try to maintain an even temperature during cooling and, if using a gas, oil or wood fired kiln, make sure that there is not a draught affecting one side of the pots.

Springing

Cracks often occur where a handle joins a pot. This type of failure is not necessarily confined to handles, it can also happen to spouts and lugs. There are several causes for this and most of them originate whilst the handle is being attached. The breaking away from the body of the pot usually occurs during the drying period but may not be obvious until the biscuit firing or, in some cases, even in the glaze firing.

The most common cause lies in a difference in moisture content between the pot and the handle. If one is drier than the other there will be a difference in

shrinkage which will be sufficient to create the initial weakness. Too little, or more likely, too much moisture at the join can be sufficient cause. This can happen particularly if the pot has been allowed to become too dry before the handle is attached and some slip is added or developed in the hope of achieving a join. If the handle clay is too stiff, too dry or different from that of the pot then trouble can develop. A common fault is one in which the clay being used is too short to make pulling a handle an easy task and the potter has added some plastic clay to make it easier. Unfortunately, this also has the effect of increasing the shrinkage in the handle.

A crack can also develop somewhere along the handle. Similarly, this usually occurs in the making process and may not become obvious until either the biscuit or the glaze firing. This type of break more commonly occurs in short clay which has been difficult to pull into a handle but it can also result from the handle being too thin.

Spalling

Spalling usually refers to small parts of refractory materials that come away from the walls and roof areas of kilns and furnaces but it can also happen to pots. This happens in most cases because of thermal shock when the temperature is taken up too quickly but in kilns and furnaces it can happen simply because of the wear and tear of constant firing. In a glass furnace the refractories suffer attack from volatiles, particularly from alkalis in the founding process. This results in a gradual but inevitable deterioration from which some spalling is likely from time to time until eventually the furnace needs a rebuild. There has been a recent innovation to delay this procedure, it consists of a lance that blasts a mixture of oxygen and refractory particles on to worn refractories and builds them up without the necessity of a furnace shut down. Spalling is a considerable nuisance to the glassmaker as the pieces of refractory material tend to fall into the molten glass and create stones. Whilst a glass furnace is taken up to a temperature for founding and then maintained at a lower temperature for working it is not normally allowed to cool sufficiently for silica inversions to have much effect. A ceramic kiln, however, is constantly being taken up to temperature and down again which allows a much greater possibility for silica inversions to take place. The difference between the hot face and the interior of the refractories also keeps changing which means that the resulting expansion and contraction creates stresses which can lead to some loosening of surfaces. Spalling in a ceramic kiln is not quite the drastic problem that it is in a glass furnace but any extraneous matter falling onto a soft glaze will almost certainly ruin the affected piece. Too much spalling is obviously a result of wear and tear but if rapid heating can be avoided then at least the time for remedial action can be delayed. In pots it is often caused by material such as small pieces of limestone which have found their way into the clay body, absorb water after firing which causes them to expand and prise away parts of the surface of the pot.

Bloating

Bloating, or blisters forming from the clay body during firing, is usually caused by the release of gases which have been unable to escape through the pores of the clay. There are many of these though the most common are carbon monoxide and carbon dioxide from the various carbonates in the clay. Sometimes there are also sulphur compounds and fluorides which release volatiles in similar manner. It can occur in slipware when the slip manages to create a barrier to prevent the escape of the gases but it is most likely to be found in stoneware where the pores are more likely to become blocked, particularly if there is residual carbon which has not been burned out in the biscuit firing. This carbon takes oxygen from wherever it can and burns out but the resulting gases tend to become trapped and cause bloating. If there is iron oxide in the clay the carbon will remove oxygen from this material. As a result there is often some reduction that causes the dark greys to black areas inside the clay body which become known as black core.

Slip faults

The faults which arise from the application of slip tend to result mostly from applying the slip when the pot is either too wet or too dry or by applying a thick layer of slip to a thin pot. As a result the pot will probably either crack in the drying if too dry or will warp out of shape if too wet. Experience and common sense will suggest an obvious remedy. A thinner layer of slip will often prove successful. To a lesser degree problems can also arise when the shrinkage, which is inevitable in both the drying and in the firing stages, is not reasonably similar in both body and slip. This again is a problem which tends to be more pronounced if the slip layer is thick. Shrinkage differences usually result in flaking or curling of the slip from the body and it is probable that the greater shrinkage is in the slip rather than the body.

Section of a piece of bloated pot

If the flaking happens before firing then there are some possible causes and cures:-

(1) The pot may be too dry when the slip is applied. It is usually better to aim at the slip being applied as early as possible but not to the extent that the pot will warp or collapse

(2) The slip layer is too thick for the pot - apply a thinner layer and dry more slowly

(3) Some of the materials in the slip may have settled to the bottom of the container - make sure that the slip is well stirred before use

(4) The proportion of plastic clay in the slip is too high - try substituting china clay for some of the plastic clay

There are rare occasions when the body may be shrinking more than the slip and this tends to be evident in the slip flaking in flat pieces rather than curls. As before, applying a thinner layer of slip may help but apart from this the cure will be the reverse of some of those indicated earlier.

For instance, a higher proportion of plastic clay or a small addition of bentonite could be effective.

A reduction in the amount of filler material such as grog could also help. If these measures fail, then an addition of gum or a commercial binder could be tried.

Sometimes the flaking may not occur until the biscuit or, as is more likely, the glaze firing. In this case the natural compression of the glaze puts the slip under more pressure, forcing it to break away from the body. The traditional method of carrying out a simple test is to add some of the glaze, about 15% to 20% to the slip. This increases the firing shrinkage of the slip but also tends to develop a better bonding of the slip to the body. Again, there are some rare occasions when this does not work and the addition of a glaze or fluxing material actually makes the flaking worse. This is because the firing shrinkage of the slip is already too great for the body. The remedy in this case is either to reduce fluxing material in the slip or to add low expansion materials such as calcined alumina or flint.

Uneven colour in a slip is usually caused by colouring oxides or stains not being sufficiently well prepared or not being evenly distributed throughout the slip. Slips need to be mixed thoroughly before use and also allowed to stand sufficiently for any entrapped air bubbles to escape. Just as colour can migrate to a glaze from the ceramic body, it can also move into a slip, particularly at stoneware temperatures.

Faults resulting from the use of casting slip

As the process of slip casting requires the mould to absorb sufficient of the water from the casting slip for it to form a layer of clay on the surface of the mould, it is very easy for the mould to become saturated before a satisfactory layer is produced. In order to make the process more viable, it is the normal custom to prepare slips of the required fluidity which will pour well and pick up the fine details of the mould but which attain the fluidity whilst containing less liquid. This is achieved by adding appropriate deflocculants to the slip (see Slip casting page 31). The deflocculants have the effect of causing the clay particles to repel each other. This results in them being separated, being able to pack better and needing much less water to achieve fluidity. This packing of the clay particles can cause a lack of permeability after the initial layer is formed onto the surface of the mould so it is standard practice to include some fine grog, 10 to 20%, or similar filler in a casting slip to maintain a degree of porosity. The amount and types of deflocculant added to produce a casting slip are critical to the success so failure to produce the right proportions or the right materials is a major cause of faults in slip casting. For example, sodium silicate and sodium carbonate are the two most common deflocculants but sodium silicate used on its own tends to produce very brittle casts whilst sodium carbonate used on its own tends to produce very soft, flabby casts so the best of both worlds is achieved by using suitable proportions of the two materials together.

Sometimes an excess of deflocculant will cause the cast to stick to the mould in which case a little more clay can be added to the slip and the surface of the mould dusted with talc. As the moisture is removed from the casting slip by the mould more slip may need to be added to maintain the level.

Some weaknesses can be created, particularly in complex moulds, where these additions overlap and as a result cracks can develop. Slightly dampening the surface of the mould will often help to reduce this problem.

A simple method of checking the alkalinity of a slip is to use pH indicator papers as used in chemistry laboratories or for soil testing. This is particularly useful in ensuring that a newly made replacement slip is similar to a previous mixture.

Pillar, *stone and lead crystal*

Pinholes

In slip casting these are common faults. There are several reasons but the most common are dusty moulds or dust having fallen into the slip, carbon products in the slip mixture which burn out in the firing, pouring the slip too quickly so that air becomes trapped, including reclaimed slip without further reprocessing and not allowing sufficient time for air to escape from a slip after mixing. The remedies for these faults are obvious.

The use of a new mould will often cause pinholes and it is good practice to make an initial cast and return it to the blunger rather than fire it before proceeding with any production. Mould porosity is an important factor which is often ignored and it is necessary to introduce the correct of amount water to plaster when making a mould.

Glaze faults

Glaze fit

It is essential that a glaze must be compatible with, and able to bond to, the fired clay body to which it is to be applied. Both body and glaze need to be reasonably in tune or a whole series of faults can develop. Despite this, prepared clay bodies and glazes are commonly supplied to potters without any indication of expansion and content. If they then fit, it is often a result of good fortune and a considerable amount of toleration in the materials rather than of calculation. There are several methods available to correct faults and these will be described later but it is not always as easy to be successful as it would seem. The major factor in whether or not a glaze will fit a body is the relative expansions and contractions of both. This is not necessarily the whole picture as several other items such as the firing cycle and the nature and amount of silica present can have a significant effect. Practically all materials expand as they are heated and then contract by the same amount as they cool provided there has been no chemical change. They also tend to be constant in these movements.

There is an inevitable involvement in compression and tension. If a force is applied to both sides of a material it will be under compression. On the other hand, if the forces are pulling at both sides then the material will be under tension. It is normal to try to achieve a state in which the glaze is put under some compression in order to avoid the possibility of it crazing. There is always a degree of compromise required in matching a glaze to a body as they may not expand and contract equally at the same temperatures. Much of the necessity for this compromise arises from the fact that there is a sudden contraction in the body due to a silica inversion which takes place at about 220°C. This usually has a beneficial effect as it provides the compression that the glaze needs but if there is too much or too little then faults can follow. Because of this, a glaze, and in some cases a body, needs to be sufficiently elastic and have sufficient physical strength to absorb the inevitable compression or tension without breakdown.

A certain amount of stress is always there and as expansions are likely to be different in body and glaze at different temperatures the results of this stress may not show up immediately after the glaze firing but may occur when the ware is in use. This becomes evident particularly if the ware is used for cooking where resistance to thermal shock becomes an essential quality. The problems may be such that they can only be cured by installing a buffer layer between the body and the glaze to ease the effect of any stress. This is often applied in the form of an engobe applied to the raw ware or by washing a layer of soft flux on to the biscuit before the glaze is applied. The engobe is usually made from equal mixtures of a clay body and glaze and potters often take the opportunity to add a little colour or alternatively produce a white engobe which will soften the effects of colour which could migrate from the original body. A buffer layer can also be developed by longer soaking at the glaze temperature so that the molten glaze can flux the surface of the body. The resultant layer is often more alumina rich than the glaze and can tend to promote crystal growth. A thick buffer layer usually develops naturally in porcelain and this can often be thicker than the actual glaze layer.

As expansion and contraction is so important there are many aspects of this which need to be explained. They need to be considered over the full range from the annealing temperature to room temperature. Expansion and contraction can be altered by modifying the composition as some of the materials such as potassium oxide and sodium oxide produce high rates of expansion and contraction and are much more likely to cause crazing than other fluxes. All the other basic oxides such as those of lithium, barium, calcium, lead, magnesium and zinc have lower coefficients of expansion than the sodium and potassium oxides as can be seen from the tables below. This means that, within reason, a certain amount of substitution can be effective in reducing the possibility of crazing. Lead oxide has the additional advantage of increasing the elasticity of a glaze. Boric oxide is often introduced for the same purpose. It is a glass former but also acts as a very effective flux. It also has a very low coefficient of expansion so the introduction of boric oxide or a suitable borax frit in place of the soda or potash is a fairly common method of reducing the expansion of a glaze. Sometimes the addition of an opacifier to a glaze will affect the expansion and contraction considerably. Crystalline glazes are in general less likely to craze than others but zirconium oxide or zirconium silicate will lower the glaze expansion, sometimes to the extent that the body is put under so much tension that it breaks. The use of zinc oxide as a flux can have a similar effect.

Comparative ordering of approximate thermal expansions of the common ceramic and glass materials:-

High expansion	sodium oxide
	potassium oxide
	calcium oxide
	chrome oxide
	cerium oxide
	cobalt oxide
	lead oxide
	iron oxide
	titanium dioxide
	antimony oxide
	lithium oxide
	phosphorous pentoxide
	zinc oxide
	copper oxide
	manganese dioxide
	magnesium oxide
	tin oxide
	zirconium oxide
	aluminium trioxide (alumina)
	boric oxide
Low expansion	fused silica

An important factor in achieving glaze fit is the nature and amount of free silica in the body. This changes its crystalline form at about 570°C from alpha to beta quartz In further heating to about 1100°C as is the normal practice in firing biscuit for earthenware, some of this beta-quartz becomes beta-cristobalite. On cooling this changes again to alpha-cristobalite at about 220°C accompanied by a contraction of about three percent. As a glaze is a form of glass, any silica will have become part of the random glass matrix and, therefore, this simply does not happen in the glaze which by this temperature will be solid. It is this sudden contraction which puts the glaze under compression and helps to prevent crazing. This means that one essential point when preparing an earthenware body is to ensure that there is sufficient provision of finely ground flint to provide the amount necessary to convert to cristobalite. Small additions of calcia or talc are often introduced as catalysts to help the conversion. Ground sand or quartz is not generally considered as being as good as ground flint.

Crazing

This is one of the commonest faults to occur in glazing. It usually shows as fine cracks in the glaze surface and is much more of a fault in earthenware than in stoneware where in many cases it is deliberately induced as a decorative feature. Whilst an earthenware glaze can be a form of decoration its prime duty is that of making the ceramic form impervious to water. When the glaze surface becomes covered with fine cracks it allows moisture to enter the body underneath the glaze whilst it is still porous.

Crazing is most likely to be caused by either too great a difference in the expansion of the body and that of the glaze, a lack of the formation of sufficient cristobalite to provide an adequate squeeze on the glaze or underfiring at the biscuit stage which has a similar effect. Another possible cause is that the flint has not been ground fine enough to convert easily at biscuit temperature.

The differences in expansion can be modified by changes either to the body or to the glaze but only a few people seem to prefer to make changes to the body rather than to the glaze. As a general indication it is usual for a fired earthenware body to have something in the region of 75% silica in order to provide sufficient cristobalite to provide adequate compression. The most common practical steps to remedy crazing by modifying the body are:-

    increase the biscuit firing temperature slightly (firing too high would be counterproductive because more of the silica would be turned into glass)
    substitute some of the plastic clay in the body with quartz
    reduce the amount of feldspar in the body
    grind the flint more finely

When modifying the glaze it is possible to reduce its expansion and contraction by increasing the silica and/or the china clay content at the expense of some of the flux material. This may seem to be strange advice as it has also

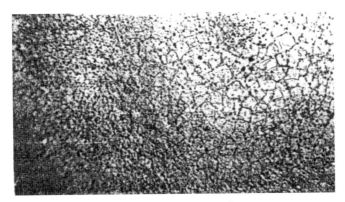

Crazing in a stoneware glaze

been suggested that increasing the silica in the body will make the expansion and contraction greater. This is because in the case of the body, some of the silica converts to cristobalite and provides compression as a result of the silica inversion whereas in a glaze it converts to a glass with a low expansion. As a general rule, an increase in the silica or china clay hardens the glaze whereas an increase in the fluxing material tends to soften the glaze and produce greater expansion and contraction. Some of the fluxes in a glaze, particularly the alkaline fluxes soda and potash, have a very high coefficient of expansion and substituting them to some extent with fluxes of lower expansion will often help.

Boric oxide is a glass former but as it melts at a low temperature it also acts as a flux with a particularly low expansion so amounts of up to 15% as part of a frit as a substitute for some of the alkaline flux can be very effective. The use of lead oxide in an earthenware glaze, whilst being currently under something of a cloud because of its toxicity, is very effective in reducing crazing because it produces a very elastic glass layer.

In stoneware, the body tends to be non-porous and so does not need a glaze to make it impervious. As a result crazing of the glaze is not usually considered to be anything of a problem. It is an effect which is often deliberately cultivated and it is a common practice to rub cold tea into the cracks to accentuate the effect. The name also changes from crazing to crackle or craquelle.

Shivering

Biscuit firing for stoneware is often carried out to a relatively low temperature in order to avoid the formation of cristobalite because if it is present in quantity in very dense stoneware it can lead to dunting or shivering. This usually consists of long sharp slivers of glaze together with some of the body which tend to spring away from the rims and similar sharp edges of pots. It happens much more to stoneware than to earthenware as in this case the bonding of glaze to body is much deeper. The glaze fit is at the root of this problem which is caused by an excess of compression on the glaze.

This can be remedied by either reducing some of the low expansion components of the glaze and substituting materials with higher expansion. Reducing the amount of free silica in the body which is available for conversion into cristobalite may seem to be a remedy but in fact at the higher stoneware temperatures and particularly in a long firing cycle much of this turns to glass in the form of vitreous silica. As this material has a very low coefficient of expansion it has the effect of reducing the amount of contraction in the body. This means that a prolonged soak might result in a reduced body contraction and consequently less tendency to produce shivering but, unfortunately, there is a down side as it also tends to make the body more brittle.

Peeling, shelling and flaking
These seem to be similar faults to shivering but in fact they usually occur on low fired ware where an inadequate bond is established between the glaze and the body. There is a bond failure which is usually due to the normal expansion and contractions of body and glaze combined with underfiring.

Occasionally, if a slip is not a good fit or has been applied badly, then the bond failure will occur at this layer.

Crawling—sometimes known as creeping, rolling or beading
It is often caused by the glaze becoming too viscous when it is melted but there are many other possible reasons. If the glaze layer is seen to have fine cracks when it is applied to the pot and dries then these cracks develop and allow the glaze to separate along them.

This usually happens if the glaze is applied too thickly or if a highly plastic clay has been used in the glaze composition and causes excessive shrinkage in the drying. Overgrinding of the glaze materials can also produce excessive shrinkage.

Glazes with a high surface tension are prone to crawling.

A different cause is that of insufficient flow in the glaze as it matures. This is often as a result of the temperature and/or soaking being inadequate for the particular glaze, insufficient flux material or the presence of alumina or opacifiers such as tin oxide or zirconia which all increase the surface tension. If the glaze has been applied to a dusty surface or one which has been painted with underglazed colour then the glaze can crawl. The surface must be free from dust or grease. A little flux can be mixed with the underglaze colour if this is the cause of the problem.

Crawling is common in glazes using zinc oxide and this can be countered by calcining the zinc oxide with some china clay. It also happens in the celadons which have a high alumina content and may have been overground. Glazes which contain materials that release an excess of volatiles can also cause crawling. Colemanite or borocalcite is a prime example as this material tends to release considerable quantities of steam and should only be used as a relatively small part of a glaze batch. The various carbonates such as whiting also release carbon dioxide in the firing and this can occasionally produce similar effects.

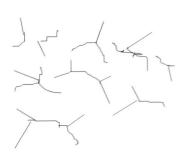

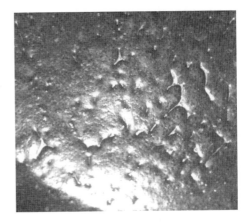

Crawling in a stoneware glaze.
Crawling is often preceded by the appearance of small cracks in the unfired glaze layer.
When fired the glaze seems to withdraw within itself and forms rolls or beads on
the surface of the pot

One of the less obvious causes and yet one which is quite common is that of glaze firing before the pot has become completely dry after the glaze application.

Cut glaze

Also known as matting or starved glaze. This is an effect where the glaze appears not to have been applied, or is evident in parts only as a very thin and almost bare layer. It happens usually because the biscuit fired ware has been unable to accept the glaze application successfully. This can happen because the biscuit has been fired too high with the result that the porosity has been reduced or that the surface has been affected with dust, oil or grease. Perspiring fingers or a damp surface can also have the effect of reducing the porosity. As with crawling, overgrinding can also help to promote cut glaze. A common remedy, apart from the obvious necessity for good housekeeping, is to introduce some binder into the glaze.

Flashing

This is a common fault when firing. Some glazes such as those which produce volatiles, release these into the kiln atmosphere with the result that they affect other ware or simply provide variations in the glaze on the ware to which the glaze has been applied. The materials can be fluxes such as the oxides of sodium and lead, boric oxide and perhaps rather less obviously, the oxides of barium, zinc and potassium. They can also be colouring oxides, chrome-tin pink is an obvious example. Salt glazing is a prime example of the action of volatiles on a clay surface. In this case the wet salt, often mixed with some borax, is thrown on to the fires when the kiln reaches an appropriate temperature. It then volatilizes and reacts with the silica and alumina on the clay surface to form a glaze.

A glaze which has not been allowed to mature and as a result is full of bubbles

Bubbles, pinholes and dimples

Pinholes and dimples are usually caused by insufficient firing to enable any blisters or craters which evolve during the melting process to blend together into a uniform surface. These blisters and pinholes result from gases that develop during the melting process. Overfiring can also cause similar effects because the higher temperature may induce further release of gases from both the glaze materials and from the clay body. Bubbles are as inevitable in glaze forming as they are in glass making.

Similarly, the small bubbles tend to be collected by the large ones which can more easily reach the surface and escape. Molten glass has the advantage of being in a liquid state which can flow and move as the gases rise to escape but a glaze is generally much more viscous because of the alumina which tends to stop the glaze from flowing. In a good firing, bubbles gradually reduce in size and number until they are not significant. They cause more surface defects than seems to be generally appreciated and soaking at the correct temperature to avoid these defects should always be considered. The number and size of the bubbles in a glaze is important as is their location in relation to the surface and to the body interface where free crystalline silica protruding from the body can have a significant effect on bubble formation. A glaze will tend to have a dull surface if there is a large number of small bubbles present. Where bubbles have reached the surface and burst they can leave craters if the glaze has not been allowed to settle into an even surface after the craters have been formed. When bubbles are still present just underneath the surface they often cause a textured finish which, if they don't create too much fragility, can be pleasant on some decorative ware.

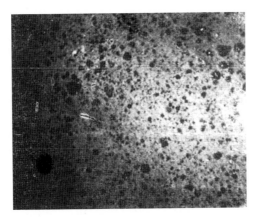

Iron from the clay body breaking through a stoneware
glaze to produce typical spots on the surface

These are conditions caused by either the effects of sulphur compounds in the fuel or by zinc or calcium in the glaze. In the case of the sulphur, various sulphates are formed which remain in the surface of the glaze and form crystals on cooling. Zinc and calcium can also create crystals in the glaze, particularly if the glaze is held at temperature between 700 and 850°C. These are of course deliberately cultivated in the case of crystalline glazes.

Movement, *fused borosilicate glass*

Surface tension

This is a term which emerges quite often in relation to glazes. It refers to the quality that affects a liquid and gives it the appearance of being held together as if in a plastic bag. It can be seen most readily when water is spilled on to a surface which will not absorb it immediately. The water tends to gather itself into globules that are distributed on to the resistant surface. Some liquids have a higher surface tension than others and it is often apparent when a liquid of low viscosity such as petrol or white spirit is spilled onto a surface and immediately spreads to cover it whilst one of a higher viscosity such as water forms globules. This ability to cover and spread across a surface is known as wetting. Some glazes will develop a relatively low surface tension and will wet a ceramic surface easily whilst others have much more difficulty and as a result create all sorts of problems, particularly that of crawling.

The effects of various oxides on surface tension are indicated below in order to give the opportunity to correct wetting problems by the substitution of materials:-

High surface tension	Alumina
	Magnesia
	Zirconia
	Calcia
	Tin oxide
	Zinc oxide
	Baria
	Silica
	Titania
	Boric oxide
	Lithia
	Lead oxide
	Sodium carbonate
Low surface tension	Potassium carbonate

For further reading on ceramic faults *The Potter's Dictionary* by Frank and Janet Hamer, and *Ceramic Faults* by Harry Fraser, both published by A & C Black Ltd, are strongly recommended.

Faults in glass

The most common faults which occur in the early stages of glassmaking are seeds, stones and cords.

Others that arise later include problems associated with annealing, incompatibility and very much later, decay.

Seeds

Most seeds are formed as the glass batch is being melted. They comprise small bubbles of gas that have become trapped in the molten glass, and are usually found in glass because the fining procedure has not been sufficiently effective. If they remain in the glass the fine bubbles are known as seeds and large bubbles become known as blisters. In the founding it is essential that any bubbles which are formed by the volatiles released from the batch materials, particularly from the carbonates which release quantities of carbon dioxide, are able to rise to the surface. Atmospheric gas can also become trapped in the batch materials and eventually form bubbles. In order to reduce the possibility of seed in some high quality commercial glass the melting procedure is carried out under a vacuum.

Large bubbles rise quickly and easily and one authority suggests that whilst small bubbles of about an eighth of an inch in diameter can rise to the surface in about ten minutes, very fine bubbles may take a few weeks. As large bubbles tend to collect smaller ones as they rise, it becomes important to create quantities of large bubbles at the right stage of a founding. This is part of the procedure is known as "fining" or "refining" and is a chemical process

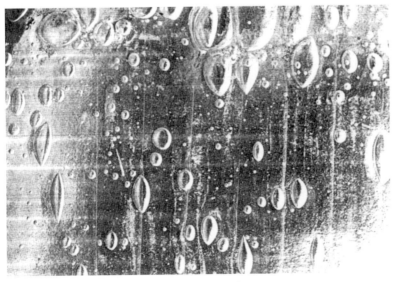

Seeds in flat glass

in which fining agents are introduced into the batch to stimulate convection currents in order to produce an homogeneous glass. Varying the temperature in the furnace has the effect of increasing and decreasing the density and viscosity of the glass to help the bubbles to rise to the surface. Small additions of calcium fluoride (0·5%) to the batch have a similar effect because they reduce the viscosity of the melt. A more common fining combination is that of adding about 0·04% arsenous oxide together with 1% of nitre to the batch. This works by releasing quantities of oxygen late in the firing to help the batch to absorb the bubbles. Antimony oxide is sometimes used in place of the arsenous oxide.

As many studio glassmakers tend to melt cullet rather than batch there is much less release of gas but fine seed is quite common and chemical fining is not easy to arrange. Many of those melting cullet have to revert to the ancient technology of plunging a potato on the end of a rod into the molten glass to release quantities of steam. The cullet must be washed thoroughly to remove any dust which could promote seeds and on completion of the founding, the temperature of the glass can be reduced about 100°C (180°F) below the working temperature for about an hour before returning it to working condition. This helps the glass to absorb the fine bubbles and is known as conditioning.

Stones

These are small inclusions of refractory matter or devitrified material in the molten glass and probably lead to more rejected pieces of work than any other fault. They can be caused by inadequate founding in which coarse material has not been fully melted into the glass, by material which has actually formed from the molten glass by devitrification and by material which has entered the molten glass as a result of attack on the refractories or from spalling resulting from thermal shock or general wear and tear. The first of these can result from using the wrong particle size of batch materials (large sand grains, etc), poor batch mixing, founding temperature too low or insufficient founding time, batch materials too wet, rubbish in the batch or cullet and insufficient stirring action in the melt. They are usually siliceous in character but are not necessarily so. Clay particles from improperly washed batch often cause stones.

Devitrification stones can form from the molten glass and this is usually because the furnace either has cool spots or has been left ticking over at too low a temperature. Some glasses are more prone to devitrification than others but it is a false economy to leave a glass furnace running at a low temperature when it is not being worked simply to save fuel costs.

Refractory stones often occur because of thermal shock on the hot refractory surfaces. This can happen when cold and often wet batch or cullet is loaded into the hot furnace. They can also result from the attack by flame from badly placed burners, by hot corrosive volatiles, from attack by equally corrosive materials in the process of melting or simply by aggressive materials within molten glass. Refractories in a glass furnace have a particularly hard life and

Contamination by inclusion of low grade firebrick particles in the batch (×150)
Courtesy of Pilkington PLC

eventually there is likely to be some break down which will create stones in the glass. The nature of these stones depends on the part of the furnace affected and the types of refractory used. For instance, the crown and side walls of a furnace are often made from silica bricks. Attack by alkaline vapours causes a soda–lime–silica glass with a high silica content to form on the surface of the refractory. This glass can fall into the melt as a "dropper" or gradually flow down the sidewalls, often becoming partly devitrified to form stones.

Contamination by an iron pellet in the batch with associated bubble. (×100)
Courtesy of Pilkington PLC

Contamination by sand grains/cristobalite from a sand clay sealing patch (×150)
Courtesy of Pilkington PLC

These droppers often appear to be pear-shaped and sometimes display a tail. They can also carry some of the original refractory material. As this will usually have had a long exposure to high temperatures, much of the silica will have been converted into tridymite and/or cristobalite which can also grow into stones. The surfaces of refractories in contact with molten glass are inevitably attacked and will eventually release material into the melt. The aluminosilicate refractories such as pot clay or sillimanite contain very small crystals of mullite which are recrystallised into much larger forms. Corundum and nepheline stones are often formed from material eroded from aluminosilicate refractories.

The positive identification of stones is usually quite difficult. Sometimes the pear shaped droppers or larger pieces of refractory material can be seen without magnification or by the use of a hand lens. As stones are crystalline they will tend to form shapes built up by a regular arrangement of atoms and will

Large corundum stones from decomposed refractory blocks above the glass line

Stones arising from a clay refractory below the glass line consisting of this plates of beta alumina

CERAMICS AND GLASS: A BASIC TECHNOLOGY

show a refractive index particular to their origins. Unfortunately, the shape of stones can easily be affected by the action of the surrounding molten glass which tends to round any corners and edges. The use of a good quality petrological microscope is a considerable help but this and x-ray diffraction equipment is not likely to be readily available to the studio glassmaker so if stones are a continuing problem the best solution to identification may lie in enlisting the help of a university materials science or physics department or a factory with its own laboratory.

Cords

These are comprised of strings of glassy material, usually more viscous than the bulk of the molten glass, that appear on the surface of the melt and, if disregarded, on the surface of the finished ware.

They have several causes. They can result from insufficient stirring action in the melting process to create a glass which is completely homogeneous. They can result from the formation of a silica rich layer on the surface of the glass which develops because of the release of volatiles. They can result from a continuing reaction between the glass and the refractories and from the remelting of stones.

Cords that are caused by droppings from the corrosive action of volatiles on the furnace roof can usually be identified because they tend to be pear or worm shaped.

Lots of glassmakers regard them as little more than a nuisance that can be circumvented to some extent by simply raking the surface of the molten glass before taking a gather. They are likely, however, to have a different viscosity

Cords (striae) in sheet glass
From Stones and Cord in Glass, *Society of Glass Technology*

from that of the melt and as a result can also have a different coefficient of expansion. This can result in the creation of strain within any completed ware in which they may appear. They usually have a different refractive index from the remainder of the glass and this produces some visible distortion of the light transmission. When the material is in wide areas rather than in strings it forms what is known as striae and can often be seen easily because of its difference in its refractive index from than that of the surrounding glass.

Decay in glass

Most studio glassblowers are approached about the possibility of dealing with the results of this problem at sometime in their careers. There are several names for decay including glass rot, crizzling, and sick glass. They all refer in general terms to the various ways in which a glass surface deteriorates under attack. There is usually some deterioration in the strength of glass over the years and much of this is due to the interaction of the glass surface with the surrounding atmosphere.

It has been a considerable problem for curators and collectors over the years but, unfortunately, it is not only old glass that can be affected. There have been several recent instances in which quite modern and very expensive pieces have caused concern. The usual symptoms are surface weeping, layers of crazing, the formation of weathering crusts and occasionally the formation of plugs.

A glaze is not usually subject to quite the same attack because it normally has a high alumina content which tends to produce a much better resistance to decay. It can, however, suffer from attack from under the surface because of moisture getting into a porous ceramic body.

There has been something of a myth about the relative resistance of ancient glass to that of later times and whilst there can be no doubt that some ancient glass has been remarkably well preserved we can have no idea just how much has simply disintegrated or disappeared whilst that which just happened to have the right balance of materials and a suitable firing survived. It is well known that much of the Roman soda–lime–silica glass survived much better than medieval glass. This tended to have a high lime and potash content from the beech wood which was used both for firing and to provide the ash used in the founding. There is a body of opinion that suggests that as more processed constituent materials began to be used rather than those "as found" at a time when the melting action was not fully understood the resulting glass was not as stable as it might otherwise have been because the so-called impurities in some of the natural materials may have helped to provide a better bond. It is known that a glass with sufficient alumina or phosphorous pentoxide in its composition will tend to have a surface that is more stable than a glass with very little alumina. The lime content can also be important. If it is present in the glass up to about 10 mol% then it also acts to provide a stable surface but if the proportion increases above this percentage then the stability starts to decrease rapidly. In general, glass with a high proportion of silica to modifiers will tend to be stable whereas if the proportion of modifiers is high then the glass will be much more readily attacked. Ultraviolet light is known to increase surface corrosion and the presence of sulphur in the atmosphere is also known to increase weathering problems.

The chemical nature of decay is varied and very complex. Some of it, such as the weeping and crizzling caused by an excess of alkali and a lack of stabilisers in the glass, is fairly simple but the results of attack by water can be much more complicated. The surface of a glass tends to react with water or even with a humid atmosphere and starts a continuing process in which the effect progresses further into the glass.

A normal glass surface lends itself to this because the surface ions are not completely co-ordinated and this allows a certain amount of replacement by other ions. This is then followed by further reaction with molecules of water and/or oxygen to the microporous substructure. In the process, alkali ions tend to become leached from the glass to be replaced by protons of smaller volume. It is thought that potash glass is more susceptible than soda glass because the potash ions are larger and leave greater gaps when they are leached out. This leaching creates a certain amount of shrinkage and the formation of crizzled layers which then again allow access to further attack. There is a possibility that any material such as lichen or gaps such as those in poorly leaded stained glass which might allow moisture to accumulate could lead to decay. There is a growing tendency for studio artists making sculptural pieces which may have to stand outdoors to use silicone sealant as an adhesive. This seems to work well in most cases but unfortunately, if the sealant has areas exposed to the weather then there is a considerable attraction to dirt and to the growth of lichen which would obviously attract moisture and possibly create decay.

Poor storage in the very damp conditions that often prevail in the cellars of museums can be a considerable contributory factor to this form of decay but there can be no doubt that poorly formulated glass, which has not been well stabilised or has been made with a high alkali content in order to achieve low founding temperatures makes the surface vulnerable to attack.

There is a particular problem which has surfaced because of the relatively new system of melting pelletised batch rather than melting cullet or standard batch. Pelletised batch is convenient to studio glassmakers because it is safe to handle, is consistent and will melt at relatively low temperatures. Studio glassmakers have traditionally used cullet for melting because of the low founding temperatures required and the reduced risk of handling toxic chemicals. Some have preferred to melt batch because in general it produces better quality glass. When pelletised batch became available it seemed to provide all the advantages of both systems. In standard batch the silica is in the form of sand which becomes coated and attacked by fluxes in the melting process. In pelletised batch, the silica is in the form of very fine grains which have been coated with caustic soda. This has the effect of shortening the melting process. Unfortunately, some of the glass produced from pellets has shown all the signs of crizzling and decay that we associate with glass which has been poorly stored or badly founded. Much of it has been affected to the extent that opacity has developed. Crizzling and decay has traditionally developed over years but some of that developing on glass made from pellets has been appearing within days. This a current problem which is exercising many technologists at the time of writing and, hopefully, a solution will soon be found. Glass decay in general is usually a complex problem about which there is a considerable amount of on-going research. It is also much too large an area to cover within the bounds of this book but for those who wish to pursue this subject further then there is an excellent section on glass decay in the book on *Glass Conservation* by Roy Newton and Sandra Davison and published by Butterworth Heineman. There is also an analytical investigation relating to this process in an article by A. A. Salem in *Glass Technology*, Vol 39, No 3, June 1998.

Annealing and compatibility

Many of the faults which occur in ceramics result from shrinkage, from poor firing schedules or from not taking sufficient account of the various silica inversions. Many of the faults which arise in glass, however, result from poor founding practice. There are two faults in particular which again relate to shrinkage. The first of these relates to the situation in which two or more different types of glass are fused together.

Most materials expand or contract when heated or cooled. The amount of change is expressed as a coefficient of expansion and refers to the change in length per unit length of a material as its temperature changes by one degree centigrade. Every glass has its own coefficient of expansion. Some, such as the borosilicates, tend to have low expansion whilst the common soda–lime–silica glass tends to have a high expansion.

The following table gives approximate thermal expansion coefficients of a range of sample materials for purposes of comparison:-

Material	Temperature range (°C)	Coefficient ($\times 10^{-7}$)
Silica glass (fused silica)	0–1000	5
Borosilicate glass (Pyrex)	0–600	32
Soda–lime–silica glass	0–500	90
Refractories (Fireclay)	0–1000	55
Mullite	0–1000	53
Porcelain	0–1000	60
Aluminium	0–500	230
Copper	0–90	170
Platinum	0–1000	90
Mild steel	0–1000	150
Stainless steel	0–1000	160
Perspex	0–80	850
PTFE	0–80	550
Polythene	0–80	2500

The figures used to express coefficients of expansion are given in two ways. This can cause some confusion to those artists not conversant with the expressions. The first is usually a two figure number such as 90×10^{-7} for a typical soda–lime–silica glass and the second a single figure $\times 10^{-6}$ which for the same glass would be 9×10^{-6}. Obviously, both of these mean exactly the same.

The manufacturers of colour rods try to make their production within as close a range of expansion as they can but as it is virtually impossible to make them all the same there will inevitably be compatibility problems with some colours. Tests on two colour rods from Klaus Kugler revealed a variation of between 88×10^{-7} for one colour to 99×10^{-7} for the other. When two colours from another manufacturer were tested for comparison one was 115×10^{-7} and the other was 111×10^{-7}.

Compatibility of colour rods and grains to a glassworker's basic glass seems to provide one of the major headaches for studio glassmakers. Unfortunately, the expansions quoted for particular rods and for various glass recipes can be very misleading as there are differing tables of material expansion factors from which calculations may have been made over the years so figures quoted, particularly for old glass recipes, cannot be taken for granted.

Schott glass have made an effort to alleviate this problem for glassblowers by producing two ranges of colour rods, chips and powders one with an expansion of $91\pm2 \times 10^{-7}$ and the other with an expansion of $98\pm2 \times 10^{-7}$. This should increase the possibility of establishing a range of colours to suit a basic clear glass. Plowden and Thompson have followed a similar path and have produced a wide range of compatible clear and coloured rods, mostly for lampworking or beadmaking in both soda–lime–silica and in borosilicate glass. They also produce mutually compatible chips and grains of coloured soda–lime–silica glass and lead glass in various sieve sizes for picking up from a marver or for use in casting.

For studio workers who fuse glass, the Bullseye Company in the US has produced sheets of coloured glass, grains and stringers for some years. These are compatible with each other but Schott have also entered this market by producing a compatible range of industrially produced coloured sheet glass with an expansion of 94×10^{-7}. This expansion should offer the advantage of matching much of the clear glass melted by studio glassblowers. This material from Schott is called their "Artista" glass and is a development of their antique glass 75. It is designed to resist devitrification, is available in large rolled sheets up to 1800 mm $\times$ 1500 mm with a standard thickness of 2·5 to 3 mm and is free from bubbles and cords making it relatively easy to cut.

If pieces of glass of different expansion are fused together it is inevitable that some strain will be created when expansion or shrinkage occurs. If the coefficients are close then the glass may be able to withstand this strain but more often than not, cracking or breakage will develop. There are many studio artists or craftsmen who do not have a strain viewer to check their work and rely simply on using particular colour rods which appear to suit their basic glass. There is an obvious danger in this as residual strain may not be immediately apparent and it is quite common for pieces to crack or even explode months or even years after they have been made. The expansion of glasses is usually assessed by calculation and this is acceptable if the same tables are used for all the glasses concerned. If this cannot be guaranteed or if a composition is not known then the practical solution is to carry out a thread test. This consists of heating a strip of each sample of glass until they are hot enough so that they fuse together when pressed. The joined strips are reheated and then held at each end with a pair of pliers or grips and pulled apart to form a fine straight thread. A section of the thread is broken away and left to cool. If the two glasses are compatible then the thread will remain reasonably straight but if a curve bending more than half an inch in a twelve inch length develops then the expansions will be different and the glasses will probably prove to be incompatible. If the curve is greater than one inch then the difference is too great to risk. This would be the equivalent of about 10% mismatch in the coefficients.

Unfortunately, differences in coefficients of expansion are not the only reason for problems of strain.

The differential cooling caused by the varying rates at which heat travels through the glass and is given off through its surface can create strain. This can be quite marked where dense, opaque colours are used, particularly if thick sections of these are used together with clear glass. Blue glass for instance absorbs and releases heat more slowly than most other colours. Fortunately, the effects of differential cooling can be mitigated to some extent by prolonging the annealing and cooling cycle to allow the slower cooling coloured glasses to cool at the same rate as the clear glass. Studio activities which are plagued by problems of thermal expansion are those of fusing two or more different glasses together or, for potters, when ceramic body and glaze have differing expansions. The stress caused becomes most evident when there is rapid heating or even more critically, when there is rapid cooling.

The effect can be illustrated by placing one piece of glass upon another and applying heat until they fuse together. Whilst they are achieving a seal, the glasses are sufficiently soft to move equally but as they begin to become rigid and during subsequent cooling each glass will contract according to its thermal expansion coefficient. If this is the same for both glasses there should be no difficulty, but if not, then one glass will try to contract more than the other. If the glass samples are thin they may be able to bend sufficiently to accommodate the stress. If they are not, then some stress is inevitable. The glass with the higher expansion will be under tension and the one with the lower expansion will be in compression. A certain amount of stress can usually be accommodated before fracture or crazing develops. As a rough guide about five percent of the expansion coefficient is the limit of the difference that should be attempted though it would be prudent to try to produce a better match because there are usually other factors such as opacity, colour, differing annealing points and variations in thickness involved. Most artists use high expansion glasses such as soda–lime–silica or lead crystal with coefficients of expansion in the region of 90×10^{-7} and very few would try to fuse other glasses to this which are lower than 85 or higher than 95×10^{-7}. It is not always realised that when fusing low expansion glasses such as borosilicates which may have expansions as low as 32×10^{-7}, the expansion of the second glass needs to be much closer to that of the first. It is good practice when casing blown glass to try to ensure that the glass on the exterior surface has a slightly lower expansion than that of the inner glass so that the surface glass is in compression thus forming a stronger article which will resist breakage as this compression has to be overcome in addition to the natural strength of the glass.

The expansion of most soda–lime–silica glasses and lead glasses falls between 85 and 105×10^{-7} but many of the commercial borosilicate glass tend to be considered as being around 32×10^{-7}. This may be a reasonable assumption for much of the borosilicate table ware but many other borosilicate glasses are produced for high temperature lighting and optical purposes. Many of these are designed to be sealed to various metals and have expansions considerably greater than this. Because of this, mixing borosilicate glass when casting or fusing could easily lead to failure.

If a piece of glass is heated to a molten or plastic state and is then left to cool naturally the external surfaces will cool more quickly than the inside and the differences in the rates of shrinkage will create residual stress. Similarly, thin pieces of glass will cool more quickly than thick ones so if different thicknesses are present in an article this will also create residual stress. It is essential that any stress is reduced to acceptable limits by the process of annealing. If this is not carried out properly the glass will probably crack and, in the case of thick articles, the result could be much more dramatic. This will probably take place within a few days but it is quite common for it to happen years later.

The stress is reduced by allowing the glass to cool to a temperature near to what is defined as its annealing point. It is then held for a length of time to enable the external and internal temperatures to become reasonably similar before the glass is allowed to cool further. The process of holding the glass at such a temperature until the values are reasonably constant is known as "stabilisation". This time is related to the thickness of the glass, its coefficient of expansion, the amount of surface exposure, the colour, its opacity and the amount of residual stress required.

A small amount of residual stress is normal for most glass but for optical glass in particular it needs to be reduced to a minimum. This means that optical quality glass of some thickness such as that used for large astronomical telescopes may require many weeks of treatment. This is because in addition to the obvious physical weakening caused by stress, other properties such as the density and the refractive index can be affected. Differences in the refractive index cause ripples in images which would seriously affect optical properties.

It is essential that as far as possible, the glass is kept at a uniform temperature at or near to its annealing point for sufficient time to remove stress. When the glass is allowed to cool further, temporary stresses will be created by the temperature gradients but when room temperature is reached and the glass stabilised these stresses disappear.

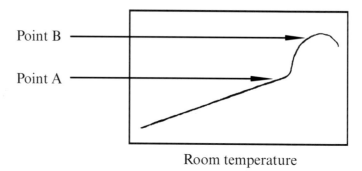

Point B

Point A

Room temperature

Typical expansion curve for glass (Glass, Borax Consolidated)

Annealing can take place over a range of temperatures but, if not known, the upper limit of an annealing range can be established by taking a rod or strip of the glass and, after supporting it at each end, heating it until it just begins to sag under its own weight. This establishes an approximate softening point for this particular glass (sometimes known as the M_g point) and a safe upper limit for annealing would be about 20°C below this temperature. It must be stressed that even with exactly the same glass, this temperature could vary slightly according to the weight and thickness of the particular articles being annealed.

If a length of glass is heated from room temperature the expansion is nearly linear until point A is reached and a typical expansion curve commences which reaches its highest point at B. This is known as its upper annealing temperature. Point A indicates the lowest part of the annealing range and indicates where the glass is changing from a solid material to a material which is becoming a liquid.

Strain is usually removed or reduced by a process of holding the ware at or near to point B (the upper annealing temperature) followed by gradual reduction to point A and beyond. In practice there is some latitude in the process of annealing. It can also be reduced, though more slowly but not ideally, when the glass is held in what is called the annealing range. In a soda–lime–silica glass this would probably extend between 550°C and 480°C and for a high lead glass between 450°C and 390°C.

This offers the advantage that a piece of glass which, because of its weight and shape might deform at a temperature just above its given annealing point, can be given a much longer soak at a slightly lower temperature. It also means that the common studio practice of running the annealing kiln on the waste heat from the furnace becomes more viable because of this latitude in the annealing cycle.

Studio artists and people operating in small workshops and producing blown ware are tempted to be casual about annealing because for thousands of years glassmakers have cracked off work and placed it in a compartment above or to the side of the furnace and produced a rough estimate of an annealing cycle simply by gradually moving work away from the source of the heat as new pieces were introduced. This system would appear to have worked reasonably well as is evident by the amount of work still around. Unfortunately, it is also impossible to estimate just how much did not survive.

Annealing in the studio tends to be a different process from that in a factory where work travels through various controlled heat zones on a belt moving at a speed regulated to the required annealing time cycle. This piece of equipment is called a "lehr". In a studio or workshop, however, it is usual to find an annealing kiln which is held at a particular temperature within the annealing range whilst work is being made followed by a programmed annealing and cooling cycle.

In industry it is also commonplace to find that work is allowed to cool naturally as it is produced, in which case the creation of some stress is inevitable. The pieces are then annealed by reheating them as part of the programme for passing them through the lehr. This system seems to work well with production ware that is reasonably uniform in thickness but would be unlikely to find favour with people operating in studios or workshops.

If batch, cullet or pellets are obtained from a particular supplier it is usually convenient to obtain annealing schedules pertaining to the material and to extend this to make allowances for the nature of studio production which can be complex in form and often contains coloured elements and differing thicknesses of glass.

It is a common fallacy that prolonged treatment will remove all kinds of stress. This is not so. The strain which is caused by the incorporation of incompatible elements, whether they be from coloured glass, stones or cords, etc, will never by relieved by any extension or variation of the annealing cycle.

A typical commercial schedule for a glass with a coefficient of 90×10^{-7} is:-

Thickness of glass	3	6	13 mm
Cooling to 5°C above annealing point	5	15	30 minutes
Cooling to 5°C below strain point	4	1	0·3°C per minute
Cooling for the next 50°C	8	2	0·6°C per minute
Final cooling	50	11	3°C per minute

This is a fairly conservative schedule for clear glass of even thickness but due allowance must be made for studio glass which often has differing thickness and colour. The schedule for borosilicate with a coefficient of expansion of 33×10^{-7} would require similar rates to 5°C below the strain point but cooling rates could be increased considerably after that because glass with a low coefficient of expansion has a better resistance to thermal shock than glass of high expansion.

Blown glass is generally much easier to anneal than cast glass and many glassblowers use a very simple general formula of annealing for one hour per 6 mm thickness followed by at least a similar time for the initial cooling over 150°C. and a similar time for cooling to room temperature.

Keith Cummings who has many years experience of glass casting gives some of his annealing schedules in his excellent book *Techniques of Kiln Formed Glass*.

He suggests as examples that a soda–lime–silica glass 12 mm thick should be held at its annealing point (557°C) for 30 minutes and then reduced to its strain point (525°C) over a period of 173 minutes, reduced further to 457°C over 83 minutes and then to 60°C over 132 minutes. The kiln can then be left to cool to room temperature.

The amount of surface area that is exposed makes a considerable difference to the annealing times. A piece of flat glass resting on a kiln shelf with only one side exposed would need twice the time that a piece of glass with both sides exposed would take. Blown ware of even thickness with only a small area of its base in contact with a shelf would have all of the interior surfaces and almost all of the exterior surfaces exposed and could be seen to become annealed with reasonable ease whereas glass which happened to be cast into a mould but had the upper surface exposed could pose problems as the heat would tend to escape much more quickly from that surface than through those which remained in contact with the mould. The usual solution to this problem is to place a slab of insulating material over the cast to allow the heat to disperse evenly.

Glass which has been cast into a mould leaving no surfaces exposed will often anneal successfully simply because the mould restricts the heat loss heat to the extent that it is likely that any differential between the exterior and the interior temperatures of the glass is reduced considerably. It may seem contrary to all that has been said for the need for glass to be annealed but there is one process in which the theory seems to be reversed. If glass is taken to a temperature above the strain point and the surface cooled quickly with forced air until it chills, a very considerable temperature difference is created which produces a tough surface with an interior which is under strain. The glass is then said to be toughened. There is a strong resistance to fracture but when this occurs the glass shatters into small, relatively harmless pieces

In the case of a glaze, the actual thickness of the glassy layer is so slight that whilst a similar contraction takes place as it solidifies, the normally slow cooling process which occurs in firing pottery and the fact that it becomes bonded to a ceramic body means that there is much less likelihood of the development of stress faults because of a lack of programmed annealing. Some glazes do craze on contraction but this is usually due to differences in expansion between the glaze and the ceramic body as explained earlier.

If a glass which has been annealed and allowed to cool is then heated fairly quickly to a temperature below its annealing range then some temporary stress will be created. If the heating is too rapid for the thickness and type of glass then this action could be sufficient to cause damage. Even if there is no effect during the heating process, if the glass is then cooled quickly the temporary stress may again be sufficient to cause some damage. If on the other hand the glass is heated and cooled relatively slowly then any temporary stress should disappear.

XIII.
Furnaces and kilns

The kiln is such a basic essential for any potter and for any glassworker dealing with kiln formed glass that its design and construction has been a constant topic for discussion and debate whenever groups of potters or groups of glassworkers get together. Similarly, the glass furnace has promoted an equal interest to glassblowers where the subject of discussion has often centred on such subjects as "tank or pot," types of burner system, types of refractories, gas, oil or electricity, automatic operation and safety.

The design of kilns and furnaces is extremely varied and obviously relates to the type of ware and the nature of the production required. Essentially, they consist of one or more chambers which are heated to a specific temperature, held at that temperature for a certain amount of time and then cooled, usually at a programmed rate. The main difference between a kiln and a furnace in this respect is that a kiln will probably be held at its peak temperature for a relatively short time whilst a furnace may be held at its operating temperature for months or even for years before being allowed to cool for the inevitable rebuild. The types of fuel used also varies considerably and depends largely on economics, efficiency, suitability and availability.

There are many excellent books on the design and operation of kilns for firing ceramics but at this moment I have only found two which really gets to grips with the design and operation of studio glass furnaces and related equipment such as glory holes, annealing kilns and types of burners. The first is: *Glass Notes* by Henry Halem, published by Franklin Mills Press, Kent, Ohio, USA at 30 dollars. It is an excellent book, full of down to earth information, often culled from experienced friends of the author and is a must for the studio glassmaker. There is a lot of information which would equally be of use to the studio potter. Another important source is the book *A Glassblower's Companion* by Dudley F. Giberson, published by The Joppa Press of Warner, New Hampshire at 35 dollars and again full of down to earth advice on equipment for the glassblower.

The emphasis on efficiency and economy has increased greatly in recent years because of continually developing pressure from the environmentalists so the nature of the combustion system, the insulation of the chamber(s), the reuse of what was formerly waste energy and the monitoring of exhaust gases have come under close scrutiny. These environmental demands are constantly being upgraded, particularly those relating to toxic emissions in the exhaust gases. At the time of writing the current top level in Britain for lead is five milligrams in one cubic metre of exhaust gas and for arsenic, one milligram. This has forced several firms who had been melting lead glass to stop production. Fortunately, studio glassmakers who melt cullet escape this particular legislation at the moment but it is doubtful if this exemption will continue for long.

Glass pots being made at the former factory of Joe McCarthy

Many potters and glassmakers have turned to using recuperators to reduce emissions and to increase thermal efficiency and this action certainly results in considerable reductions in many of the emissions. Because of the considerable reduction in the temperature of the exhaust gases as they pass through the recuperator much of the toxic material remains and the craftsman then has the distinctly hazardous job of removing this material from time to time and, if left, it soon begins to impair the efficiency of the recuperator. The problem is greater for glassmakers than it is for potters because the release of noxious material is a much more continuous process. Another unfortunate fact is that the hot lead based vapour is a powerful flux and attacks the stainless steel of the recuperator very quickly so that expensive replacements often become necessary. Some glassmakers have turned to using covered pots to reduce the amounts of lead and arsenic getting into the exhaust system. They then collect the toxic material on to sheets of ceramic fibre so that it can be readily and safely removed.

The use of oxygen to supplement or replace air initially gained some popularity in industrial fuel systems, the costs of the oxygen in industrial quantities having been reduced to an acceptable level. One of the suggested benefits of this system is that fuel is not wasted in heating the huge quantities of nitrogen which enter the system in the air. Another important environmental benefit is in the possibility of a reduction in the amounts of nitrogen oxides released into the atmosphere.

In industry there has been an almost feverish activity to find methods of reducing emissions from kilns and furnaces. As new legislation and the resultant pressure to decrease nitrox emissions reaches the studio operator there are suggestions to consider the introduction of oxy-fuel burners. There has also been a further suggestion that the introduction of oxygen would lead to more efficient use of energy resources but this seems to disregard the fact that in basic environmental terms the energy used in the initial production of the oxygen should be taken into account. Either way there is a likelihood of problems with the cost of oxygen especially if it has to bought in the relatively small quantities likely to be used by studio potters or glassmakers.

Efforts to reduce nitrox emissions are causing considerable concern at the moment and whilst some advocate the addition of oxygen into air/fuel systems, others see this as not being a successful answer and that a better approach might be through specially designed low NO_x burners. It is suggested that whilst it is obvious that oxy-fuel burners which do not use air would produce little or no NO_x as this could only come from the fuel, when the system is simply oxygen enhanced then the greater heat of the flame could actually increase the possibility of the production of NO_x. Other industrial possibilities being explored include the injection of ammonia into the exhaust gases to neutralise the NO_x and the cleansing of the exhaust gases in a regenerative system. At the time of writing this is one of the most discussed and researched aspects of firing procedures in industrial situations. Whether or not any of the results can be adapted to reach the needs of small studios is questionable.

There are many difficulties to overcome and just one of them involves the effect of oxygen enhanced flame on the refractories. In general, the high alumina refractories stand up very well but silica refractories used largely above the glass line tend to be attacked. Part of this tendency for corrosion is due to the higher level of water vapour in the furnace atmosphere.

One of the approaches to reducing NO_x emissions has been developed by Pilkington and involves the controlled introduction of fuel into the regenerator system. This reduces the NO_x to nitrogen. Schott have also recently introduced their own system and claim considerable success in reducing NO_x release.

Dr George Mattocks, who is a member of the Society of Glass Technology, is an acknowledged expert on this subject recently advocated the controlled introduction of oxygen into part of the exhaust gases that are recirculated from the regenerator and has also developed a system using a form of artificial air.

The urgency of the problem is such that various solutions are likely to be developed or suggested in quick succession. It is a matter of some concern to the small workshop operators that legislation on such matters as acceptable standards of nitrox emissions and various metal volatiles will be negotiated with the large pottery producers and with the flat glass and container industries. As a result, what might be reasonably achieved in large plants may provide a virtually impossible target if they are then imposed upon small workshops. The regulations agreed in the European Community in 1996 are an obvious example of this and much will depend on the understanding and flexibility of the local supervising authorities.

XIV.
Refractory and insulating materials

Potters and glassmakers have had a long tradition of building their own kilns and it is not many years since these were all made from dense, heavy firebricks which absorbed much of the input of heat energy. The scene has changed drastically, however, and there is now a tendency to use purpose made refractories especially designed to suit specific circumstances. Some of these are extremely efficient in their qualities of insulation, but as a result are often so light and fragile that they have very little structural strength. This means that when kilns and furnaces are designed today there are various factors which need to be considered that once were given little thought. Some sort of compromise now often needs to be reached between achieving maximum thermal efficiency and the essential physical strength required to ensure that the structure does not degrade or collapse.

The maximum operating hot face temperature required for the refractories is obviously something which must be established before anything else but in deciding suitability for the purpose, the extent to which the refractories will be liable to attack from volatiles, flame, thermal shock, from active chemicals in melting batch and from corrosive molten glass must also be considered.

Another calculation which is easily missed is whether or not the refractories will be taken up to a particular temperature and then after a short time, cooled down as is the case in a normal kiln firing or taken up to a high temperature for a glass founding, reduced somewhat to a working temperature and then held at that temperature, often staying at these high temperatures for several months. A refractory which is perfectly suitable for one might well be totally unsuitable for the other.

Refractories are materials which will withstand high temperatures and most of those that are used for making kilns or furnaces are still made from clay related or clay bonded materials though the number of modern refractories which can no longer be described in those terms is steadily increasing. Pure oxide refractories are used for some very high temperature applications and such materials as platinum and recrystallised alumina are now used for making crucibles.

Most of the kilns used by potters are designed to withstand temperatures up to approximately 1300°C in order to be able to accommodate stoneware firings whereas those used for kiln formed glass are rarely used above 900°C. A glassmaker also uses an annealing kiln which would be unlikely to need an operating temperature greater than 550°C. He also uses a glory hole which is used to reheat the glass whilst it is being formed and which will probably withstand very rapid temperature rises of up to about 1150°C. The major temperature requirement, however, is that of the glass furnace which in a studio will probably need to be built to withstand a founding temperature of something up to 1450°C and then be able to hold a continuous working temperature of around 1100°C.

In glassmaking the refractories have to withstand a much tougher regime than that which is likely to prevail in ceramic kilns so they will be considered first. In this case it is essential to use materials, particularly those which are in contact with the molten glass, to be as free from iron as possible, which will have sufficient mechanical strength, and which will resist attack both from the hot glass and from any volatiles which may be released.

Fireclays which form the base for many traditional refractories are composed of kaolinite together with some free silica and various impurities, but for practical purposes can be considered to be composed of alumina and silica. Both of these materials have high melting points, silica at 1713°C (3115°F) and alumina at 2050°C (3720°F). Interestingly, 5% to 6% alumina together with silica will produce a theoretically lower melting temperature of approximately 1600°C (2900°F). When the proportions reach alumina 30% and silica 70% the theoretical melting temperature returns to about 1713°C (3115°F) and with higher proportions of alumina the melting point will rise smoothly until it reaches that of 100% alumina at 2050°C. This relationship between silica and alumina is described in greater detail under Eutectics, page 103.

Firebricks are usually designated by a number which corresponds to their alumina content. This means that a firebrick 38 is sold as having a 38% alumina content. This system can be misleading because high temperature insulation bricks are also given a number which suggests a hot face temperature in Fahrenheit whilst to confuse the issue further, ceramic fibre products are given a number which indicates a hot face temperature in degrees centigrade.

As clay based refractories consist of both crystalline and glassy materials they tend to slump when they reach a temperature at which the glass pockets begin to absorb the crystalline material. Most fireclays are more refractory than other clays simply because they tend to contain more alumina and less flux so, in general, the higher the alumina content the more refractory they become. Whilst the nominated melting point might indicate a temperature at which a refractory would begin to fail this can only be considered as applying to refractories which are not under load. Whilst under load, deformation can take place at temperatures more than 100°C (180°F) below a theoretical melting point so any structural requirements affected by this need to be taken into account.

High alumina refractories may contain anything between 45% and 80% alumina but are expensive to produce because of the cost of high firing and the cost of the calcined bauxite which needs to be introduced to achieve the necessary high alumina level. Refractories such as kiln shelves which often have to withstand a heavy load without warping were traditionally made from high alumina fireclay, the presence of the silica in the fireclay helping to reduce the effect of thermal shock.

Aluminosilicates are generally more resistant to thermal shock than products made from fused alumina and the natural kyanites and mullites are considered to be more successful than fireclay products as materials for the manufacture of kiln furniture. Mullite and cordierite mixtures are now often used for kiln shelves as cordierite has a low thermal expansion and thus increases the resistance to thermal shock. Many manufacturers simply add talc to mullite to provide the cordierite in the shelves during firing. In subsequent firings it seems that more cordierite is produced, lowering the thermal expansion even further and increasing the resistance to thermal shock. The big disadvantage of these shelves is that they are not suitable for use above 1300°C as other magnesium products begin to evolve which reduce the shock resistance and can start melting processes which lead to shelf distortion.

Strong but more expensive shelves with a high resistance to chemical vapours usually have a zirconium silicate content but shelves which are likely to find considerable use at temperatures above 1300°C for glazed porcelain, etc, tend to be made from silicon carbide. This is the best kiln shelf material for resistance to thermal shock but is not very suitable for general use at temperatures below 1300°C because of its tendency to oxidise, causing the shelves to swell. This can be countered to some degree by coating silicon carbide shelves with alumina.

Glasshouse pots are traditionally made from relatively iron free fireclay into which grog is introduced to reduce shrinkage. Ground and previously fired fireclay was often used to provide the grog but latterly it has become common practice to use Molochite (calcined china clay) as this has a negligible iron content and is sufficiently refractory for this purpose.

Small pots suitable for studio furnaces are also available in vacuum cast sillimanite from various manufacturers. Some studio glassmakers, particularly those who only wish to run a furnace for a few days at a time, make their own glass pots. These are easily coiled or thrown to an appropriate size and thickness using clay as described above and fired to a biscuit temperature. They offer the advantage of being relatively thin which means that they can be taken up to temperature quickly and are so easy and cheap to produce that it does not matter if they can only be used for a few foundings.

Crucibles to be used for glass tests can be produced in a similar manner. The following are three traditional recipes:-

	Parts by weight
(1) Fireclay (low iron content)	60
Molochite grog	40
(2) China clay	45
Ball clay (low iron)	10
Molochite grog	45
(3) China clay	35
Ball clay	10
Calcined alumina	10
Molochite grog	45

If the crucibles are to be thrown then the grog will need to be suitably fine and a little bentonite can be added to improve the plasticity. If they are to be slip cast then the deflocculant (a mixture of sodium silicate and sodium carbonate) needs to be calculated on the clay content and the slip prepared before adding in the grog and/or alumina (see Slip casting, page 31). The amount of deflocculant is often reduced or omitted altogether because of the possible fluxing effects of the sodium carbonate but commercially prepared deflocculants which do not have the same fluxing effects are available.

There is considerable scope for varying the above recipes. Zirconium silicate is sometimes included. If the material is not to be thrown, the ball clay is often reduced or omitted.

Sillimanite and mullite refractories are commonly used in glass furnaces for the areas which are in contact with the glass. The two terms overlap somewhat because the best mullite refractories have until recently been made mainly from sillimanite and kyenite, although the use of kyenite has declined recently because of difficulties caused by variable quality and content of the source material so most sillimanite is now made from a mixture of molochite and calcined alumina. A certain amount of mullite is formed whenever an alumina–silica compound is fired over 1200°C (2200°F), the amount varying in relation to the form, the firing and the impurities present.

Mullite is an important refractory as it is the one alumina–silica compound which remains stable at temperatures approaching 1800°C (3270°F).

Traditional sillimanite refractories were made by calcining raw sillimanite or kyenite at high temperatures and after suitable grinding, the results were mixed with sufficient fireclay and water to bind the mixture together and to make it workable in preparation for the process of forming, drying and firing.

Fusion cast alumina–zirconia–silica (AZS) refractories are common for tank floors when the glass being melted does not have a high potash content. Molten glass attacks refractories largely because of the corrosive action of the alkali. The temperature and the porosity of the refractories are also important factors in the ability of the material to resist this attack. Coloured glasses can have an increased tendency to attack refractory surfaces because dark glasses in particular are usually hotter on the surface than a similar clear glass.

Silica refractories, as high as 96% silica, are commonly used in industrial furnaces for tank roof and walls above the glass line. They tend to spall during heating and cooling at temperatures below 600°C (1110°F) but above this temperature they work very well though they may be gradually attacked by volatiles from the founding, releasing drops of silica rich material into the melt which create cords and stones in the glass.

Fusion cast refractories are made by melting a refractory batch to a viscous liquid in an electric furnace which is tapped to allow the liquid to run into special moulds. The furnace is taken to very high temperatures (up to 2500°C, 4530°F). Whilst there were earlier experiments into the process it was Corning Glass Works in the USA who succeeded in producing fusion cast blocks of 72% alumina in 1925. It provided immediate improvements both to the life of glass furnaces and to the quality of the glass. There have been continuing developments in the range of fusion cast refractories. ZAC (AZS) which is based on alumina–zirconia, and Monofrax which is based on pure alumina became the most popular for many years. The zirconia content was increased from a standard 32%, first to 41% and eventually reached a high specification casting containing 94% zirconia which is used for the production of fluorine opals, special borosilicate glasses, lead crystal and TV glass. Other fusion cast blocks containing 26% Cr_2O_3 have been produced and are used mostly in the glass fibre industry.

Many refractories are now chemically bonded with materials such as ethyl silicate instead of the traditional clay. There are several advantages to this. They can be manufactured very quickly as there is no necessity for a long drying process before firing. No clay is involved so there is little or no shrinkage either in the forming, drying or firing schedule. There is also a much improved resistance to thermal shock. Complex forms can be cast to fine limits to a predetermined surface quality. Large forms can be made precisely which means that they can be installed easily and quickly thus considerably reducing the number of joints which are a major cause of heat loss in kilns and furnaces. These casts can made as sufficiently precise modules to enable the refractories to be assembled dry and can also be made with various materials quite easily.

Calcined alumina, zircon, sillimanite, mullite, fused silica granules, silicon carbide, etc, can be bonded in proportions to suit a particular requirement. Insulation is also something which can be built in. It is possible to prepare a cast with a suitable hot face which is backed up in the same cast with material which contains bubble alumina, bubble mullite and even ceramic fibre to produce a material with the necessary thermal conductivity value to suit the degree of insulation required.

Crushed and powdered fused silica can also be chemically bonded to provide furnace roof blocks. A kiln or glory hole is different from a furnace as calculations need to take into account the fact that a furnace may need to stay at a high temperature for months on end whilst a kiln only needs to attain a certain temperature in a relatively short time and is unlikely to need to maintain that temperature for more that an hour or so. Modern glory holes in the studio tend to be heated to a high temperature very rapidly as required and then allowed to cool just as quickly so they usually consist of a steel barrel shape lined with high temperature insulation material which will withstand both the thermal shock and flame attack. Even in production conditions they are unlikely to stay in operation for more than part of the working day. Because of this and because of the fact that they are unlikely to encounter the corrosive attacks to which furnaces are subjected, most kilns and glory holes are often made nowadays almost entirely from insulation materials. The use of heavy refractories in this context has almost disappeared.

If a kiln or furnace is a complex shape such as the catenary arch kiln or the egg shaped furnace it has been common practice to cast the refractory and/or insulation material, usually *in situ*. In this case aluminous cements such as "Ciment Fondu" or the similar but higher temperature cement known as "Secar" are used to produce a concrete by being mixed with suitable crushed refractory or insulation brick. Ready mixed castable materials are also available from most suppliers. They offer advantages in having considerable structural strength when fired and not suffering from the heat loss between brick joints. They tend, however, to be more dense than other materials and, if possible, are best used together with a suitable layer of efficient insulation material. An initial firing needs to be reasonably slow and the fact that the casting will have little mechanical strength until it has been fired must be taken into consideration.

Insulation for furnaces, kilns, glory holes and lehrs, etc.
There are many differing insulating materials used for these and the designer needs to consider the various qualities required. These include:-

> The hot face temperature
> The material which will best stand this temperature
> The physical strength

It will then be necessary to calculate the progression of the various insulation materials needed to give an external temperature of less than 80°C (175°F). This is necessary because those materials which are likely to give the greatest amount of insulation are often those less likely to withstand high hot face temperatures and may not to have the physical strength required.

A suitable illustration of furnace or kiln insulation will often be produced by manufacturers to demonstrate the difference between the hot face temperature and the cold face at different thicknesses using various materials. This usually refers to a situation such as that which applies to a glass furnace where a temperature is often maintained for a long time.

Specifications of insulation and refractory materials tend not only to give the hot face temperature at which they can safely be used without deformation but also their density and their rate of thermal conductivity. Due allowance must therefore be made for different requirements. For instance, the progression of the heat through a material is subject to a time factor and when this is calculated it is likely that a glass forming or pottery kiln which spends very little time at its top temperature may need considerably less insulation material to achieve a suitable exterior cold face than that which would be calculated for a furnace.

Another factor to be taken into consideration is that the more dense the material the greater the capacity to store heat so heavy refractory material which will absorb a lot of heat, will cause the kiln or furnace to take a longer time to achieve a temperature and, subsequently, a longer time to cool than if a lightweight insulation material is used. As a dense firebrick will absorb four to five times the amount of heat than a similar insulation brick there is a considerable saving to be made in calculating the layers of insulation material very carefully.

The sides, top and base of a kiln or furnace are often composed of layers of different materials rather than being made from one type, depending entirely on its usage. It would be normal practice to use the data from the manufacturer to calculate the temperature drop across the inner layer in order to find the interface temperature at the next layer, to then fit a suitable insulation material to stand rather more than that temperature and carry out the same procedure to fit the outer layer of insulation. This should be calculated to give a cold face temperature which would be safe to touch. Because heat will travel more easily through

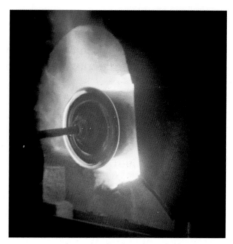

Reheating at the glory hole

solid material than through air most of the insulation materials contain numer-ous fine sealed pores which are calculated to provide both insulation and an ability not to be deformed or melted at a given temperature.

Heat is transferred through insulation materials by:- conduction through solids, convection in gases, transmission of infrared radiation and molecular conduction in gases. The solid materials used are normally those giving low thermal conductivity which by virtue of the creation of numerous voids, present a low cross section in the path of any conduction. In many modern thermal insulation materials as much as 90% of the volume is taken up by air which is trapped in small cavities. This means that gaseous convection is virtually elimi-nated. The distance available for intermolecular collision can be reduced by making these cavities as small as possible.

The transmission by infrared radiation increases rapidly as the temperature rises so various materials are often introduced to reflect and to scatter the radiation.

A mixture of clay and sawdust was often formed into bricks which were then fired so that the sawdust burned out to leave a porous matrix. Some craftsmen still make their own insulation bricks in this way but as the price of commercially produced insulation bricks to set and calculable standards is reasonably low, there seems to be little advantage in making them in the studio. There is constant research and as a result production has became more sophisticated and varied. High temperature insulation bricks, known as HTI's in Britain and as IFB in the US, are now manufactured to high specification to withstand a range of hot face temperatures. They are des-ignated by the hot face temperature Fahrenheit which they have been de-signed to withstand. Thus a brick HTI 23 would be designed to withstand hot face temperatures of 2300°F (1260°C). For small furnaces HTI 28 grade bricks are commonly used. Higher grades are readily available but at a much greater price.

The development of ceramic fibre has made a considerable impact on the design of kilns and furnaces and to easier achievement of high temperatures. It is basically an aluminosilicate refractory material which is melted and then blown into fibre in a similar method to that used for the production of fibreglass. It is then formed into a number of different composite materials which have excellent insulation properties and have a degree of flexibility. Unfortunately, they have also a major disadvantage in that they have very little structural strength. They are produced in many forms; blanket, boards, loose fill, mouldable materials, tubes, modules, and when necessary, can be made into complex vacuum formed shapes. There are several grades available some of which can be used for temperatures up to 1600°C.

They can be cemented to bricks or metal and can also be pinned with specially prepared ceramic and stainless steel fastenings. They have excellent resistance to thermal shock. They have little weight and do not store heat to any appreciable extent. They resist most chemical attack except that of hot alkaline and hydrofluoric acid vapour. One difficulty which can arise, particularly with some of the boards is that they can have a shrinkage of up to 4% on initial firing. Analysis of various grades of ceramic fibre board show an increase in resistance to the effects of temperature in a similar manner to that of firebricks as the proportion of alumina is increased. For example:-

	Classification temperature		
	1260°C	*1400°C*	*1600°C*
Al_2O_3	35%	49%	56%
SiO_2	64%	50%	43%

Special cements are available from most manufacturers of ceramic fibre. These are particularly useful for bonding layers of fibre blanket or board to insulation brick.

Perhaps not so well know to potters and studio glassmakers is "Micropore". This is probably the most efficient of the materials currently available for furnace and kiln insulation This has a remarkably low thermal conductivity and is available in many forms. Unfortunately, it has a top temperature limit of 1025°C (1880°F), so for furnace work and for most ceramic kilns it can only be used as back up insulation to a more refractory material. It is rather more expensive than most of the ceramic fibre materials but the additional cost should soon be recouped by savings on fuel. It is largely made up of silica and titania with small amounts of other oxides.

A sample analysis shows:-

SiO_2	64·68%
TiO_2	31·90%
ZrO_2	0·23%
Al_2O_3	2·37%
Fe_2O_3	0·33%
P_2O_5	0·02%
B_2O_2	Trace

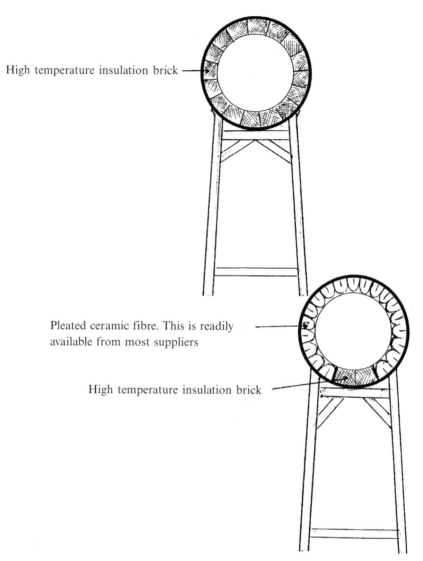

High temperature insulation brick

Pleated ceramic fibre. This is readily
available from most suppliers

High temperature insulation brick

*Sections through two common types of glory hole, one using conventional insulation brick and
the other ceramic fibre*

Complex and very accurate shapes can be produced by the makers by the use
of laser cutting equipment. They will only supply the material cut to size and
packed in a special material which burns away once the Micropore is in position and firing commences. Whilst Micropore is made largely from silica and
titanium oxide it is amorphous and the only crystalline silica dust likely to be
encountered would result from contamination of a surface by alkali vapour
together with subsequent firing to temperatures above 800°C. This could cause
the production of cristobalite. Alternatively, continued usage over 1000°C

(1830°F) could also produce cristobalite. This in itself would not create any problem until the material was broken up. It would, therefore, be most advisable to take all necessary safety precautions when renewing material which might have been affected in this way.

To give some indication of the insulating properties of the material, the manufacturers suggest that if a hot face temperature of 950°C (1740°F) and a normal outer cold face of 80°C (176°F) is assumed, as would be common in a glass forming kiln, and assuming a continuing exposure at this temperature it has been calculated that the following measures would all achieve the required temperature difference.

In practice continuing exposure at high temperatures would be unlikely to be required in a glass forming kiln so these figures could be reduced accordingly. Unfortunately, the porous nature of Micropore which produces its thermal efficiency also means that it is a very fragile material and it would be prudent to use it behind a layer of ceramic fibre slab or even behind a layer of insulation brick.

In general, the more efficient the material in terms of its thermal conductivity the weaker it tends to be in terms of its physical strength.

In a stoneware kiln and assuming a hot face requirement of 1280°C Micropore would be totally inadequate on its own but would provide an excellent backing material to appropriate ceramic fibre or insulation brick. If a potter wishes to apply the layers as suggested above for thermal conductivity to a kiln required for stoneware then one further layer of an inch of ceramic fibre on the hot face would probably suffice. The figures worked out by manufacturers are often based on the presumption that the kiln will be taken to its temperature and then held for a considerable time. If, as is often, the kiln is only to be taken to its temperature, given an appropriate soak and then cooled, then the insulation layers can be modified considerably. Many potters make up temporary stoneware kilns from little more than a layer of firebrick lined with an inch of ceramic fibre or even more simply of ceramic fibre fastened to a wire mesh frame.

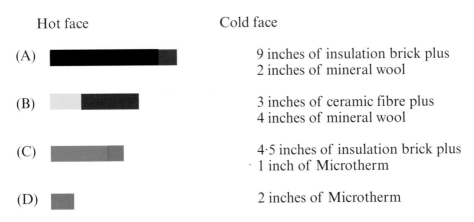

	Hot face	Cold face
(A)		9 inches of insulation brick plus 2 inches of mineral wool
(B)		3 inches of ceramic fibre plus 4 inches of mineral wool
(C)		4·5 inches of insulation brick plus 1 inch of Microtherm
(D)		2 inches of Microtherm

Different insulating measures required to achieve an outer cold face of 80°C if the hot face temperature is 950°C

Micropore (Microtherm International) and most manufacturers of ceramic fibre or insulation bricks are usually happy to give advice on appropriate insulation layers to suit particular applications.

Appropriate forms can now be made from bubble alumina and bubble mullite by a process of chemical bonding to produce an insulation material which has much greater strength than the various forms of ceramic fibre and is also highly refractory. The process also offers the advantage that denser materials can be incorporated into the same casting as a solid layer. This means that materials with the requisite qualities to form a hot face and/or give the necessary mechanical strength could be effectively bonded to appropriate insulating layers in the same monolithic block. Precise monolithic lightweight blocks can be made to suit a construction thus making the procedure of dismantling and reassembling a small furnace or kiln a relatively quick and simple operation.

One insulation material occurs naturally. The raw material, diatomaceous earth, is found in Denmark, France and the United States and is formed from the siliceous shells of tiny single cell organisms in former sea beds. The result is a very porous material which can be bonded with clay and fired into an effective insulating refractory material or simply cut into suitable insulating blocks.

It is relatively cheap and has been a common backing material for kilns and furnaces for many years.

Another relatively cheap material which is often used as back up insulation material is calcium silicate slab. This is made by several manufacturers and whilst it is only useable to temperatures of approximately 1000°C It is more substantial and more rigid than the ceramic fibre boards and can take a greater structural load. As annealing kilns in studios are unlikely to be used to temperatures above 550°C many glassmakers use this material in a suitable steel frame to make such kilns.

Some craftsmen use mineral block as backing for other types of insulation material, particularly for annealing kilns. There is no doubt that this is very cheap and very effective. The fibres, however, easily become airborne and present quite a hazard so care must be taken to see that mineral block is completely and securely contained.

The data on the various forms of thermal insulation are often given by manufacturers and suppliers as W/(mK), occasionally as kcal/(mh°C) or as Btu in/(ft²h°F). The conversion factors for these so that they can be compared adequately are:-

$W/(mK)$	$kcal/(mh°C)$	$Btu\ in/(ft^2h°F)$
1	0·86	6·93
1·163	1	8·06
0·124	0·144	1

XV.
Firing

There are basically four different methods of firing required by the potter and the glassmaker but they all involve similar regimes of heating material to specific temperatures and either maintaining that temperature or producing a controlled reduction to room temperature. They are:-

(1) the process of taking a glass furnace to a temperature commensurate with the introduction of batch materials, their subsequent melting into useable glass and then maintaining that temperature as necessary to ensure that the molten glass remains in a good working condition

(2) taking a kiln to a temperature at which glass may fuse, slump or be cast into a mould and then controlling the cooling cycle to suit the particular circumstances, thickness and annealing requirements of the glass, the temperature rise normally being governed by the nature of the mould materials and whether or not it is necessary to avoid any cracking or shattering as the glass is heated

(3) the process of converting clay materials to a hard ceramic by the use of heat

(4) taking a kiln to a temperature at which glazes may be formed or at which decorative processes involving enamels, lustres, etc, can be matured

The first is described in the chapter on glass melting and the second in the chapter on moulds and casting.

There are various physical and chemical changes which inevitably occur during the process of converting clay materials to hard ceramics by firing. To achieve these successfully there must be a consideration of the time factor in close association with the achievement of particular temperatures. Any organic matter present needs to be safely burned away and various volatiles released need to be removed completely but the major changes occur as dry clay changes to hard ceramic in a process in which water which is released in stages and various chemical and physical bonds are broken and formed.

The rate of firing relates strongly to both the nature of the clay and to its thickness. Whilst ceramic ware of normal thickness can be fired to biscuit temperature at approximately 100°C to 150°C per hour, preferably with an initial period at 60°C per hour to at least 120°C, the firing of firebricks is usually done over a period of several days.

A glass pot which may be up to two inches thick but needs much more careful handling is normally dried over several weeks and takes at least five days to fire in a pot arch to achieve a temperature at which it can be safely transferred to the pot furnace.

The firing of clay to ceramic is much the same procedure whether it is of delicate table ware or of heavy refractories. It is only the time involved, the temperatures achieved and the actual amount of heatwork which differ according to the type of clay and the size of the ware to be fired. Objects formed from clay are placed into a kiln cold and are then heated gradually at a predetermined rate to a set temperature which is held as necessary and then cooled down gradually, again at a predetermined rate. There are various chemical changes and water is released as steam at different stages during firing, so there is a considerable amount of clay shrinkage involved, whilst at the same time, water is expanding into steam. If this cannot take place at an appropriate pace, then there is likely to be some cracking or shattering which may or may not be apparent at the end of the firing but may develop later. There is also a physical change in the cooling cycle which again if rushed through, can cause damage.

Most modern electric and gas fired kilns are fitted with programmers which make the procedure simple and easy to control. There are, however, kilns without such provision and there are also potters who for various reasons still prefer to use simple hand controls or to fire a kiln by burning wood or by using oil drip systems. The main reason for firing kilns with wood is largely one of aesthetics as the fly ash tends to settle on to surfaces which are relatively horizontal rather more than on to surfaces which are nearer to being vertical. The ash changes the balance of the glaze and often provides a useful emphasis, particularly on rims and shoulders.

These firings are successful when operated by somebody with experience but it is all too easy for a beginner to build a kiln, pack it with ware and start to fire it, without fully understanding the complexities of what they are doing. Unfortunately, it is remarkable just how quickly a kiln will heat up in the early stages when in fact, it should rise slowly. Equally unfortunately it be can obstinately resist reaching the required temperature in the latter stages.

The pore water in clay which remains after drying and reflects the atmospheric humidity is removed between room temperature and about 120°C (250°F). This temperature must be reached slowly to allow the steam to be released which can be a rapid process after the boiling point is reached. If the kiln is being fired by electricity it is normal practice to leave out the plugs to allow steam to escape. If other fuels are used then the steam will escape together with the products of combustion. This stage of the proceedings is known as "water smoking". As considerable amounts of steam can be generated it is essential that it is allowed to escape or there can be a considerable risk of damage to the fabric of the kiln.

Most organic matter starts to decompose at about 200°C (390°F) and, as the temperature rises further, burns away. The water in the interlayer starts to be released at about 450°C (840°F) and continues to about 600°C (1110°F), when the water held in the crystal structure should be fully released. At this stage the plugs in the kiln can be replaced. The kaolinite crystals change to metakaolinite crystals which do not contain water so the clay is irreversibly changed from a material which can be made plastic by the addition of water to one which is permanently solid but still very fragile and porous. This stage is known as the "ceramic change" and is usually considered to have been completed by 700°C (1292°F).

At 573°C (1063°F), known as the dunting point, there is a change in the crystalline structure of the silica which produces a rapid increase in volume of about 2%, so the kiln should be taken reasonably slowly through this temperature. Any carbon and sulphur present in the clay then begins to burn out, the carbon usually being removed by about 900°C (1650°F) and the sulphur taking somewhat longer and occasionally not being clear until about 1150°C (2100°F). If carbon and/or sulphur is not removed there will be a considerable possibility of bloating in later stages as trapped gases try to escape. Prudent potters often slow down the firing or soak the kiln at about 800°C for about an hour whilst the body is still porous if they are firing clays known to contain carbon and/or sulphur. This period should be extended if the clays are heavily contaminated. Bloating is caused by the failure to remove these materials during the biscuit firing but usually only becomes apparent in the later stages of a stoneware firing when the outer layer has become impervious and any volatiles which develop cannot escape.

Fireclays and the clays used for brickmaking tend to be prone to having a high carbon and sulphur content and, because of the size of many of the products for which these clays are normally used, it may take several hours of firing to ensure that the carbon and sulphur products are removed completely. The presence of carbon or sulphur can also cause problems in once fired ware and it is essential to ensure that these products are burned out before the glaze melts and seals the surface.

These materials must have access to plenty of oxygen in order to convert into gases and escape from the clay and ultimately from the kiln. The volatiles produced can also create hazardous conditions if there is inadequate ventilation in the kiln area. If carbon monoxide is released it is a very toxic gas which is not easily noticed because it has no smell. The sulphur can cause emissions of sulphur dioxide gas which can rapidly convert to sulphurous acid. Fortunately, this is easily detectable by its particularly pungent smell.

At this stage, the clay particles are just sintered together at small points of contact and the structure is reasonably solid but fragile. It is strong enough to hold together to accommodate the changes involved in the silica inversion but still needs to be fired further to attain sufficient strength to stand the glazing process or to be used as a simple unglazed ceramic material.

At about 800°C some of the fluxes in the clay body, mostly potassium and sodium oxides, together with the free silica begin to fuse into pockets of glassy material within the pores of the clay particles in the process known generally as vitrification.

At 980°C some amorphous silica is released as the metakaolinite enters its transitional stage and as the temperature reaches 1050°C crystals of two forms of mullite begin to form and more amorphous silica is released. The first form of mullite consists of small crystals which increase mechanical and thermal strength whilst the others which tend to develop later are needle shaped and help to tie the structure together and strengthen it further. They also help to produce a strong interface with high temperature glazes.

With further increases in temperature there is further fusing until the pores become filled, usually by about 1250°C. and accompanied by a rapid decrease in size. The clay particles around the pores are also gradually attacked and incorporated into the glassy material. In general, ware fired above 1250°C is no longer porous and becomes impervious.

As the glassy pockets solidify on cooling they help to bind the clay particles together and give additional strength. The temperature at which the glassy material begins to form and the degree to which they then attack the silica depends on the particular chemicals available in the clay. If too much glass is formed the ceramic body can become brittle or may even reach the stage at which it will deform. If there is insufficient glass then the ceramic form can be weak. It must be evident from this that the glass plays an important part both in the structure and in the strength of a ceramic body.

The hard porcelains and high fired stonewares tend to be in the nature of glassy material bonded by needles of mullite crystals. In a similar manner, the calcium phosphate in bone china forms long crystals of tricalcium phosphate which strengthen the glassy matrix formed by the fusing of kaolin and feldspar.

As structural changes occur during the quartz and cristobalite phases of a firing the resulting movement in crystal size can create sufficient stress to cause cracking. The significant temperatures are 226°C (440°F) and 573°C (1065°F) and where it is known or suspected that there might be sufficient free silica or if amounts of cristobalite may have been formed then it is essential to take the firing and cooling very slowly through a few degrees either side of these temperatures.

In the cooling cycle some of the previous changes made to any free silica are reversed and the quartz–cristobalite inversions become responsible for sudden contractions. The major contraction affecting a ceramic body occurs at 226°C and is particularly beneficial in a glaze firing when it imposes a compression on the glaze known as the cristobalite squeeze.

The free silica in clay is in the form of quartz and whilst there is some change to cristobalite before 1100°C (2010°F), it begins to convert very rapidly after this temperature and this is the reason why this temperature is the usual limit for biscuit firings. Whilst there is obvious advantage to many glaze firings in maintaining a presence of some cristobalite an excess can lead to a great deal of trouble by creating too much contraction as it changes from the beta to the alpha phase on cooling.

The sequence of these inversions is that when a ceramic body is heated the crystal structure of silica, a compressed form of quartz known as alpha-quartz, begins to change to beta-quartz which has an increased crystal size at a temperature around 570°C. This is the first of the inversions and creates sufficient expansion to produce a shock to the ceramic body. On cooling, any beta-quartz remaining reverts to alpha-quartz at the same temperature with a corresponding shrinkage which also produces some stress on the ceramic body. However, there is a further change which occurs as some of the quartz converts to beta-cristobalite and this takes place mostly as the ceramic body reaches 1100°C but is unable to revert back to quartz during the normal time of a firing. It remains as beta-cristobalite which then suffers a reversion to alpha-cristobal-ite at around 226°C (440°F), again accompanied by a sudden and significant contraction. Once cristobalite has been formed there will be repeat inversions as it is reheated and recooled but it cannot revert to quartz in this time scale so this temperature remains an important point for slow temperature movement in considering further firing and cooling cycles.

Glaze firing

The application of a glaze to a ceramic body is largely to make what would otherwise be a porous material impervious. Glaze is also applied purely for decorative reasons and for the simple practical matter of providing a surface which will clean easily. In order to satisfy these criteria, the firing of the glaze and the ceramic form must be carried out thoroughly to the correct time–temperature cycle.

A glaze firing does not only affect the glaze. As it usually involves firing to a higher temperature than that achieved in the bisque firing there tends to be further development of the glass pockets in the ceramic body which helps to develop the fusion of the glaze.

The greatest problem is ensuring that the glaze and the ceramic body fit together despite their expansion differences, a glaze being a thin layer of glass with an amorphous structure and the ceramic body being largely crystalline with some glassy inclusions. Because of this they tend to expand and contract differently at various times. An earthenware glaze becomes fairly rigid by about 500°C as it cools and a stoneware glaze by about 625°C.

If the relative coefficients of expansion of the ceramic body and glaze are approximately compatible then they will cool together with reasonable har-mony until the sudden contraction in the body occurs with the cristobalite inversion at about 226°C. This squeezes the glaze which, if all the calculations have been correct, will be sufficiently elastic to benefit from this. If, however, there is too much or too little beta-cristobalite the glaze can be forced either to craze or to shiver away from the body.

Most ceramics are fired at least twice. The first being intended to turn the clay into a solid material and the second to produce a glaze on the resultant surface. Both processes can be successfully combined into one firing in what is known as "raw glazing". In this instance, the glaze is applied to the unfired pot, usually at the leather hard stage, and then the pot is fired so that both pot and glaze mature together.

Porcelain is probably the prime example of glaze and body being fired to-gether until a thick and strong body–glaze layer is created. Another example is that of salt glazing in which the pots are fired to the necessary temperature and then salt or a mixture of salt and borax is thrown onto the fire in two or three sequences after the kiln reaches a temperature of about 1100°C. This mixture volatilizes and the soda and the boric oxide react with the silica and alumina on the hot surface of the ceramic body to form a layer of glaze which is chemi-cally very resistant.

The once fired method offers advantages in producing savings in both firing and in the labour of kiln packing but whilst this was once the norm there is no doubt that at the present time most glazed ceramic ware is fired twice as this method offers greater quality control.

Raku firing is something which confounds many potters who are concerned with the effects of thermal shock and controlled cooling. There are many variations but the most common involves bisque firing clay with an open texture (an addition of 40% grog is quite usual), to a low temperature of about 900°C. A low firing glaze is applied and the pot reheated, usually in a temporary kiln until the glaze is melted and shining, when it is removed from the kiln with a pair of long tongs. It then can be simply left to cool down, subjected to reduction by covering it in sawdust or even being dipped into cold water which has the effect of producing a crackled surface.

The production of industrial earthenware usually involves a bisque firing to temperatures in the region of 1100°C or over to ensure sufficient cristobalite is formed to provide a glaze squeeze followed by what is called a "glost" firing in which the glaze is fired on to the surface at a somewhat lower temperature. This produces a relatively weak glaze–body layer which does not begin to compare with the strength of that produced in porcelain or in stoneware where there is a much greater integration of glaze and body.

The various stages of a glaze firing from room temperature are as follows:-

To approximately 120°C	any moisture absorbed by the ceramic body from the glaze application which has not dried out is removed slowly. If this stage is taken too quickly the glaze layer may be forced away from the ceramic body
At about 600°C	the various fusion processes start as the fluxes, particularly the soda, potash, lead oxide and boric oxide begin to react with the silica. This process follows the usual path of glassmaking with different fluxes becoming effective at various temperatures until the glaze becomes fully mature
At about 1000°C	earthenware glazes begin to mature
At about 1150°C	stoneware glazes begin to mature and to form a bonding layer with the ceramic body

At maturing temperature the mullite crystals tend to encourage other crystals to devitrify from the melt to strengthen the body–glaze layer and, in some cases, promote the development of matt or crystalline glazes. On cooling, the rate at which the temperature reduces affects the growth of crystals until about 700°C. It also affects colour and the surface brilliance. After this, the glaze sets slowly but the final colour may not be established until the temperature is considerably lower. There are two different points at which difficulties may arise during cooling. These are at the dunting points at 573°C and at 226°C when, if the cooling is too rapid, some cracking may occur.

The following table describes the general aspects of firing both biscuit and glaze:-

To 120°C	This is the drying period during which most of the pore water is removed so the firing needs to be slow and the kiln plugs out to allow plenty of ventilation. Water content needs to be less than 1% or there will be a considerable risk of cracking
120°C to 200°C	The remainder of the pore water is lost so the kiln still needs to be well ventilated
200°C to 350°C	Organic matter starts to decompose. Ventilation still needed but firing rate can be increased
350°C to 500°C	Most of the chemically held water is released. Chemical change starts. Some carbonates begin to release carbon dioxide
573°C	This is the point at which inversion from alpha- to beta-quartz takes place
700°C to 1000°C	Most carbon and sulphur should be burned out, vitrification begins and particles start to sinter together. Clays with a high carbon content need slow firing. The kiln plugs can be inserted. Glaze particles start to sinter. together and body shrinkage occurs
1000°C to 1100°C	Glass starts to form in the body. Mullite crystals begin to form. Glaze–body interface starts to seal according to type of glaze. Strength of body increases
1100°C	This is the usual top temperature for earthenware biscuit firing
1100°C to 1400°C	As the glazes mature the temperature needs to be slowed or held to allow gases to escape and bubbles to settle into a smooth surface
1400°C	All pores in the clay become completely filled

On cooling:-

Top temp. to 750°C	Most glazed ware can be cooled quickly but crystalline glazes will need slow cooling to allow crystals to develop
750 to 500°C	This is a period of reasonably slow cooling whilst the glaze solidifies and moves through 575°C because of the inversion of remaining beta-quartz to alpha-quartz. Fast cooling at this stage could result in cooling dunts
300 to 150°C	Slow cooling again desirable because of the inversion of beta to alpha-cristobalite at 225°C

Kiln fired glass

When glass is refired in a kiln it is usually in the form of granules or blocks of cullet and as it is a non crystalline material with no water content to consider, the firing schedules are considerably different from those used for ceramics. The main difficulty centres around the temperature at which the particular glass starts to change from being a solid material to one which initially becomes plastic and eventually to one which becomes a liquid. It becomes much more critical when the process is reversed and the glass starts to revert to being a solid. It is of necessity a relatively slow process and it is easy to lose the sense of vitality which often accompanies the process of blowing or manipulating hot glass directly from the furnace. Some careful planning of temperature and time is essential as the opportunity for visual monitoring and making adjustments is decidedly limited. Coloured enamels which are basically low melting glass particles are often introduced to provide areas of colour and some artists also use these to fuse other glass granules and fine metal inclusions onto or into the cast glass. If the cullet is in the form of granules the change as the temperature rises can be largely disregarded but if large pieces or blocks of cullet are involved then the firing needs to be taken reasonably slowly until the temperature is approaching the annealing range. It is then prudent to allow a period of time at this temperature to allow the glass to become uniform in its temperature distribution. After this, the kiln can be heated fairly rapidly. Much depends on the type of glass being heated. A high expansion glass such as a typical soda–lime–silica glass will need more care than a low expansion glass such as a borosilicate. It is necessary to be much more careful in the cooling process. When a block of glass is being heated the outside tends to expand and soften before the inside so the pressure generated is relatively small whereas on cooling the outside starts to solidify before the inside and time must be calculated to allow the glass temperature to become uniform before the glass becomes too rigid to allow any stress to be released before further cooling takes place. This process is described under "Annealing" and the temperature at which this takes place varies considerably from one type of glass to another.

The temperature to which the kiln is fired depends on how the glass needs to be processed. If it is simply to be softened sufficiently to deform or slump into a mould the this can usually be achieved at temperatures below 650°C. If glass sheets or particles are required to sinter together then 700 to 750°C will often suffice. Glass sheets will appear to fuse together at temperatures below this but such a join is unlikely to be strong enough to be stable. If the glass needs to soften sufficiently to become a liquid which will run into a mould then most glasses other than the low expansion borosilicates will do so at temperatures around 830°C though it will be necessary to soak the kiln until the glass has filled the mould and settled. The kiln should then be cooled fairly rapidly to annealing temperature to avoid any possible difficulty with devitrification. It then becomes necessary to start an annealing schedule appropriate to the type and volume of the particular glass as described under "annealing."

Carved and polished lead crystal

Glass founding

Founding in the small workshop is the process of introducing batch chemicals, cullet or a mixture of both into a preheated furnace and melting them into a homogenous liquid suitable for hand working.

The furnace is heated to founding temperature either by electricity, oil or gas and nowadays, very occasionally by wood. After this temperature is achieved the batch material and/or cullet is introduced, usually in a sequence of amounts, but sometimes as one lot and the furnace temperature drops initially and then gradually regains its founding temperature as the materials melt. If batch chemicals are involved the process follows that of glaze melting in that water of crystallisation and gases such as carbon dioxide, etc, are released until a homogenous liquid is formed and all crystalline materials have disappeared. It is necessary to ensure that all the gas bubbles have been removed and this process is known as "refining" or simply as "fining" and usually needs no more than holding the furnace at its founding temperature for some time before reducing the temperature to 50 to 100°C below the working temperature and then raising it to the temperature suitable for the glass processes required. After this the furnace temperature is maintained until the glass has been worked sufficiently for another founding to be necessary to replenish supplies. The furnace would not normally be cooled completely until a rebuild becomes necessary or until there is to be a sufficiently long break in production to merit a shut down.

XVI.
Moulds and casting

Moulds for ceramics can be complex and require considerable care and skill in making. They are, however, used cold and a straightforward and simple mixture of water and good quality potters or surgical plaster will prove perfectly adequate for this purpose in the studio. The ratio of water to plaster used is usually in the region of 75 to 85 parts by weight to 100 parts of plaster. The higher the proportion of water to plaster produces a more porous mould but one which is somewhat weaker. The main properties required, apart from the ability to set to a particular form fairly quickly, are that the resulting mould will be absorbent, provide a smooth surface and be sufficiently strong to hold the clay which is being processed.

Moulds for glass on the other hand are used for a variety of processes so they need to be able to withstand a considerable amount of heat and, in some circumstances, a great deal of thermal shock. As a result a much wider range of materials is used. For most kiln glass forming however, the moulds are also mostly based on plaster of Paris but with other materials added to strengthen them and/or to give them a greater resistance to heat. More permanent moulds for kiln work are usually made from ceramic or from various compositions based upon aluminous cement.

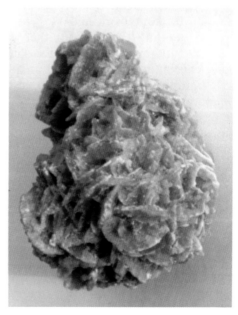

A piece of gypsum showing the natural crystalline structure

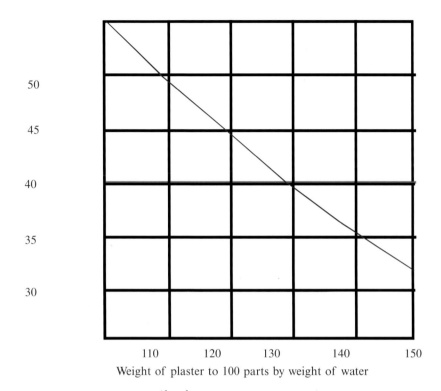

50

45

40

35

30

110   120   130   140   150

Weight of plaster to 100 parts by weight of water

Absorbency as percentage porosity.
The diagram above shows the ratio of water to plaster in the mixing affects the absorbency of the resultant cast. What it doesn't indicate is that it also affects the setting time and the strength of the mould

Plaster of Paris is a white powder which is made by removing the water of crystallisation from gypsum by heating the mineral in large steel pans.

In use, the powder is added to water when, after mixing it begins to revert to its original state and solidifies. It is usually described as being semi hydrated calcium sulphate, $2(CaSO_4.2H_2O)$ which on heating becomes $2CaSO_4.H_2O$ having released $3H_2O$.

The ratio of plaster to water can have a significant effect on the strength, the setting time and the resulting absorbency so this ratio is capable of being varied to suit the mould characteristics required. Nine parts of water to 10 parts of plaster by weight is about the safe limit for a light absorbent plaster which would start to set after 7 or 8 minutes whilst a much more robust mixture which would have less absorbency but would have much greater physical strength would be 10 of water to 14 of plaster and this would begin to set rather more quickly at about 4 minutes. Pouring times would be rather less than the times quoted but care is needed in using old plaster as this tends to set rather quickly.

The setting time can be slowed by adding very small quantities of acidic materials to the water. Alum and sulphuric acid are popular retardants but vinegar, gelatine and borax are also used. The use of warm water not hotter than 30°C will also slow down the setting. If the water is more than 30°C it will start to act as an accelerator and will speed up the setting. Other common accelerators are:- previously set plaster, ground and sieved to a powder and various alkaline salts. It must be emphasised that the quantities of these materials must be very tiny as it is surprisingly easy to mix a plaster which takes hours to set or one which allows no pouring time. The actual proportions vary from one material to another but it is well worth the small amount of time taken to make sample tests to ensure that they are right. As the plaster begins to set some heat will be generated as the crystals are formed and this should peak after about half an hour. At this stage the mould should be sufficiently strong to handle but the crystal formation continues and the achievement of maximum strength will probably take about 24 hours.

In a small glass workshop casting is usually carried out either by:-

(1) ladling hot glass from a furnace into a preheated mould

(2) melting glass in a crucible from which it is poured into a mould

(3) heating both mould and glass together in a kiln until the glass assumes the form defined by the mould

In industry, moulds, usually made of fine steel or bronze, are designed for long term repetition blown or pressed ware and are very expensive to produce. Because of this they are rarely used in a studio where the glassmaker is unlikely to need continuous production of similar forms. Moulds for studio use tend to be made from simple, cheaper and readily available materials such as fine plaster or aluminous cement and various forms of refractory grog.

The most popular mixtures for moulds suitable for kiln forming are usually based on plaster so the details given for making moulds for ceramics apply equally to those made for glass forming. The difference lies in the fact that the mould used for studio glass forming must be able to withstand temperatures up to about 850°C without disintegrating or warping so the plaster usually needs to be re-reinforced with other materials. It also needs to release the glass easily from the mould and leave as fine a surface as possible to avoid laborious grinding and polishing.

The most popular mould recipe to suit these criteria is a simple mixture (by volume) of 50% dental plaster and 50% ground flint or quartz though the proportion of silica is often increased slightly for higher temperatures. Another which seems to be used successfully is 40% plaster, 30% ground flint and 30% prefired plaster which has been ground down. This is said to reduce the likelihood of cracking during the casting process but the inclusion of prefired plaster has the added effect of reducing the available pouring time considerably so this needs to be taken into account when using this material.

Another popular variation is to introduce crushed high temperature insulation brick in place of the prefired plaster. The proportion of water to the plaster/silica mixture is approximately 1 pint of water to 2 lb (or 1 litre of water to 1·6 kg) of the mixture. This 1 pint of water to 2 lb of mixture should make approximately 40 cubic inches of mould or 655 cc of solid investment. With

An industrial mould for blown forms

practice the weighing out process becomes unnecessary and the amounts can readily be estimated by eye. Some artists prefer to use warm water (above 30°C) for mixing in order to speed up the process.

Another rather more complex mould recipe which is believed to have originated at Corning and which has been highly recommended is:-

2·25 lb or 1 kg of plaster
2·25 lb or 1 kg of flint
7 oz or 200 gm of china clay
0·7 oz or 20 gm of alumina fibre
0·7 oz or 20 gm of heavy paper such as paper towels
3 pints or 1700 cc of water

The fibre and paper is liquidised to a pulp with some water in a domestic blender. The pulp is then washed and drained. The rest of the ingredients are introduced to the water and after they have been absorbed the pulp is added and the whole stirred lightly by hand before being stirred vigorously either in a blender or with a paint stirrer in an electric drill for a few seconds. The mixture sets very quickly so it needs to be poured on to the model soon after stirring. Suitable wetting agents are recommended to allow the mixture to flow and to allow the rather fragile mould to release from the model when it has set. The mould needs to be shaken gently after pouring to move any bubbles away from the contact surface. When a plaster based mould has dried it is essential to prefire it gently to about 100°C (212°F) to remove any moisture before actually using it for the casting process.

A well known Dutch artist whose production consists almost entirely of kiln cast forms recommends a mould which can be used several times if treated carefully. It consists of a two layer mould consisting of an inner layer made with 60% plaster and 40% talc backed up with an outer layer of 50% plaster and 50% grog.

Aluminous cements such as "Ciment Fondu" or "Secar" together with similar aggregate materials to those used with plaster can be used successfully for making more permanent moulds. These moulds need to be dried slowly, prefired to the manufacturers recommended temperatures and, if to be used without an inner plaster based mould, need a light dusting of a suitable separator such as talc or whiting before use. While plaster based inner moulds are usual, it is possible to make double skin moulds in which the inner one is of the alumina cement with an equal part of fine powdered flint or talc and the outer layer with one part of the cement to four or five parts of an appropriate high temperature aggregate, usually a mixture of fine and coarser aggregate. The Secar or Ciment Fondu mixtures need to be dried slowly and when dry, fired slowly to about 850°C.

Other mould mixtures are:-

50% plaster
25% silica
25% Molochite

50% plaster
25% silver sand
25% Investrite
50% Investrite
30% plaster
20% talc

50% plaster
50% silica   often used as an inner mould and surrounded by an outer
                  mould composed of 20% Ciment Fondu and 80% grog

40% plaster
20% Ciment Fondu
40% flint

40% plaster
10% Ciment Fondu
40% Molochite
10% ceramic fibre

20% Ciment Fondu
80% grog

Moulds made from plaster mixtures need to be dried thoroughly and to be prefired to about 100°C before being placed into a kiln for the actual casting process. Many craftsmen often leave them in a warm oven overnight to achieve the same result.

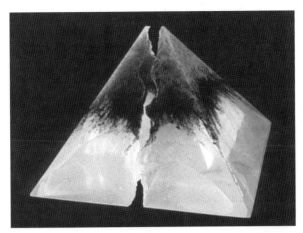

Glass cast in a mould then polished, Colin Reid

The mixing process is important to the results. The plaster and silica need to be well mixed, preferably in a sealed plastic bag in order to avoid the possibility of breathing siliceous dust. The plaster/silica mixture is added to the water carefully to avoid introducing air and left for a minute or two to soak, then mixed into a slurry, preferably by plunging the hand into the mixture and gently shaking it from one side to the other. Taking the hands in to the mixture tends to introduce air. It therefore needs to be left to settle to allow any bubbles to come to the surface. These should be skimmed off carefully and any excess water poured away. At this stage the material should be ready for pouring into the cottle.

Before any casting can take place it is necessary to ensure that the original model will release from the set plaster. Damp clay will present no problem but models made from wood or porous materials will need the application of some kind of sealant or separating agent. There are several of these on the market and suppliers of casting equipment and materials will supply a range of suitable products. Porous materials can be coated with either a couple of coats of shellac or quick drying lacquer before applying the separating agent.

Separators are used to prevent the original model from sticking to the mould, to lubricate the surface, and to form a very thin uniform film between the mould and the model. Potter's soap is a very common separator. It needs to be thinned down with water and it is usual to brush on several coats before giving a final wash after which the surface of the mould should feel slippery to the touch. Another separator is made by mixing warmed flakes of stearic acid with paraffin (kerosene), 1 lb of stearic acid to 1 quart of paraffin. When completely mixed it is applied to the mould with a soft brush. Petroleum jelly thinned with paraffin can be used similarly. Other separators in the form of coats of thin machine oil, warm olive oil or spirits of camphor can be sprayed on to a metal model.

The "Cire-Perdue" process commonly used for casting metals is probably the most popular method for producing full three-dimensional forms in a kiln

Detail of a large cast and polished sculpture by Zora Palova and Stepan Pala and sited at the National Glass Centre in Sunderland. Photgraph by Zora Palova

using the plaster mixtures previously described. Resin bonded sands, obtainable in small quantities from foundries are good for casting from the furnace. Some craftsmen use sand bonded with about 7% sodium silicate and which is then set by treating the mould with carbon dioxide gas.

Solid blocks of graphite which can easily be worked with appropriate woodworking tools can be shaped into moulds but have the disadvantage that this process can create an incredible amount of black dust which must be removed carefully and completely. Graphite is expensive but is a very good material for moulds as it withstands the thermal shock of hot glass very well. It is advisable to drop some hot glass into the mould and to remove it before the actual cast is made so that the surface of the mould is hot enough to avoid cooling the surface of the glass casting too rapidly. Relief casts are usually made by making a mould directly from the original model. This will probably be made from soft clay, modelling wax, or vinyl type material.

Moulds made from aluminous cement mixtures or from fired ceramic must be coated with an appropriate release agent so that they will release the cast glass cleanly. Ceramic fibre paper works well on simple shapes such as shallow bowl forms or flat kiln shelves but more complex shapes need to be covered with a thin application of release agent such as talc or a commercially prepared release agent.

A kiln shelf can used for casting slabs by ensuring that it is perfectly flat, if necessary first rubbing over it with a diamond abrasive pad to remove any material which may have become fused to the surface. A sheet of ceramic fibre is laid on the shelf and cut at the corners so that it can be turned up along the edges to form a box. These edges are then supported by narrow strips cut from kiln shelf material. Deep box forms made in this way will probably need to be supported in place by further pieces of refractory placed along the strips to ensure that they do not spring apart when the glass melts into the form.

Most makers simply lay in sufficient cullet into the mould when making relief casts and then melt it into the form. If the glass needs to flow into the form, rather than simply being placed there the cullet can be placed into a suitable ceramic plant pot which is placed so that when heated the molten glass will run through the hole in the bottom of the pot and into the mould.

Some makers deliberately introduce small amounts of fine glassmaking sand into casts of clear glass to give some internal movement or flow which often emerges as a fine cloud effect. This can be done quite haphazardly by sprinkling the sand amongst the cullet or by making half the cast, putting a small amount of fine sand on to the surface, spreading this with the fingers or a brush into a pattern as necessary and then casting the remainder of the glass on top of this. It must be emphasised that the amounts of sand used must be very small and must be finely distributed.

It is normal practice to use finely ground glass for the production of the more delicate forms of pate de verre. Sometimes this is slip cast using a suitable commercial deflocculant or is carefully built up on to the interior surface of a plaster mould in thin layers using an organic adhesive. Whenever fine particles are used the result will be opaque, or at best, translucent. This is because of the presence of lots of tiny bubbles. These cannot be removed either by prolonged or by increased heating and it is a good policy to accept that this is an essential part of the character of this type of pate de verre.

Moulds to the glassblower are those made of metal, wood or graphite used for forming blown glass or are the metal moulds used for the production of pressed glass. Glassmakers in small workshops do not normally need the expensive permanent moulds used in factories as they are rarely concerned with long production runs so they tend to make their own. Simple box moulds can be made from slabs of wood. Moulds for bowl shapes are easily turned from blocks of wood. Cylindrical moulds are made from steel tubing lined with wet paper and from various plaster/grog mixtures.

Refractory cement mixtures can be used for more complex moulds. The plaster mixes for blowing moulds are usually formed from approximately 60 percent plaster and additions of aggregates such as grog, molochite and powdered flint or quartz. The dry components are often mixed in a domestic type blender, sometimes together with some ceramic fibre before being introduced into the water. It is possible to blow several pieces from these moulds with careful use before they start to disintegrate. They always need to be prefired before use.

Refractory cements such as Ciment Fondu and Secar make more permanent moulds when used with suitable refractory aggregates. In Eastern Europe a popular mould mixture for blowing was made by adding dextrin, carpenters animal-hide glue and small quantities of fibreglass to the plaster.

The procedure is to mix approximately 1 lb of dextrin to one pound of water and stir into a stiff paste.

Use a carpenters double glue pot to melt about 6 ounces of glue to 1 lb of water. Mix four ounces of the melted glue together with about three cups of the dextrin paste and allow to stand for about twelve hours. This is mixed with the plaster–water in the proportions of 1 part of paste to 30 parts of the plaster–water but should be introduced into the water before the plaster is added. A handful of fibreglass is mixed in before the plaster mixture is poured.

Blow moulds need to be used wet and may need to contain small holes leading to the outside surface to allow steam to escape. The resin bonded sands used in foundries for metal casting are also very good for making moulds for blowing. These foundries are usually willing to supply the small quantities required by the studio glassmaker. Simple moulds made from steel rods welded vertically from a steel base can also be used to blow corrugated forms and loose moulds made from wire mesh can be used to produce individual irregular pieces.

Separators

One of the major problems for artists casting glass into moulds or fusing glass together in a kiln is to ensure that the surface of the mould is reproduced as faithfully as possible and that the glass and the contact areas will part cleanly leaving a surface which needs little or no polishing. There are many mould mixtures which can be used for casting glass. Unfortunately, without further attention, many of them, particularly those made from ceramic material or cement based materials will cement themselves firmly to the surface of the glass. As a result it becomes necessary to introduce a fine buffer layer of material from which the glass will release cleanly. These materials have become known as separators. They are not to be confused with the soap or oil based materials used when making a plaster or investment mould from an original model. They need to be of materials which are resistant to high temperatures (up to 850°C).

The most popular of these for flat or nearly flat areas, particularly kiln shelves, is a thin layer of ceramic fibre. This is readily available from many suppliers in rolls of different sizes and thicknesses and is easily cut to the required size. It tends to leave a slightly textured finish but this can be reduced by slightly damp-ening the surface of the fibre when it is in place and then running over it with a hot domestic iron. Another popular separator is talc. This is basically a natu-ral form of magnesium silicate which is usually of an extremely fine particle size and sometimes sold as French chalk. It can just be rubbed lightly on to a mould surface or kiln shelf but is probably best applied by mixing it with water or alcohol and lightly spraying the mixture on to a warmed surface. This offers the possibility of a much finer finish than can be achieved by dusting, brushing or rubbing in the separator. Magnesium carbonate can be used in a similar manner to talc.

Head modelled in clay by the author and cast in black glass

For lower temperature applications such as bending or fusing where temperatures are not likely to exceed 700°C the same separators can be used but white emulsion paint not based on vinyl can also be used. If this temperature is exceeded when using emulsion paint there will be a tendency for the glass to bubble. For temperatures up to 650°C the type of graphite paste sold in tubes for applying to domestic grates, etc, is very good. It needs at least two or three applications but can be rubbed and polished to produce a fine smooth finish. At higher temperatures it tends to burn away.

Both separators and moulds are affected both by the temperature and the amount of time that they are held at a top temperature. Plaster based moulds tend to crack once the temperature has exceeded 850°C. The extent to which a separator or mould surface becomes embedded in the glass is largely dependent on temperature but this is not the whole picture. Some glasses are much more invasive in this respect than others so it is prudent to test a sample of new glass on the separator or mould material before making an actual cast.

For high temperature work, boron nitride is an expensive but effective separator.

XVII.
Adhesives

There is a growing tendency for artists working in both glass and ceramics to produce sculptural works which involve the use of adhesives to cement various elements of a construction together. Conservators also use specialised adhesives to repair broken artefacts. There are many of these adhesives which are perfectly suitable for joining ceramic material but which may not be suitable for use with glass or with glazed surfaces.

Glass and glaze presents problems in that the surface contains molecules which are not chemically satisfied and as a result, layers of moisture are attracted to the surface. When glass is clean and dry it can be wetted both by adhesives and by unwanted grease and dirt. It is necessary to be sure that before applying any adhesive that the glass or glaze surface is thoroughly degreased and cleaned.

It may be necessary to ensure that much of the water layer is removed from the surfaces in order to increase the area of contact if the adhesive is to perform with efficiency. This applies in particular to some of the organic based adhesives. The surface may still attract more moisture if it can and this could eventually result in a breakdown of the adhesion.

Many polymer based adhesives are not completely waterproof so when moisture manages to penetrate through the skin it can cause a reaction at the interface between the adhesive and the glass or glaze which again will reduce adhesion and result in possible failure.

Special silane coupling agents are available to reduce this effect and enhance the adhesion of polymers to glass considerably but, particularly when used on constructions which are located outside and have to withstand the weather, it is inevitable that eventually the water penetration and subsequent glass decay will cause the adhesion to fail.

There are various adhesives available for both glass and ceramics, some of which have been in use for many years but as new materials, particularly from developments in polymer chemistry have emerged, more adhesives have come on to the market. There are several of these which are designed specifically and are used principally by people who are involved in conservation work but those in most common use in small workshops at this time are:-

    polyester resins
    epoxy resins
    silicone sealants
    UV curing acrylate adhesives for glass

Polyester resins are often used as gap fillers and in general, they initially produce good mechanical strength. They are thermosetting and are in the form of liquids consisting of unsaturated polyester and styrene. There is a peroxide based liquid which is used to start and to accelerate the reaction. The proportion of this liquid can be reduced to some degree if the reaction needs to be slowed.

The polyester resins are available in various forms including some which are clear and designed for embedding and some which need to be applied in layers. Most of them can generate considerable amounts of heat if mixed in quantity and the peroxide needs to be handled very carefully as it has a strong oxidising capability. Various inert fillers can be mixed with polyester resins and as a result they have been very popular as gap fillers in ceramic conservation. There are disadvantages in using these materials for glass in that there is a tendency for yellowing to develop when there is exposure to light and for there to be a possibility of attack by moisture.

During curing, fumes are given off which can be harmful and should be extracted. It is also advisable to use a suitable barrier cream on the hands and to use appropriate gloves to avoid contact between the resin and the skin.

Epoxy resin is used much more than polyester resin by glassmakers. It is usually in the form of a two mix resin and hardener. Over the years the most popular has been Araldite AY 103 with hardener HY 956 but now similar material is available from many manufacturers. It is sometimes used by potters but its greatest use has been by studio glassmakers. There are rapid setting varieties and these are very useful though they do not seem to have the strength of the standard material. There is a tendency for the resin to become yellow in time.

One common use is that of gluing pieces of float glass together to make blocks or laminates which can then be cut and polished. This process seems to be very simple but it does pay dividends to take great care in carrying it out. At a demonstration of the technique, pieces of 10 mm glass were cut to size, cleaned thoroughly three times with acetone and then places between layers of paper to avoid any dust falling on the surfaces. The glass was then placed into a kiln and gently warmed so that as the adhesive was applied to the centre it would spread easily. At this stage, any bubbles were removed with a pin or the point of a knife. The next piece of glass was lowered on to the layer of adhesive from one end until it was flat and there were no bubbles. Pressure was then applied with a padded stick to press out any excess adhesive. Further layers were added similarly until a block of sufficient size was formed. This precise use of adhesive to form blocks which are then meticulously ground and polished is very evident in the Czech Republic and Slovakia but is becoming very popular throughout the world.

In homes or in the controlled atmosphere of a museum or art gallery the life expectancy of such a bond is likely to be considerable.

For general sculptural work where complete clarity is not essential, glass must be degreased before the resin is applied and where there is a need to achieve maximum adhesion some abrading of both ceramic and glass surfaces can be considerable help.

In cold weather the resin can become too viscous to use easily and is best applied at temperatures above 30°C (86°F). It is also advisable to mix the resin in small quantities because there is a danger of generating an exothermic tem-

Illustration of sculpture by the author. Glass bonded with epoxy resin

perature rise from any mass of the mixture. This will certainly result in shortening the working life of the mixture and in sufficient quantity can create enough
heat to produce noxious fumes.

Eye protection and rubber or plastic gloves are advisable. Good ventilation
is essential. Suitable barrier and cleansing creams are available. Skin which has
been in contact with epoxy resin should be washed well with soap and warm
water. Spatulas, brushes and any other tools can be cleaned with acetone or
cellulose thinners before the resin has set.

For bonding pieces which need to be held in position whilst curing, rapid
setting resins are available but setting of most resin can be accelerated by heating the glass or ceramic surfaces. Curing of the AY103/HY951 mixture can
take from 20 minutes to 24 hours depending on the temperature of the surfaces affected. Suitable schedules are available from the suppliers.

Clear silicone sealants

When gap filling and/or flexibility is required clear silicone sealant is often
found to be the most suitable adhesive. It is usually supplied in pistol grip type
tubes and can be spread easily with a spatula or knife. The contact surfaces
should be degreased with methylated spirits (alcohol) or acetone. The adhesive
stops being tacky after about an hour but achieves maximum adhesion after

about twelve hours. It is cheap, reasonably waterproof and easy to use but it contains acetic acid which is an irritant so care is needed to ensure that it does not get on to the skin. It is also surprisingly strong, especially when used over large areas. It is also gap filling.

It is available in bulk and Dow Corning offer a dense, strong silicone called Dow Corning 732 RTV. They also offer a very strong silicone adhesive called 795 sealant and a rather expensive but crystal clear sealant called 2001 Ultraclear.

Any excess material can be cleaned off immediately with methylated spirit or, alternatively, left until it has just ceased to be tacky when it will usually pull away in strips. If it is left to cure it can still be removed by cutting and scraping but will require much more work with a sharp knife or razor blade. A silicone sealant remover is available at most retailers.

Silicone based adhesives offer the advantage that they retain a considerable amount of flexibility which can often prevent damage in circumstances in which the materials come under strain or physical attack. Where this quality is of great importance a low modulus sealant with a greater than normal flexibility can be obtained from most suppliers. The major difficulty with this material is that any adhesive left exposed on edges or faces will inevitably attract dirt. This will remain on the surface and may even penetrate into the material to leave a dark line or area which could be very difficult to remove. Some of these adhesives also tend to attract lichen and such materials when used outdoors. However, adhesive containing a fungicide to deter this is readily available. In the US the General Electric Company of 260 Hudson River Rd, Waterford NY makes a construction grade silicone sealant SC1200 which is highly recommended.

Silicone is a term which relates to various compounds formed from silicon and organic radicals. They divide into two basic groups, the silanes which have excellent weatherproofing qualities but have less strength than the elastomers which form the other group. These are available as one part silicones, usually provided in a sealed tube and as two mix silicones which are reputed to be not as strong.

UV curing glass adhesive

This is a remarkably strong but relatively expensive material and the most popular supplier at this moment in time seems to be Loctite. It can be obtained in a variety of size of containers. It is not commonly used for joining ceramics or opaque glass as it usually needs access to ultraviolet (UV) radiation before it will cure. It is possible, however, to buy an activator for some of the UV adhesives.

An ultraviolet lamp is useful for curing but reasonably strong sunlight will work just as well. Close fitting surfaces are essential for good bonding and this material should not be used unless the surfaces fit well together.

The bonding action is very rapid so when the adhesive has been applied it is essential to ensure that the glass is in exactly the right place before it is exposed to UV light. Setting can be complete within a few seconds. Prior degreasing of

A large stone and glass sculpture by the author using silicone adhesive.
Grizedale Forest Sculpture Park

the surfaces by acetone or cellulose thinners is advisable. The same material can be used for cleaning any excess adhesive immediately after setting as this will not cure as rapidly as that which is trapped between the layers of glass. If the excess is left to harden it can be very difficult to remove and sometimes in the process of being scraped off will lift part of the surface of the glass. There have been reports of crizzling on some glasses caused by the use of a UV light source and where there has been a pocket of adhesive left to fill a gap there have been instances of the glass cracking.

Cyanoacrylates

The various cyanoacrylate products sold generally as "superglue" provide a good quick setting adhesive for ceramics but are expensive for general studio use and tend to be used mostly for conservation, particularly when dealing with small fragments.

They offer an advantage for artists building up multiple element constructions in that they set in seconds, allowing further elements to be added almost immediately. This quality does produce its own disadvantages in that the pieces

Example of glass sculpture using UV curing glue as the adhesive

to be joined need to be placed precisely as there is little time to make adjustments. There have been suggestions that they may gradually break down from exposure to light and from attack by alkalis.

Several adhesives with particular applications in the field of ceramic conservation are described fully in *The Conservation and Restoration of Ceramics* by Susan Buys and Victoria Oakley, published by Butterworth-Heinemann.

Reference. *A Dictionary of Glass*, C. Bray, A & C Black Ltd, 1995.

Fraxbond

The Carborundum Company who make the ceramic fibre insulation called Fibrefrax has brought out a range of adhesives suitable for high temperature applications. They are marketed under the trade name "Fraxbond". The first of these, number 702, is a powder which is mixed with water. When it is cured it is claimed to have good adhesion to glass, ceramics and metals and will stand working temperatures up to 900°C (1650°F).

The second and third, numbers 715 and 716, are both specifically intended for bonding ceramic fibre and are supplied as paste or liquid ready for use. They have a top continuous working temperature of 900°C (1650°F). Adhesive number 803 is a two mix powder best used on non porous surfaces and has a continuous working temperature of 1000°C (1830°F). It is recommended for bonding refractories. The last of the group, number 900 is two part mix of base and hardener recommended for glass bonding where high temperature usage is envisaged. It has a recommended top continuous working temperature of 900°C (1650°F).

The bonding of glass to glass can usually be achieved successfully by one means or another. Greater difficulties can arise if it becomes necessary to bond glass to other materials such as metals, rock, ceramic, etc, particularly when working on a large scale. The differences in expansion mean that any adhesive must have a degree of elasticity whilst retaining its bonding strength to both materials. Fortunately, modern car design has produced a demand for such adhesives and much research is currently taking place to find suitable material. No doubt the results will soon appear on the market.

Reference. *A Dictionary of Glass*, C. Bray, A & C Black Ltd, 1995.

Sealing glasses

There is another alternative to adhesives which does not seem to have been exploited to any degree by artists or craftsmen. This involves the use of so-called "sealing glasses" for joining glass to metal and "solder glasses" used for joining glass to glass. These are usually made from low melting glasses, usually lead borate silicate glass and specially designed to have a specific expansion to suit the materials to be joined and to have other physical and chemical characteristics as required. When used as seals to metal, the boric oxide content also brings the advantage of providing a high resistance to thermal shock. A considerable number of sealing glasses have been developed for the lighting and electronics industries. There are many possible complexities and the subject is developed in *Glass to Metal Seals* by J. H. Partridge and published by the Society of Glass Technology. Studio glassmakers might find more to interest them in the solder glasses used mostly for joining glass to glass. These solder glasses are melted and ground to a powder, suspended in some suitable medium and applied to the surfaces to be joined. They melt at temperatures as low as 370°C in order that the components to be joined can be heated together without slumping whilst the powder fuses to both surfaces. Needless to say, the expansion of the solder glass must be sufficiently near to that of both components to avoid the development of strain.

XVIII.
Colloids

Colloids are used considerably in both ceramics and in glass. They are usually composed of finely divided particles of material dispersed in another substance and often show different characteristics as a result. They are often described as being halfway between a suspension and a solution, the fine particles being known as a dispersed phase whilst the materials in which they become suspended become the dispersion medium. Both together become a colloid.

There are different kinds of colloids. "Sols" are small solid particles dispersed in a liquid. "Emulsions" are colloidal systems in which both the dispersed and continuous phases are liquids. "Gels" are colloids in which both dispersed and continuous phases have a three dimensional network which forms a kind of jelly.

These fine particles play an important part in many aspects of clay, glaze and coloured glass. In a clay they make a considerable difference to its plasticity and very plastic clays tend to hold a large proportion of colloidal material. In slips, particularly in those made from plastic clay, they are responsible for particles remaining in suspension because the surface charge repels one particle from another. This means that a material which can be more than twice the weight of water, can remain in suspension and defy the force of gravity. These fine particles can move freely in the water because the electrical charge applies its force from all sides. When a small amount of electrolyte such as calcium chloride or even vinegar, known as a flocculant, is introduced into the slip the electrical charge is reduced and the particles are able to gravitate together and form larger masses called flocs. As a result the slip tends to settle. The process whereby the particles aggregate is known as flocculation.

Many colours are the result of colloidal dispersions. Sometimes this colour results from the actual colour of the colloidal material but often results from the fact that the particles are so tiny that they are actually smaller than the waves of light and interfere with these by bending them to produce an opaque, translucent or coloured effect rather than one of transparency or of simply reflecting and/or transmitting light. These particles tend to take no active part in the formation of the random network of the glass or glaze but remain as discrete dispersed material suspended in the molten mass and eventually in the solid glass or glaze. They can be composed of amorphous solids, crystals or gases.

The colloidal effects may not necessarily be caused by solid material. They can also be created by tiny pockets of gas dispersed in a similar manner. These are more likely to occur in a glaze than in a properly founded glass. The gases should be removed from glass during the founding process but in a glaze there are many materials which release gases at various stages of a firing and some of them can easily become incorporated into the glaze to produce translucency or opacity. Fine bubbles can also be created when glass is re-heated for kiln casting and this is one of the main causes of the opacity which can develop in this process.

Colloidal silica is now used increasingly as a bonding agent for ceramic fibre insulation and together with zirconium silicate as a batwash for kiln shelves.

Bubbles of gas are quite common in glazes and enamels and when these are extremely fine they form colloids responsible for much opalescence. Some gases may also become part of sulphates, chlorides and fluorides in the glaze. An important material is phosphorous pentoxide. This is actually a glass former but can remain in part as fine colloidal particles in the glaze which do not enter into the network. They produce a blue opalescent quality. Arsenic oxide is another glass former which acts in a similar way.

The effect of many of these materials depends considerably on the control of the cooling cycle. Many potters try to achieve beautiful Chun glazes and keep modifying their recipes without success whilst more often than not they would be better served by trying to reach a satisfactory cooling cycle. If this is too rapid then there will be little or no effect. If it is too prolonged then the result will probably be too opaque. (See Opacity and translucency, page 225, also Dichroic glass, page 212)

Perhaps the most famous example of colloidal dispersion in glass is that provided by the Lycurgis cup in the British Museum. It appears opaque green in reflected light but becomes wine-red in transmitted light and is often quoted as a prime example of dichroism.

Several heavier metals go into a dispersed phase to produce colour. Very small quantities of gold and copper can each produce ruby. Silver can produce yellow. Cassius purple results from the use of colloidal gold and tin.

Some non-metals also become colloidal suspensions. Carbon and sulphur which together will produce amber, and selenium, particularly in association with cadmium, is widely used to produce a range of yellows and reds.

Heat treatment is often required with some of the colours to enable them to strike.

XIX.
Colour

Colour is a major element in much glass and ceramic production. It is a wonderful quality when used with due consideration and sensitivity but unfortunately in some glass production the makers are seduced into producing very loud and garish effects. It is a phenomenon which creates a sensation when light of different wavelengths falls on to the human eye. There is a visible spectrum ranging from approximately 390 nm to 740 nm running from violet through indigo, blue, green, yellow and orange to red. All these as found together in normal daylight produce white light. Other colours can be produced by varying the proportions or by omitting some components altogether.

There are three particular colour qualities. They are:-

(1) Its hue which depends on its wavelength,

(2) Its saturation which depends on the degree in which it moves away from white light and

(3) Its luminosity.

The colour that we normally see from an opaque surface such as that of a painting usually results from the pigment which has been used. For example, the colour in a red tablecloth seen in a white light results from the fact that the surface absorbs all the other colour wavelengths except the red.

Glass is different because whilst it produces the reflected colour sensation in a similar way to that in paintings, it also deals with light which is transmitted through the material, reflected from small particles in the glass, or in the case of a glaze, reflected from the ceramic surface. This is very evident when a very thin layer of copper lustre will register as being the colour of copper metal when we see the reflection of light from the surface of the glass but will appear as being blue when the light actually comes through the glass. The so-called precious metal lustres such as silver, platinum, gold and copper leave a thin film of the metal on the surface which reflects light in a similar manner to that of polished metal rather than by creating interference layers like the other lustres.

We know a glaze is a thin layer of glass bonded to a fired clay body but what is not generally appreciated is that an enamel is also a layer of glass which may be bonded either to another glass, to a glaze or to a metal. It has a relatively low melting point in order that a glass object being enamelled does not deform in the firing when the enamel is fusing together. On a glaze, the melting point of the enamel does not need to be quite so critical but whilst it can be applied to a hard glaze it is better if it is able to bond to a softening layer of glaze without becoming sufficiently fluid to run and disperse. It is also essential that enamel is not overtired or it can start to bubble or produce muddy colours.

The bonding of enamels to another glassy layer and the bonding of glaze to a ceramic body is explained under bonding and under ion exchange. The compatibility of glazes, enamels and glass is explained under compatibility, coefficients of expansion and glaze fit.

The colouring of a glass can be a very complex and involved subject. Whilst there are plenty of simple colour recipes for both glazes and glass, a glance through the excellent comprehensive book on coloured glass by W. A. Weyl, published by the Society of Glass Technology will give a very good indication of both complexities and possibilities.

Many ceramic glazes and some old glass is coloured naturally by virtue of the impure batch materials and the nature of the firing processes used at the time. As a result the colours were rarely brash and were often softened by the associated materials and by the action of flames and kiln atmosphere. Many of the metallic oxides have traditionally been introduced as carbonates and this has often meant the inclusion of smaller particles which are more easily incorporated into the glass or glaze than some of the raw oxides. In the case of glass, the release of carbon dioxide from carbonates also helps to produce more even dispersion. Some of the more refractory materials have also been introduced as materials which will provide the oxides in a form which can be more readily accommodated. Manganese dioxide is an example of a refractory material which is sometimes introduced as potassium permanganate. Chrome oxide is similarly often introduced as potassium bichromate.

Most modern glass and ceramic glazes are now coloured either by the effect of small quantities of the oxides of transition metals in solution, in colloidal dispersions of insoluble particles, or by the introduction of previously prepared coloured material. The colour is rarely a constant produced by a particular oxide in isolation. The arrangement of the electrons surrounding the atoms of a particular colouring material are affected by the light energy and by the magnetic energy of adjacent atoms. This means that the nature of the remainder of the batch can have a considerable effect, producing the opportunity to create colour variation by using various combinations of atoms. Different glasses also have differing refractive indices which affect the resulting colour. For example, when nickel oxide is used with a soda glass or glaze a brown or grey colour of some sort will result even if it is in association with other materials such as barium, boron, calcium or lead. If, however, the soda is replaced by potash the colour becomes violet and remains generally so with the same materials in association.

In general the replacement of soda by potash in a glass or glaze will have a beneficial effect on colour largely because of its tendency to produce a glass with a better refractive index.

The colour produced by the introduction of a single oxide can be very raw, particularly in the case of cobalt and it has become the habit of most discerning potters and glassmakers to make the colour less garish by introducing small quantities of other oxides or stains to modify the result. This occurred naturally in much early glass and glaze and the local deposits of minerals were rarely as pure as the chemically prepared pigments that we tend to use today. Cobalt is an example.

CERAMICS AND GLASS: A BASIC TECHNOLOGY

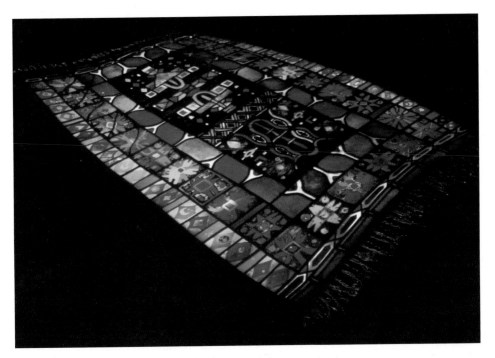

The Magic Carpet, *John Patsalides*

It is relatively easy to obtain, therefore it is cheap but as a colorant in early times it was usually beneficially affected by the presence of other minerals. Zaffre was a common cobalt based material which was exported from Germany to many countries. It was mostly made from natural cobalt arsenide sulphide and cobalt arsenide. Other minerals found in association with cobalt and affecting the colour are:-

Aluminium (Egyptian glass)
Nickel–arsenic (Saxony)
Zinc–lead–indium (Freiburg and Italy)

Several of these associations have become well known and many experienced potters will tend to use a lead glaze to produce a good amber colour from iron, a bright green from copper, brown from manganese and a red at low temperatures from chrome. Similarly, an alkaline glaze will tend to make the blue from cobalt have a slight tendency towards purple, will produce a purple colour from manganese and a blue moving towards green from copper.

The oxidising or reducing atmosphere in the kiln or furnace also has a significant effect as some of the colours can exist in the glass in more than one valency state. The obvious example is that of iron oxide. It can reduce to ferrous oxide (FeO) and produce a blue colour or it can also become ferric oxide (Fe_2O_3)

to produce the green and browns of bottle glass. In fact ferric oxide and ferrous oxide are rarely found alone but as various proportioned mixtures of both. Copper oxide will be blue-green in a normally oxidised alkaline glass, but it can also be reduced to produce reds within the glass or to produce a thin layer of metallic copper on the surface. In contrast, colour such as that resulting from the effect of cobalt ions tends to remain largely similar in both oxidising and reducing atmospheres.

Colouring oxides

In considering the problems of colouring glass the required effects are largely concerned with the reactions between various metal oxides and glassy materials, but with glazes there are other considerations. Whilst most generation of colour, control of opacity, etc, is the same or is very similar for both areas there are some essential differences. A transparent glaze can be affected considerably by the colour and nature of the underlying ceramic material to which it is bonded. In a low firing transparent glaze such as in earthenware, the underlying colour would be important and is often usually deliberately introduced as in traditional slipware. In a higher firing glaze such as that used on stoneware there would always be a strong possibility of fluxing resulting in colouring material migrating from the clay body and affecting the glaze. This is particularly apparent when there is some form of iron in the clay body as this often comes through and produces speckled areas. Wood ashes in a glaze also affect colour as they usually contain sufficient phosphate material to create some opacity and enough seeding materials to promote crystal growth. Long mullite crystals can also grow from a stoneware body into a glaze and whilst helping to provide a strong bond can also promote crystal growth in the glaze. The variations in content of many of the materials used in ceramics produce considerable numbers of possible permutations and mean that simply adding colouring oxides to a given glaze recipe can easily produce totally unexpected results. Experience will often lead to greater facility in handling problems which arise. For instance, additions of iron oxide to produce a tenmoku or kaki glaze are not likely to need precise calculation. as there is considerable latitude in possible proportions. However, both the quality and quantity of the iron oxide in a chun glaze is likely to be critical to success and careful consideration is essential The preparation of oxides can also have a marked effect. Some oxides such as cobalt oxide will produce decidedly speckled distribution in stoneware glazes if they are not ground or milled finely before their introduction.

Another consideration is that the proportion of alumina present in a glaze and a normal glass differs considerably. It is likely to be less than 2% in a glass whilst it can be anything up to 15% in a glaze. There are also circumstances when there can be more than this, particularly when the so-called alumina matt glazes are created. Alumina and manganese are often fused together commercially to provide a pink stain because both materials are very refractory and are not usually introduced together directly simply as colorants to produce this pink. If however, there is a prolonged soaking at high temperature this colour can appear and can be disconcerting if not required, particularly as it can occur in patches. One of the main reasons for making colouring stains is that the atoms of the colouring material tend to have a preference in materials to which they will become associated. There is a tendency for them to attach to the opacifiers tin oxide and titanium dioxide, the other colouring oxides, the glass formers silica and boric oxide. Alumina is well down this list so colours requiring an association with alumina are usually commercially produced as a stain by calcining the colouring oxide with the alumina in isolation rather than by simply adding them to an alumina rich glaze.

Most commercial glasses are made within a fairly narrow range of temperatures and the colouring materials are chosen to suit them. Over the years a comprehensive range of colours has been built up to suit these temperatures and despite the romantic assertions of some historians, there is very little that has been produced in the past that cannot be achieved today.

There are colours resulting from some materials, however, particularly in low firing enamels, which are becoming very difficult to achieve simply because of the restrictions imposed by the regulations appertaining to health and safety. A considerable amount of research is being constantly pursued and the range of safe colours is extending all the time.

There can be considerable losses during a glass founding but as most volatiles usually disappear up the flues it simply means a loss in material and it is standard practice to calculate for this loss.

Some volatiles in a glaze firing, however, can easily affect other pieces. A prime example of this occurs with chrome. On its own it will produce a range of greens and at suitably low temperatures can be made to produce yellow greens and even reds but together with tin will produce a pink. If a glaze containing chrome oxide is fired in a kiln which also contains tin glazed ware, the volatile chrome can migrate to produce pink splotches on the tin glaze of other pieces.

When a metal is not dissolved into the glass or glaze but remains dispersed as small particles, the size and shape of the colloidal dispersion affects the colour. Silver, copper and gold are commonly used in this way to produce yellow, red and orange colours. Very often these dispersions give very different colours according to whether they are viewed in a transmitted or in a reflected light (see Colloids, page 193).

Glasses coloured by copper, gold, selenium and silver often need to be reheated to enable the colour to strike but this is rarely seen as a problem affecting glazes. The temperature required to strike colours can differ considerably so the correct one and the time that it is held must be established in order to avoid disappointing results. The colouring atoms tend to form groups of nuclei but in a normal cooling process the crystals formed remain too small to produce any effect.

The reheating of the glass and holding at temperature, however, allows these crystals to grow until they are large enough to scatter the light waves.

One of the problems often met by glassmakers who reheat glass, either in the process of kiln forming or in glassblowing is that colours can change substantially at different temperatures, in different kiln or glory hole atmospheres, or simply because of differing time schedules. Glass and glazes coloured by cadmium–selenium are particularly prone to this and it can be very disconcerting to expect red-orange colour and find instead that the result may be black, brown, green, or yellow, etc.

At the same time it is also possible to find that transparency has turned to opacity.

Carbon ambers are also prone to change and almost inevitably darken when reheated.

Whilst both the methods and the oxides used for the colouring of glass and glaze are very similar, there is a difference in emphasis. Apart from its use in wine and beer bottles, iron plays a relatively small role as a colorant in glass but in glazes there is little doubt that it is most significant. It is found in considerable quantities in many minerals including clay and sand. Perhaps because of this, and the fact that it can be used to produce a wide range of colours it has assumed a major role in ceramics. Most of the classical Chinese potters relied almost exclusively on iron to produce their coloured glazes either by introducing iron containing minerals directly into the glaze or as colour which migrated into the glaze from a clay body. The celadon and tenmoko glazes and the rich colours in iron based aventurine glazes are examples of totally different results which can be achieved by the use of iron.

The effect of aventurine glasses and glazes results from the presence of large particles which have not been able to be incorporated into the glass structure because of saturation (see Aventurine glass and glazes, page 229).

Some of the oxides used to produce colours and which have managed to become dissolved into glass are described below.

Chrome

In very small quantities (up to 2%) it can be used to produce yellow greens in lead glass and green in soda–lime–silica glass. Together with tin oxide it will produce pinks in a glaze.

Weyl in his book on coloured glasses gives an interesting comment on chrome-tin pink. It is:-

> If chromium oxide is introduced into a glaze its behaviour depends on the furnace atmosphere and the glaze composition. Its normal green colour can be changed to yellow or orange when oxidising conditions are maintained.

Later he continues:-

> An entirely different stain can be produced when small amounts of chromium are introduced into glazes which contain tin oxide as an opacifier. The pink pigment can be obtained easily by calcining mixtures of chromium oxide and tin dioxide, especially when fluxing agents such as calcia or boric oxide are added.

Chrome oxide is a very refractory material and is sometimes introduced as potassium dichromate because of its low solubility. Even so, with high acidity

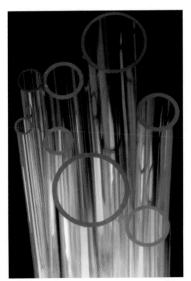

Glass tubing with very low inclusion levels and virtual optical quality produced on Corning's new purpose designed tubing melting unit

glasses there is still a tendency for chromium to remain undissolved and so produce black stones in the melt. All chromium glasses have a high transmission in the red part of the spectrum therefore it is recommended that it would be better to use copper for producing strong greens with small quantities of chromium added as necessary to modify the colour as required.

Chromium was used for the production of aventurine glass and glaze because of the formation of large crystalline plates of Cr_2O_3. In blown ware these plates tend to align themselves approximately parallel to the surface to give strong reflections (see Aventurine glass, page 229).

It is not a very popular glaze colorant. It is very refractory and only a small proportion dissolves into the glaze, the remainder being responsible for the uninteresting green colour which normally develops. It is, however, often used to modify other oxides, particularly copper and cobalt. In the form of iron chromate it is commonly used to produce grey colours.

It can be used to produce a low temperature (about 900°C) red or orange colour in a lead glaze with a low alumina content but the result is too toxic for ware which might be used for domestic purposes.

Cobalt

This is the strongest of the colouring oxides giving a range of blues in most glass and glazes. As little as 0·5% will produce a strong blue. This colour is often deliberately muted by adding iron oxide or manganese dioxide. Glasses and glazes containing magnesium move the colour towards pink. In early times cobalt was rarely introduced on its own but as an addition to copper it was used to produce the earliest known blue colours. One such blue vessel from

Mesopotamia is dated 2000 BC, Egyptians often used both cobalt and copper together in their glass and glazes.

In ceramic glazes however, cobalt oxide was frequently used for decoration, particularly in China, from the earliest times. As the raw ore was often contaminated with small amounts of other oxides the resulting colour was usually warmer than that produced by the purer forms of cobalt oxide which came to be used in the West. The carbonate is often used in preference to the oxide but both disperse relatively easily. It should be remembered that the oxide is used in about one third the quantity of that required by the carbonate to produce a similar density of colour.

Dark blue glass from the use of cobalt became very popular in Europe after 600 AD but really developed in Venice from whence it moved to Germany and the Netherlands. In Britain it reached great popularity with the introduction of Bristol glass. It is still produced in considerable quantities today in most parts of the world as it is one of the easiest colours to make and to use because of the tendency of cobalt to be constant in its colouring effects even after heating to a wide range of temperatures.

As a general rule, most glass assumes a blue colour when cobalt is introduced. In potash glass the blue is rather better than that achieved in a soda glass. In a borosilicate glass the blue from cobalt tends to be a rather warmer colour.

As a glaze colorant it can be used successfully throughout the standard temperature range used by the potter. It has a strong fluxing action but as it is only added to a glaze in small quantities, this is rarely a problem. It is often used together with small proportions of copper oxide to produce deep blues and rich black colours but if the additions are too liberal they can create a metallic surface.

Copper

In a soda–lime–silica glass made in an oxidising atmosphere copper oxide tends to produce a blue colour and in a lead glass a green, though there are several possibilities for the production of turquoise colour. The addition of boric acid, calcia, baria or magnesia to a glaze or glass will tend to move the blue colour towards green. Additions of around 15% titanium dioxide as an opacifier to a soda–lime–silica glass containing copper as a colourant will also produce green.

In a reducing atmosphere copper can be used to produce a ruby and in high proportions (about 10%) it can make an aventurine glass by saturation. It was probably one of the first materials used to produce a ruby colour and there is some evidence of it being produced and melted in a reducing atmosphere in the seventh century AD. Copper ruby was, however, not made with any real degree of consistency until the 17th century.

It produces quite a range of colour in glazes, much of the variation being due to nature of the basic glaze and to the type of firing. In an oxidised alkaline earthenware glaze coppers will tend to produce blue-green colours whereas in a lead glaze it will tend to produce greens. (If adding copper to a lead glaze it is essential to become familiar with the regulations relating to lead release.) It can be used, with additions of about 5%, usually together with a little cobalt oxide, to produce a rich black. With this amount of copper, however, its strong fluxing action can cause a glaze to run. If a rich turquoise colour is required the alkaline glaze will need to be rather low in alumina so it will then need a little calcia to stabilise the glaze. Unfortunately, the presence of calcia will move the colour back towards green so only small amounts can be tolerated. If some of the alkali is replaced by lithia or boric oxide the turquoise colour will be enhanced.

Copper in reduction can produce blues and grey-blues. Small additions, (under 1%) can, with appropriate firing and together with other associated materials, produce copper reds. This not the easiest colour to achieve. As oxygen is removed in the firing the copper moves towards its metallic state as fine colloidal particles which disperse through the glaze. These particles develop through the glass as fine crystals which, because of the difference between the refractive index of the crystals and that of the glass produce the red colour. The following points are relevant.

It helps to hold or to slow the kiln temperature at an appropriate stage during the cooling to allow the crystals to form.

An alkaline glaze containing some boric oxide which becomes fluid will help the crystals to disperse.

It is common practice to include some tin oxide.

The colour can be moved towards purple by the addition of small amounts of cobalt and titanium dioxide.

Calcia can move the colour towards orange.

If the colour of the body is affecting the colour of the glaze it should be first coated with a fine white slip.

Iron

Much of the concern with iron in glassmaking is to counter its effects in order to produce clear transparent glass whereas in glazes and in stoneware in particular it is a major colouring oxide. Used in proportions from 0·5% to 10% to give a range of greens from very pale to a green bordering on black. Strong reduction will move the colour towards blue. It was responsible for most of the green coloured glass which has been in evidence from the beginnings of glassmaking and was characteristic of the forest or "Waldglas" in Germany and in Britain. It is still used in the production of wine and beer bottles where the colour often results naturally from the iron content of the sand and other batch materials. It is often used together with manganese to produce ambers but with different base glasses and firing conditions a much wider range of colours can be achieved. Rich amber colours are also formed by iron in association with carbon and sulphur.

The brown colours found in wine and beer bottles is often achieved simply by the introduction of an oxidising agent such as pyrolusite. The oxidising process is also used to decolorise glass. Compounds of arsenic, antimony and cerium are used in this context and move the proportions of the FeO–Fe_2O_3 balance towards Fe_2O_3 and at the same time provide additional oxygen in the furnace atmosphere to cover any minor variations which might occur.

Iron assumes a much more important role in glazes than it does in glass. It occurs naturally in many forms of clay and in many of the minerals used in ceramics so perhaps it was inevitable that for many hundreds of years it became the major colouring material both for clay bodies and for glazes. Simply by controlling the kiln atmosphere, potters using iron oxide in the Far East managed to achieve a wide range of coloured glazes which have long been sources of considerable admiration in the West.

Iron oxide is responsible for much of the natural colour in clay bodies. Terracotta will have up to 6% and brick clays can have substantially more than this. When fired in a reducing atmosphere the colours move from buff through grey to a dark brown. The iron can also migrate through a glaze, particularly at higher temperatures, to give speckled effects. In transparent earthenware glazes iron oxide produces colours varying from yellow to dark brown according to the amounts introduced. In a lead glaze the colours will tend to be warmer than those in a leadless glaze. In oxidised stoneware glazes similar colours will develop but will tend to be somewhat duller.

The thickness of application is important, a rich brown black will tend to emerge with amounts over 5% but this will appear an earthy red wherever the glaze happens to be thin. In reduction, small percentages up to 2% can be responsible for producing the range of pale green, grey-green or blue-green glazes known as celadons.

Some care is needed in compiling glazes which contain high percentages of iron oxide as it will act as a flux and could cause a glaze to run.

Manganese

This is used in proportions 1% to 10% to give a range of colour from pale purple to black in potash glass tending to pink shades in a soda glass. It is also used together with iron to give a wide range of ambers and browns. In general, the colour obtained from manganese in a soda glass or glaze moves towards red whilst in a potash glass it moves towards blue. Any change in the base glass in which the alkali is replaced by one of higher atomic weight moves the colour towards blue.

Manganese dioxide also has a strong tendency towards stiffening the glass and making it difficult to work. It was often used to produce a pale rose pink colour but perhaps its major usage has been as a decoloriser to counter the colour resulting from iron in the batch materials. It is very sensitive to variations in the furnace atmosphere. To obtain rich purple colour manganese glasses need to be melted at relatively low temperatures, in a strongly oxidising atmosphere and to be rich in alkali.

Both the dioxide and carbonate forms are used in glazes and usually produce brown and purple colours. The colour tending to brown in lead based glazes and towards purple in alkaline glazes though a small amount of cobalt oxide is usually added when there is a need to emphasise the purple colour. It is fritted together with alumina to produce a pink stain.

Nickel
This is not a popular colouring oxide to be used in either glassmaking or in glazes. Used in proportions from 0·5% to 4% in lead potash glass it produces purple-red colour and in soda–lime–silica glass a grey-brown. In lithia glass it produces yellows. Proportions above 4% are used to produce black.

It can be used in ceramic glazes in conjunction with zinc oxide to produce blues but its normal role is to subdue some of the more brash colours such as those produced by cobalt or copper oxides. An old recipe for a crystalline glaze giving electric blue needle crystals on a yellow ground uses a glaze containing zinc and boric oxides and smaller quantities of calcia, rutile, barium carbonate feldspar and clay plus an addition of 1% nickel oxide. It is also low in alumina.

Selenium
This produces golden browns in lead glass and pink in soda–lime–silica but is mostly used in conjunction with cadmium sulphide to produce a range of strong reds and yellows. It is a difficult colourant to use because of its volatility and tendency to produce thin colour. Additions of neodymium oxide have been found to be effective in strengthening the colour 0·6% will improve the pink and 2·5% can make an excellent ruby.

It is used in glazes but as it often needs to be introduced in conjunction with cadmium disulphide which is a very toxic material, most potters buy commercially prepared glazes rather than try to mix them in the studio. Because of the toxicity of these materials and the stringent regulations on release from fired ware, many of the colours produced by these materials are now being made with yttrium and vanadium.

Vanadium pentoxide
This is used to produce yellows but is more popular with potters than with glassmakers as it is not suitable for high temperatures. It tends to be unstable so it usually needs to be made into a stain together with a little tin oxide. This makes a good yellow stain which can be modified towards orange by introducing titanium dioxide, zirconium oxide or yttrium in the frit.

Vanadium pentoxide and zirconium oxide produce a turquoise frit.

Vanadium silicate and zirconium oxide produce green stains.

The colours suggested are very basic and wide ranges of colour are produced commercially by the inclusion of more than one colouring oxide into a mixture. Combinations of materials are often used to produce specific colours.

The range of amber colours are a case in point. In a glass they are traditionally produced by the introduction of various sulphur compounds in conjunction with carbon and are essentially reduction colours but iron oxide together with manganese dioxide will also produce an amber glass as will selenium in a lead crystal glass, both in an oxidising atmosphere.

The harsh colour produced by cobalt oxide is often modified with copper to give a different range of blues or by adding small quantities of iron or manganese simply to mute the colour. Turkish blue is produced by the additions to the cobalt of chrome, iron and copper oxides.

A wide range of greens can be produced by mixtures of copper, chrome and iron in an appropriate batch.

Silver was a traditional source of yellows but is rarely used now because similar colours can be achieved much more cheaply and more easily by using other materials. For example, a bright clear yellow for signal glasses is now made with cadmium and sulphur. It is, however, used considerably as a stain by stained glass workers where it can be used to produce a range of yellows, ambers and browns. It can also be used to produce a bright metallic film when applied as a lustre.

Titanium with cerium also makes a very attractive yellow.

Iron with manganese can give a range of soft olive yellows.

Colour blending

The studio potter is much more likely to experiment in the blending and testing of various proportions of colouring materials than the studio glassmaker who is faced with a much more difficult situation because of the lack of appropriate facilities.

Whilst it is true that the glassmaker who has access to a small kiln can melt test quantities of glass in small crucibles this process is more likely to be carried out in a suitable laboratory than in a studio. The potter on the other hand can easily produce considerable numbers of tests in the same firing. Many experienced potters simply work intuitively by adding quantities of colouring materials to a basic glaze when they think that this is necessary but there can be no doubt that for most people a methodical approach coupled to careful measurement and rigorous recording usually pays dividends in pointing out useful possibilities.

The process of blending is often achieved in a very simple form in establishing a base glaze. In this case three or four materials can be mixed in various proportions quite easily. A popular form of chart to illustrate this is formed by aligning simple proportions of each material along sides of a rectangle.

In this table the silica could be in the form of quartz or flint and the feldspar could be potash, soda, nepheline or whatever similar material the potter chooses to use. The tests indicated would produce sixteen different results of which three or four would probably be found to be useful at the prescribed temperature and others might well be found to be useful at higher temperatures. Other materials could be added or substituted as necessary. The above is a very simple example of blending but a similar approach can be made to the process of testing colouring materials. In this case it is usual to take one or more basic glazes and add to these carefully measured quantities of oxides, carbonates or stains. If a basic glaze being used is transparent, it is often useful to run a parallel test in which an opacifier such as tin oxide, zirconium oxide or titanium dioxide has been added to the glaze.

CERAMICS AND GLASS: A BASIC TECHNOLOGY

Ceramic heads coloured with oxide and stain washes Paula Armstrong.
Courtesy of Cumbria College of Art and Design

Similarly it can also be useful to run parallel tests using barium carbonate, magnesium oxide, zinc oxide and calcia but remembering that there could be some extra fluxing action which could cause glazes to run.

It might be assumed that colouring oxides, etc, should be calculated as part of the molecular formula of the basic glaze but whilst this might seem to be the logical approach it is in fact, normal practice to simply count the glaze as being 100% and to add an appropriate percentage of colour. A glaze could therefore, be calculated as being 100 parts glaze plus 2 parts copper oxide and 0·5 parts of cobalt oxide. The usual approach with a new glaze is to first try sample additions of a range of common colorants to ascertain the basic response. Some colorants are much stronger than others so the following may serve to give some idea of the proportions that could be tried:-

Cobalt oxide	0·5 to 1%
Nickel oxide	0·5 to 3%
Copper oxide	2 to 5%
Chrome oxide	"
Manganese dioxide	"
Iron oxide	1 to 10%

Many of the most useful and interesting colours result from the use of two or more colouring oxides and one simple method of investigating the possibilities is to make up a basic glaze with a fixed amount of colouring oxide such as 2% copper (glaze A) and other samples of the same basic glaze but coloured with a different colouring oxide such as 0·5% chrome oxide (glaze B1) with 1% chrome oxide (glaze B2), with 2% chrome oxide glaze B3) and another with 3% chrome (glaze B4).

A series of tests can then be made by mixing:-
25% of glaze A with 75% glaze B1
50% of glaze A with 50% glaze B1
75% of glaze A with 25% glaze B1

This would then be followed by a similar series but substituting glaze B2 for glaze B1 and again by substituting glaze B3 and then glaze B4. This simple line blend would give 12 variations but if other colorants are then used as replacements this number could increase dramatically.

A common extension of this process is to produce a line of variables which could be existing coloured glazes or one basic glaze into which different colouring oxides have been introduced. Number 1 could be a glaze with a percentage of cobalt oxide added, number 2 could be the same basic glaze but with the cobalt replaced by a percentage of iron and so on. A further line could be created by mixing equal quantities of number 1 with number 2, then number 1 with number 3 followed by number 1 with number 3, etc. The next line would consist of mixtures of equal quantities of number 2 with number 3, then number 2 with number 4 followed by number 2 with number 5, etc. The next line would start with number 3 mixed with number 4, etc, as shown in the table below.

The process of carrying out the various forms of producing tests by blending is very instructive because in addition to providing a range of samples of which several are likely to be useful it also develops an awareness of the likely results of further experiments. The previous example can easily be extended simply by carrying out duplicate tests but using a 75–25 mixture instead of the equal parts. With a little experience it soon becomes possible to be able to make a reasonable estimate of the likely results and to save a considerable

	40% silica	30% silica	20% silica	10% silica	
10% feldspar	10 feldspar 10 limestone 40 china clay 40 silica	10 feldspar 20 limestone 40 china clay 30 silica	10 feldspar 30 limestone 40 china clay 20 silica	10 feldspar 40 limestone 40 china clay 10 silica	40% china clay
20% feldspar	20 feldspar 10 limestone 30 china clay 40 silica	20 feldspar 20 limestone 30 china clay 30 silica	20 feldspar 30 limestone 30 china clay 20 silica	20 feldspar 40 limestone 30 china clay 10 silica	30% china clay
30% feldspar	30 feldspar 10 limestone 20 china clay 40 silica	30 feldspar 20 limestone 20 china clay 30 silica	30 feldspar 30 limestone 20 china clay 20 silica	30 feldspar 40 limestone 20 china clay 10 silica	20% china clay
40% feldspar	40 feldspar 10 limestone 10 china clay 40 silica	40 feldspar 20 limestone 10 china clay 30 silica	40 feldspar 30 limestone 10 china clay 20 silica	40 feldspar 40 limestone 10 china clay 10 quartz	10% china clay

amount of effort and kiln space by avoiding using combinations of colour which are almost certain to be of little use.

Several authors give details of the process of triaxial blending, which may be used occasionally in colleges or in technical or commercial laboratories but from experience is most unlikely to be used by individual potters because of the complexity and the amount of time and work involved.

Glaze tests are usually made on small tiles about 4 cm square but it is often beneficial to produce them on small thrown cylinders or vessels in which case it is easier to see the effects of any possible flow or breaks on a rim. Another advantage of using small thrown shapes is that if the glazes are likely to be used on thrown ware then the likely effect on throwing marks will be shown.

Tiles can of course, be fired at an angle which will also illustrate any tendency for glazes to run. It is advisable, therefore, to set any tests on to old kiln bats, liberally covered with alumina or batwash to prevent possible damage to good kiln furniture.

A few procedures relevant to glaze testing are as follows:-

Test tiles are best bisque fired before use.

A few different thicknesses of glaze should be applied to each tile.

Tiles should be marked on the back with an appropriate number with an underglaze pencil or with black underglaze stain. The application needs to be strong enough to remain legible after firing.

The weighing of the component parts must be made as accurate as possible.

Records of each test giving its number, contents, firing details and result must be kept if they are to be of lasting value.

Ruby glass

Ruby glass is a name which describes a wide variety of red glasses, some of which have been around for many centuries. Of these, copper ruby has been used to produce most of the wonderful reds in stained glass windows since medieval times. There can be no doubt however, that gold ruby is the finest, the richest and the most expensive red glass that has ever been produced. It seems to have originated in Roman times and was the subject of considerable research in the eighteenth and nineteenth centuries. Because of this many methods of production emerged.

It is a complex process which can easily go disastrously wrong. As gold is a remarkably strong colouring agent as little as one part of gold to 1200 parts of the basic glass will produce a strong colour. Muller carried out a lot of research into making gold ruby glass and recommended one part to 1000 as producing the strongest useable colour. Because of the strength and the expense it has become normal usage to apply a very thin flashed layer onto a clear or amber glass. Its use in glassmaking is said to have developed from the "Purple of Cassius", a frit made for glaze making and consisting of 7200 parts of powdered glass to one part of gold with additions of tin and antimony.

Forms in ruby glass

The theory that gold ruby was discovered because glassmakers threw gold coins into the melt is still maintained by some historians but this simply would not have worked. Gold needs particular preparation before its inclusion into a batch will produce the required results. Most current batches for gold ruby are based on a high lead glass. If soda–lime–silica glass is used then it is essential to include some tin oxide. The gold for the batch material is often dissolved in a mixture of hydrochloric and nitric acids and mixed with tin which has been dissolved in nitric acid, the mixture then being allowed to evaporate to a fine powder before being introduced into the batch. The ruby colour is not apparent in the resultant glass until the ware is reheated to enable the colour to strike. It is also necessary for the glass to be cooled fairly rapidly to ensure that the ruby colour will strike well on reheating. Lead based glass cooled slowly can cause the colour to turn black on reheating.

Small additions of bone ash were common in old recipes.

The striking temperature will obviously vary to some degree according to the basic glass but for a copper ruby based on a soda–lime–silica base temperatures between 610 and 760°C seem to be recommended.

Most of the modern red and amber colours are based on cadmium–selenium and are in considerable demand for light signals and reflectors to various specifications.

Ruby glasses are almost wholly produced at the present time by the use of cadmium and selenium together. The traditional materials of copper and gold are now only used for art and prestigious ware but antimony together with some sulphur and carbon can also produce a ruby with a similar transmission to that of the selenium ruby. With the strong environmental lobby against cadmium compounds it seems possible that copper as a source of ruby glass could now make something of a comeback. Some of the strong signal reds and yellows are also now being produced from combinations of yttrium, zirconium dioxide and vanadium pentoxide.

All of the rubies present various difficulties in melting and striking and those based on cadmium–selenium are particularly liable to go wrong. A glass suitable for blowing may be totally wrong for other forming techniques.

A batch for a hand working cadmium–selenium ruby glass on a weight percentage basis is:-

Sand	53·7
Potash	16·25
Soda ash	16·25
Zinc oxide	11·37
Cadmium sulphide	0·81
Selenium	0·81
Borax	0·81

It will be seen from the table that the batch contains cadmium, selenium, sulphur and zinc. The first three of these are volatile and considerable losses are possible during founding. Another founding difficulty is that metal selenides can separate and accumulate at the bottom of the tank or pot if the temperature during charging is too low. Some makers find that there is an advantage in countering the volatility loss from the three materials mentioned by introducing them in the form of cadmium selenide and zinc sulphate as these are much more stable. Similar advantages are claimed for using cadmium sulphur selenide as a replacement.

As it is normal practice to melt these glasses in sealed containers, when the selenium is being released it will create a red-yellow fume and it may be necessary to seal the furnace stopper with wet clay both to prevent the volatile escaping into the workshop and to restrict the amount being lost.

Other difficulties can arise in getting the colour to strike. Sometimes this can occur during forming processes, sometimes it can occur whilst the work is in the annealing kiln or lehr but more often than not the work has to be reheated. In this case the temperature and the nature of the batch material can have a crucial effect on the result. In most cases it is necessary for the glass to be cooled below its softening point and then reheated. If the reheating temperature is too low than the colour may tend to be orange rather than red. Extended reheating may cause the ruby to darken considerably. Some authorities recommend that traces of copper in the batch help the formation of the colour.

Many of the colours used in glazes and underglaze techniques are prepared commercially for these particular circumstances. They are available in a very wide range of colours and have one advantage over the use of oxides in that to some extent, the powdered material gives some indication of the colour it produces.

Dichroic glass

Dichroic (two colours) refers to glass which exhibits two colours according to the nature of light falling on or passing through it.

At various times throughout history, glassmakers have tried to replicate the effects of precious or semi precious stones. Small amulets and brooches made from Egyptian paste were early attempts to produce something in the nature of turquoise. During the 15th and 17th centuries in Venice chalcedony and girasole glass was developed. Both of these resulted from the introduction of small quantities of transition metals to scatter the light and produce interesting visual effects. Chalcedony glass tended to have swirls of greens, purples, blues and yellows which changed to orange-red or orange-yellow in transmitted light and was intended to reproduce the visual effects of agate and jasper whilst girasole glass was normally a milky blue colour in reflected light which changed again to orange-reds in transmitted light. The basic glass for chalcedony was a mixture of cristallo (a very good quality soda–lime–silica glass) with some lead glass and a lead glass opacified with tin oxide.

Into this was added a mixture of silver, zaffre (a type of cobalt silica), iron oxide, copper oxide and mercury sulphide dissolved in nitric acid. The resulting glass was worked at the furnace in the normal way, but in common with some coloured glasses such as copper, gold and selenium rubies, it was necessary to get the colour to strike. When ware from such glasses are made the metallic crystals formed during initial cooling tend to be very small but reheating at the glory hole can be repeated until the crystals grow sufficiently to scatter the light by having a refractive index different from that of the surrounding glass. In the case of girasole glass, a pale blue opalescence develops and in a chalcedony glass a pronounced variegated colour appears. There is also a theory that the opalescence can result from liquid–liquid phase separation similar to that responsible for the blue opalescence of chun (jun) glazes.

An excellent article on girasole and chalceony glass "The unusual optical properties of two Venetian glasses" by W. P. McCray and W. P. Kingery of the Materials Science and Engineering Department of the University of Arizona published in *Glass Technology*, Vol. 37, No. 2, April 1996. It gives several recipes, historical background, chemical analysis and technical appraisal.

Dichroic glass used as sculptural form in the National Glass Centre in Sunderland

In more recent years Kolo Moser in Bohemia, produced what he called "Alexandrit" glass. This contained about 4% neodymium oxide and was noted for its property of changing colour according to the nature of its lighting. In daylight it tended to produce a blue colour, whilst in artificial light, which tends to have little short wave radiation, it was predominantly red. A similar effect occurs in the mineral alexandrite, hence the name given to the glass. Several attempts were made around the world to copy the effect, even to using the name "Alexandrite glass" but the results turned out to be rather poor substitutes.

Dichroic glass at the present time commonly refers to commercial products which have been coated with various chemicals to give specific properties in relation to the transmission or reflection of light.

For example, the chemicals, zinc sulphide and magnesium chloride are deposited on the surface of the glass in thin alternate layers so that each layer interacts with the other, allowing the transmission of certain wavelengths of light and reflection of the others.

The effect of coatings can be easily seen in the small tungsten halogen lights used spotlights and display lighting. The reflector is coated to give a silvery finish on the reflecting surface. This sends the light forward as in a conventional mirror.

However, the coating is transparent to infrared and the heat given off by the bulb tends to pass through the reflector and is not projected from its surface. When applied to glass in specific ways. These chemicals can produce primary colours when viewed in transmitted light, a second colour when viewed at 45° and a third colour in reflected light.

Flat glass for windows and architectural use is often coated to produce decorative and/or solar control effects. This product is traditionally known as "coated" glass but more complex varieties with as many as twenty layers are essentially dichroic glass. Many materials are used including gold, copper, nickel, cobalt oxide, iron oxide, chromium oxide and titania depending on the properties and finish required. The coating can be applied by hot spraying with an organo-chemical compound, by electrical deposition in the float bath and by vacuum depression.

One commercial glass used in windows has a coating which allows light and short wave infrared into a room whilst reflecting the long infra red wavelengths from internal sources back into the room thus conserving energy. The makers of this glass have been remarkably successful in controlling dichroic effects. Apart from in exceptional circumstances as might occur in polarised light the glass appears to be normally transparent and colourless.

Stains

In glass these are used to produce traditional effects by stained glass artists and involve the application of silver and, to a lesser degree, copper salts to the surface of glass. They offer an advantage in producing colour without materially affecting the surface polish of the glass.

Silver produces a range of yellows and browns which are often used for shading. Copper produces a red stain but needs more complex treatment than that necessary for the silver. They work because of the fact that silver or copper ions can replace some of the alkali ions in a glass at temperatures below the softening range. The process originally followed that of the application of lustre in the Middle East in which a metal salt was mixed with an appropriate carrier such as clay or ochre in proportions of approximately 1 to 5. This was sprayed or brushed on to the surface and the ware fired in a muffle kiln to about 600°C. The carbonate, sulphate and sulphide all work well but whilst the chloride also works, it tends to produce a spotty surface. Most stained glass artists use commercially prepared stains as they are readily available and are reasonably cheap. The silver stain reduces sufficiently by nature of reducing agents within the glass but copper stains require assistance in this respect. The silver staining effect is generally stronger on glasses which have been refined with arsenic than on those which have been refined with other oxidising agents and tends to be less effective on borosilicate glasses than on the more common soda–lime–silica or lead glasses. Colours tend to develop more as the glass is heated to the top of its annealing range so this can be exploited if greater intensity of colour is required. After firing there is usually a certain amount of iron oxide residue on the glass but this is easily removed by brushing or by washing.

The copper stain is much more dependent on the nature of the basic oxides in the glass. Potash gives much better results than soda. It also helps to replace calcia in the batch with zinc or magnesium oxides. The process for copper staining can also require two or three firings.

The first one being in an oxidising atmosphere after which a wide variety of colours may appear, a second one in a reducing atmosphere in which the copper red develops, and, if this provides dull or dark colour, a third firing in oxidising conditions to brighten the colour.

Glaze stains are totally different from the glass stains used by stained glass artists. They are prepared colours which can be introduced directly into a glaze instead of or to complement the usual colouring oxides. They can also be applied on to bisque ware as underglaze colour but it is advisable to refire the ware again before glazing as anything in the nature of a dry powdery material on a surface to be glazed can create havoc with the results and will almost inevitably lead to bare patches. As they need to be commercially prepared they are generally more expensive than the oxides and carbonates but are likely to prove more predictable. They also offer a small advantage in that the powdered colour as supplied will have at least some resemblance to the resulting colour when fired. The biggest advantage, however, is that they can be used to produce colour which might otherwise be somewhat difficult to achieve. The usual example of this is provided by the achievement of the pink colour obtained from mixtures of alumina and manganese. These materials are very refractory and when introduced into a glaze are not always as successful as may be required. By fritting the two materials together to produce a pink stain, a much more reliable colour is possible and one which is a rather better colour than that obtained from chrome–tin.

Enamels

The process of enamelling is thought to have been derived from the tradition of incorporating cloured and precious stones into jewellery in pre-Christian times. Early enamels were made, as most of them still are now, from ground particles of glass mixed with suitable fluxes and colourants. They were probably first applied to precious metals but over the years the technique has spread to a wide range of applications to other metals, ceramics and glass. This has not been just for purely decrative purposes but has also become used for practical reasons to provide non-rusting surfaces on iron pans and for coatings which can be easily cleaned on baths, cookers, etc.

Today, enamels are made from a similar but much wider range of materials which are fritted together commercially to suit specific requirements. The resulting grains and powders are readily available from several commercial sources and are usually finely ground in order to remove much of the labour involved in their preparation. Very few artist craftsmen now make their own enamels. There is one exception, however, and that is the case of so-called "roll on" or "pick up" enamels for glass. As these are intended to be picked up directly on to hot glass from the marver they can easily be made from coloured glass of similar expansion to that being used by the glassmaker. The coloured glass is simply ground into suitable particle sizes and needs no further treatment. It is often left as small chips of material rather than being ground to a fine powder in order to give a mottled effect. Many of the suppliers of Kugler type glass rods for colouring also supply ready ground material in various grain sizes for this purpose.

Painting or spraying enamels designed for firing on to ceramics and glass are basically similar in that they are both made from inorganic pigments in a suitable glass frit or carrier. The proportions of these varies from one colour to another and to the various parameters within which the enamels must operate. A typical example of a blue enamel would consist of a suitable glass carrier together with approximately 25% cobalt silicate as the pigment. The basic carrier material would first be melted and poured into cold water to form a frit This would then be mixed with the pigment and milled for several hours. The resulting powder after further mixing and sieving would form the enamel. In use it would need to be mixed with a medium suitable to the process required.

Ceramic and glass enamels differ in the temperatures at which they are fired because they both have to achieve bonding to the ceramic glaze or to glass by a process of ion exchange and this can only occur on heating to a temperature at which ion exchange can take place. In the case of glass this is usually between 550°C (1022°F) and 650°C (1200°F), the lower temperature being that used for blown and hollow ware whilst the higher temperature can be used for flat areas such as panels of architectural glass. In the case of ceramics they are made so that they can be fired at temperatures between 750°C (1380°F) and 850°C (1560°F).

This allows for considerably greater flexibility in the manufacture and has allowed much easier progression into preparing enamels which meet the rigorous standards now required with regard to toxic metal release. The long firing cycle available for ceramic enamels has also helped with this problem as a greater time for the reaction between the substrate and the enamel than is possible with glass helps to stabilise the toxic metal release. In the case of glass enamels, however, the situation has been much more difficult as these have been traditionally prepared from a carrier based on lead borosilicate or from alkali lead borosilicate glass in order to achieve the low melting properties required. There is also the necessity of a short firing cycle in order to avoid distortion so the reaction time between the glass substrate and the enamel is considerably curtailed. In order to achieve enamels which will have good colour and satisfy the standards for toxic metal release the industry has had considerable difficulty and the achievement of so-called "leadless" enamels for glass has usually resulted in a compromise situation in which many qualities, particularly gloss and colour, have been lost in the process. Boron has become the most common substitute for lead and as this also gives a very low coefficient of expansion it also often needs to be balanced with high expansion alkalis. The resulting enamels are not as chemically durable as those previously used and some colours have proved to be particularly difficult to achieve.

Low temperature stoving enamels which fire at about 200°C are available but are a poor substitute for the real enamel and function in the manner of a paint than as a bonded material.

Enamels for painting on to ceramics or glass can be made in the studio but need considerable preparation, calculation and experiment in order to achieve success. As they need to melt at a lower temperature than the softening point of the glass or glaze to which they are to be applied, appropriate fluxes must be introduced to coloured glass which has been finely powdered. Lead frits, soda ash, lithia, borax, etc, can be used and ground together with the coloured glass powder and further colouring oxides and opacifiers as required but if the ware to be decorated is to be sold there are legal obligations relating to possible toxic metal release to be considered. The resultant enamel also needs to approximate to the expansion of the glass or glaze to which it is be applied so it is essential that this is considered in deciding the particular frits to use. Small quantities can be ground in a pestle and mortar together with a little glycerine or aromatic oil but larger quantities are best prepared by grinding the ingredients together in a ball mill until a fine consistent powder is produced.

There is no doubt that after this stage even when dealing with commercially prepared, enamels, a great deal of elbow grease expended on mulling the results together with a suitable medium on a glass plate into a fine, smooth paste pays dividends and produces enamel which is a delight to use. Turpentine or white spirit is used for thinning but this must be introduced with care. Too much will cause the enamel to run if it is applied to a vertical surface. Whilst traditional aromatic oils can be successfully used as a medium for enamels to be used on ceramics, the low temperatures required for glass enamels is best satisfied with commercially prepared medium. There is rarely any difficulty in fitting commercial ceramic enamels to a glaze but the commercial enamels for glass that are readily available in small quantities are usually made to approximate in terms of expansion to that of bottle glass as industrial container production presents the greatest source of demand. There is, however, usually sufficient flexibility for this to fit most stained glass and studio glass applications. The people who miss out are the lampworkers using borosilicate glass as the expansion difference is far too great for the standard enamels to fit. Special low expansion enamels are made for borosilicate glass but whilst the manufacturers supply these in quantity to industry they have not until recently been interested in supplying the small quantities that a solitary lampworker might require.

The demand is also insufficient for the retail outlets to be interested so the lampworker has almost inevitably been faced with the necessity of making his or her own colour. There is a little light emerging on the problem as a company in the US has seen the market and has started to produce coloured borosilicate glass rod and powders with the standard expansions to suit the needs of the lampworker. In Europe, Schott Glass of Germany produce a wide range of colour borosilicate to match their Duran range of glass rod and tubing.

Fortunately, in lampworking the colour is melted in the flame so anyone wishing to produce his own colour can do so because it can be made to melt at a fairly high temperature. This offers a possibility to experiment with mixtures of borax frit, ceramic glaze and colouring oxides in order to make colour which can be rolled on to a heated rod or tube in a similar manner to that in which roll-on enamels are marvered on to a parison for blown glass processes.

Whilst the painting of enamels can demand considerable skill the firing on to ceramic glazes rarely poses problems if the application is carried out carefully and the temperatures required are not exceeded. Most of the artists who use enamels on glass apply them to flat panels and the fine control of temperature necessary to avoid ware from collapsing is not critical in this case. Considerable care is needed, however, when firing enamels on to blown ware as it becomes necessary to take firing to a temperature at which the softened enamel will bond with the surface of the ware. In order for this to happen effectively the ware must approach its own softening point and with many blown forms any over firing would be likely to result in collapse. It often becomes necessary to provide some means of support, particularly when enamelling wide shallow bowls. It may be necessary to resort to flash firing in some cases. This means that the ware is taken very quickly from its annealing temperature to that necessary for the enamel to form and is then reduced equally quickly to its annealing temperature again.

Iridescence

There are three popular techniques used to produce iridescence. They are:-
1. Use of a reducing flame to affect metallic material in the glass or glaze
2. Fuming
3. The application of lustres to the glass or glaze surface

In glass and glazes the results of these techniques is very similar to the silky colour effects which occur when interference colours appear as a result of oil being dropped on water. The most common method of producing these effects in a studio is that of coating the glass or glaze with a very thin layer, rather less than one micron in thickness, consisting of a metallic or similar substance. The light from the top and bottom surfaces tends to be reflected equally to blend together. If the peak wavelength of one coincides with the trough of the other the apparently lost energy reinforces the other colours to emphasise their luminosity. The dominant colour effect produced in iridescence results from the particular materials used.

It is an effect which often occurs naturally as a result of thin surface layers forming on glass or glazed ceramic which has been buried for some considerable time but is also one which has been deliberately exploited successfully over the years by several artists and manufacturers.

The technique is far from new as beautiful lustred ceramics were produced in Persia in the 13th century. These were followed by equally beautiful lustres produced by the Moors in Spain.

These early lustred wares were developed by first firing an alkaline glaze on to the pot and then applying a 50/50 mixture paste of red ochre together with silver sulphate and/or copper carbonate. Occasionally, bismuth oxide was used if a mother of pearl effect was required. The pot was then fired in an oxidising atmosphere to about 600°C and then in very reducing conditions to about 700°C at which stage it was soaked for about 30 minutes. When the kiln had cooled the pots were taken out, cleaned and the surface burnished to bring out the lustre.

A similar approach was and still is used for the development of lustres from within a soft lead alkaline glaze containing a little tin and boric oxide. In this case the metal salts are applied as part of the glaze which again is fired initially

Iridised bottles by Siddy Langley

in an oxidising atmosphere and then changing to reducing conditions as the maturing temperature is near. Some potters prefer to complete the firing to temperature in oxidising conditions but to then provide strong reduction at about 650°C in the cooling cycle.

The first two techniques mentioned were often used together on glass. A piece would be made at the furnace from glass which contained metal salts. It would then be introduced into a glory hole where a strong reducing flame would be directed on to it in order to produce the lustre from the salts. The piece of glass would then be sprayed with stannous chloride suspended in water or alcohol to enhance the lustred surface.

The initial production is believed to be by Llobmeyr in about 1863, but after this the techniques were exploited considerably by Thomas Webb in England. This was then followed by a flood of production and patents in the USA in the early parts of the twentieth century. Tiffany, The Quetzal Art Glass and Decorating Company, The Durand Art Glass Company, The Union Glass Works and lastly, but far from least, Frederick Carder at Steuben all produced iridised glass. Frederick Carder is credited with introducing the technique of heating the glass in a muffle kiln and then spraying it with stannous salts dissolved in distilled water.

Louis Comfort Tiffany also developed many variations, including one of incorporating thin threads picked up from the marver. He used several single coloured iridised forms but probably his most famous production was his variegated "Peacock Ware". The procedure of introducing metallic compounds into the glass melt and then exposing the ware to a reducing flame in the glory hole before putting it into the annealing kiln is quite straightforward and often happens unintentionally in the studio. For example, when a copper glass suddenly

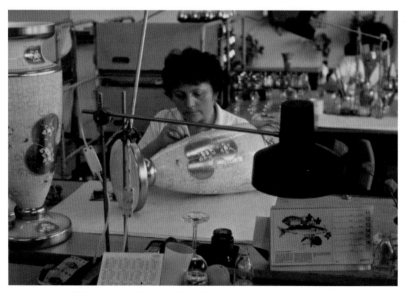

Illustration of enamel and lustre being applied at the
Crystalex Factory at Novy Bor in the Czech Republic

develops a copper red surface or a piece of lead crystal becomes a dirty grey colour simply as a result of an unplanned change in the nature of the flame.

Fuming used to be carried out in many factories by simply placing a small tin at the mouth of the furnace with some stannous or silver salts in it and then dropping a small piece of hot glass into it from a bit iron. The glass being worked was then held in the resultant fumes until the required amount of iridescence was achieved. The fact that the fumes tended to be sucked into the furnace lessened the danger from any possible toxic effects.

The popular method used nowadays by most studio glassmakers is to mix the salts to be used with distilled water or alcohol and then to spray them from a small plastic hand garden spray on to the piece of hot glass being worked. The type of small spray with a pistol type lever which can be worked with one hand is ideal for the purpose. It is essential that the spraying is carried out in some form of box with extraction facilities or to spray directly under a strong extractor to ensure that fumes are carried away from the operator. The wet mixture can also be brushed directly on to the hot surface.

The metallic salt most commonly used for the purpose is stannous chloride. Variations in colour are often achieved by using stannous chloride to form about 90% of the material, with other metallic salts, either singly or together making up the other 10%. Small amounts of copper and silver salts are those normally used. It is necessary to beware of some of the old recipes which can be found. These usually include bismuth nitrate, strontium nitrate and barium nitrate which, whilst they may produce beautiful colours, are now known to be particularly noxious and are best avoided for use in spraying techniques. Ferric chloride is sometimes used but needs to be introduced in quite a different pro-

Large glass plate with lustre decoration

portion. Up to 40% ferric chloride to 60% stannous chloride is usual.

The application of commercially manufactured lustre is the other popular technique for achieving metallic and iridescent surfaces. This has the advantage of being applied as a liquid on to cold glass or glaze surface which is then heated to produce the iridescent effect.

Early lustres were made by simmering metallic salts, produced by treating metals with hydrochloric acid, in natural resin for some considerable time. This would be carried out in a small oven by a potter but a glassmaker would use a convenient point on the furnace structure where the necessary supply of constant heat would be available. The results would be mixed with a suitable medium such as an aromatic oil and, where required, thinned with turpentine.

Today they are made by specialist suppliers but the basic materials have not changed very much. The metallic salts, usually chlorates are added to a resinate which together with the oil medium provides a built in reducing agent as it burns out during firing. Lustres are generally available ready for use in whatever quantities are required. Unless there is likely to be a lot of use, there are advantages in buying fairly small quantities of some of the colours as they do not have a long shelf life and can soon turn into an unusable jelly. This problem can be aggravated by buying from some retail outlets who may have already had the materials in stock for some time. The manufacturers are usually ready to advise regarding colours which are likely to behave in this way which can help when enquiries are being made about the date of any stock which might be purchased.

The lustres are applied with a soft brush on to cold glass or glaze surface and care must be taken to ensure that the resultant layer is not too thick as this will result in uneven cover with occasional blank areas. A little practice will soon produce good results. In the early stages of firing the kiln plugs must be

Large bowl by the author, in borosilicate glass decorated with applied lustre

left out to give some ventilation. It is also important to avoid a situation where the resultant fume might be discharged into a studio where it can collect and be inhaled. Most of the bottled lustres are toxic to some extent so the usual precautions must be taken when handling them.

The most common effect is the form of iridescence known as "Mother of Pearl" provided by a thin layer of bismuth but a variety of colours are available which are often based on bismuth together with metals such as gold, silver, platinum and copper. There is some experimental work in progress involving the rare earth metals which could soon extend the range.

Applying these lustres to glass can be difficult as most of the types of glass used in a studio begin to soften and sag at the temperatures required to produce a permanent lustre. This problem is particularly difficult on high lead glass and it may be necessary to find some way of supporting the glass in the kiln. If the glass is not too thick it may also be possible to flash fire the pieces by taking them up very quickly to the required temperature and then dropping the temperature equally quickly to the annealing point. If there is an opportunity to use a higher temperature borosilicate glass then the process of providing a lustred surface becomes much easier.

Glass lustres are made to mature at lower temperatures than those made for ceramics. This means that whilst ceramic lustres may appear to work on glass they will often wipe off or be unable to resist scratching with a finger nail. With both types of lustre it is usual to fire at first with plenty of ventilation in the kiln leaving the plugs out and then replacing them as the maturing temperature is approached. The prepared lustres have a built in provision for reducing the lustre. In firing lustre on to ceramics it is important that the stated temperature is not exceeded as the lustre may disappear.

The following old glass lustre formulae date from well before the current specialist production and would be most unlikely to find favour with any of Health and Safety authorities operating today:-

1. Iron Lustre
Boil together half a pound of rusty nails, half a pint of nitric acid and half a gallon of tar. Whilst boiling add two ounces of Canada balsam.

2. Iron Lustre (This name seems to be somewhat illogical as the recipe would suggest a copper lustre)
6 oz sugar of lead
6 oz resin
6 oz sulphate of copper
half a gallon of turpentine
Simmer gently until little more than a quart remains.

3. Gold Lustre
1 oz of gold put into a bottle with 6 oz of muriatic acid and 3 oz of nitric acid and one and a half ozs of green tin
Put into a jug 12 oz balsam of sulphur, add three pints of turpentine and stir for one hour. Drop the solution of gold into it and stir gently for four hours.

4. Gold Lustre
Put 2 oz of muriatic acid and 1 oz of nitric acid into a glass bottle. Add a quarter of an ounce of yellow gold and let it stand in a warm place. When it ceases to work add five grains of block tin and let it stand awhile. Put into a jug together with three and a half pints of turpentine and stir for four or five hours. When settled it is ready for use.

The above formulae are obviously not recommended either for use or experiment but serve to give a fascinating insight into the development of the material.

Reference. *A Dictionary of Glass*, C. Bray, A & C Black Ltd, 1995.

Optical glass
Most of the glass which is manufactured today is considered to be transparent and for nearly all purposes is considered to be colourless. In fact most of it, particularly window and container glass, is slightly coloured because of the economics of finding materials which are free from contaminants or because of the cost of decolourising. So-called clear glass is transparent because it has a similar property to that of a liquid in having no internal boundaries or surfaces near to the wavelength of visible light to reflect the light and produce opacity as is the case in nearly all crystalline solids. It transmits wavelengths of visible light, ultraviolet and infrared which pass through the glass virtually unaffected and as a result the glass is transparent. A certain amount of light is reflected from the surface of glass and, in common with most liquids, when light moves from low density material such as air into something of higher density such as water or glass its velocity is reduced to the extent that it bends. This property of bending light is called refraction and as different liquids and glasses produce this effect in different amounts, that amount can be calculated and the resulting figure is known as the refractive index. For comparison, diamond has a refractive index of 2·4173, glass varies between 1·5 to 1·7, water depending on its temperature is about 1·33 and air is very slightly above 1.

Construction in optical glass

If the wavelength of light changes as would be the case when it becomes coloured, the amount to which the refractive index changes in a particular glass can be calculated and this produces another factor known as the index of dispersion. A material such as full lead crystal which is particularly brilliant would have a high dispersion index, N. The higher the "N" value of a glass, the higher the reflection and greater brilliance.

These properties are all important in the manufacture of optical glass to be used for lenses, etc, which are now made to stringent specifications including both the refractive index and its dispersion. The glass must also be free from defects such as cords, stones, seed and strain. It must also be completely homogenous and for many years molten glass was stirred for several hours in order to achieve this.

Optical glass used to be melted in fireclay pots and when the glassmaker was satisfied with the quality the pots were left to cool. When the pot was completely cold, it would be broken and the lumps of glass removed for selection, only the best pieces were then used as blanks for lenses, etc. In later developments larger pots were used from which the molten glass was poured into moulds to form large blocks which were then annealed for several weeks. Most optical glass is now melted in platinum lined continuous tank furnaces to avoid the possibility of contamination. The glass then flows into an automatic pressing plant to produce suitable blanks for machining and polishing.

Blanks of optical glass are in considerable demand for artists who specialise in cutting and polishing and whilst blanks with slight defects which were of use to artists used to be fairly readily available, especially in France and in the Czech Republic, such sources seem to be drying up and as a result good blanks at an appropriately higher price now have to be purchased. These blanks are described in terms which are not always meaningful to the artist. For instance they may be given Abbe numbers and without going into the mathematics, a low Abbe number refers to a glass which has a high dispersion in relation to its refractive index and is almost certainly described as a flint glass.

On the other hand glasses with a high Abbe number related to their refractive index are likely to be described as crown glass. Abbe numbers occur between 20 and 90, those below 50 being classified as flint glass and those above 50 being crown glass. In addition to this form of classification, glasses can be described as light crown, heavy crown, light flint and heavy flint, the terms heavy and light relating to high and low refractive indices.

The brilliance or sparkle of a piece of glass is a quality which is valued by artists who cut and polish glass and this is usually associated with a relatively high refractive index which has been traditional achieved by the introduction of heavy metal oxides such as those of lead or barium, or more recently by the use of rare earths such as lanthanum. Some optical glass slabs, therefore, may be beautifully clear and may well polish to a satisfactory quality but if brilliance is required then it might be necessary to look for pieces with an appropriate refractive index.

Some glass artists either glue or fuse slabs or cut and polished pieces of glass together and the fusing can cause problems as there are now considerable numbers of various types of optical glass and they can have substantial differences in their coefficients of expansion. If the component parts of a construction are not to be fused, then the stringent quality requirements for optical glass is likely to ensure the possibility of finely finished pieces.

Opacity and translucency

Opacity and translucency in both glazes and in glass are usually caused by the inclusion of minerals which either remain largely as undissolved particles or which form or promote crystal growth.

They can also occur because of the colloidal dispersion of fine bubbles.

In the first case, the opacity is caused by the light being deflected by the faces of crystals such as those of tin oxide, zirconium oxide, antimony oxide and cerium oxide suspended in the glaze or glass. There is a major difference in emphasis between glass and glazes in this respect. In glass there is a strong tendency to exploit qualities of light transmitted through the glass rather than those produced by reflection so there is much more use of transparent coloured and clear glass than there is of opaque or translucent glass. In glazes there is a much greater use of opacity.

This is not just a matter of taking advantage of a particular quality. It also evolves from the fact that the growth of crystals within a glass, except in particular well controlled circumstances, can produce unstable material. In a glaze no such restriction exists because the glaze, especially stoneware glaze, is usually firmly bonded to a ceramic body. Another difference relates to both the making of the material and the forming processes involved. Glass is melted into a mass of liquid which is then worked whilst it is hot. Any excess of a material such as alumina or calcia which makes the glass too stiff to work easily has to be avoided. Alumina is, therefore, usually restricted to amounts of less than 2% and calcia less than 10% of a glass batch. A glaze on the other hand is applied cold and provided that it can bond well to the ceramic body and when heated can become sufficiently fluid to form an even layer it can carry substantial amounts of such materials. Alumina and zirconia have a similar effect on the viscosity of a glaze making it stiff. As a result very tiny bubbles tend to become trapped and these add to the opacity.

There is no doubt that most of the early Chinese stoneware glazes were made from remarkably simple batch recipes which by the nature of the materials involved contained a wide variety of oxides. The resulting opaque glazes preceded the transparent glazes in China by over a thousand years.

Common glaze batch recipes of the time included the mixing of equal parts of clay, quartz and limestone or an even a more basic mixture of equal parts of siliceous clay and wood ash. Eventually some potash was introduced in place of part of the calcia in the clay–quartz–lime glazes and resulted in some of the best stoneware glazes such as the chuns and celadons that have ever been produced. Part of the calcia tends to crystallise in the cooling cycle and produce opacity. Similar so-called high lime matt glazes are still popular with many potters today.

Wood ashes vary considerably in their make up. They all contain some potash which for glaze purposes is mostly washed out whereas when plant ashes such as barilla were used for glassmaking the potash was retained as a valuable flux.

Some ash such as that from burned rice husks produces material which is very high in silica whilst others prove to be so low in silica that in order to produce a reasonable glaze, additional silica in another form has to be provided. All wood ashes, however, tend to contain a wide variety of oxides, carbonates, etc. It is inevitable that amongst these will be some materials such as small amounts of titanium dioxide, zinc oxide and phosphorous pentoxide, and which in suitable firing processes, promote the development of opacity by providing nuclei from which crystals can grow.

There is again a difference in what some potters consider to constitute a matt or what they think constitutes a crystalline glaze. The matt glazes are virtually all caused by the presence of small crystals in the glaze so some people refer to them as crystalline glazes whilst most people reserve the term crystalline solely for those glazes which develop large and obvious crystal formations on the surface.

Many inexperienced potters can be surprised to find that they have fired what purports to be a matt glaze and it comes out of the kiln all bright and shiny. This is almost inevitably due to the fact that the cooling cycle has been too rapid to allow crystals to form. Apart from this time factor, the production of many matt and crystalline glazes is not always straightforward as one would think because many of the materials used as opacifiers have complex roles to play and an excess of a particular material can have devastating results. Zinc oxide is an obvious example. It is relatively cheap and was once used in many areas to produce the Bristol glaze which was developed to reduce the amount of lead being used in commercial glazes. Its behaviour, however, is quite complex. In general, it is successful when used in small amounts, often improving surface brilliance in shiny glazes, but creates all sorts of difficulties when more is added.

Many of the zinc matt glazes have a low coefficient of expansion and can create sufficient pull on the clay body to cause it to break. Because of its low expansion zinc oxide can be used to substitute some of the high expansion fluxes such as soda in order to cure crazing but there can be a tendency to produce crawling because of high initial shrinkage if the oxide has not been previously calcined. Zinc oxide also has the property of making many colours appear dull yet can give good colour in some situations with cobalt and copper oxides. It is an active flux above 1080°C when used together with other fluxing materials but is not successful as a single flux. As an opacifier there are situations in which it retains much of its crystal character whilst acting as a flux in a similar manner to that of calcia but in other situations it can also act as an anti-flux like tin oxide.

In glassmaking it is often introduced into a glass batch as a stabiliser to replace some of the calcia in order the lengthen the working properties of the glass and to reduce the possibility of creating devitrite. It can be introduced to produce small crystals to form smooth matt glazes or it can be encouraged in a fluid glaze containing little alumina to produce large crystals of zinc silicate which can be up to 10 cm across. The presence of small quantities of titanium dioxide in addition to the zinc oxide is particularly effective in encouraging the growth of these crystals.

A glass network is inherently not as stable as a crystalline material and, as previously stated, if the opportunity arises the glass will seek to rearrange its structure. If successful the result will be a regular crystal lattice such as that responsible for producing crystals in glaze. In theory all glasses will crystallise if held for an appropriate time at the right temperature. In practice seed materials are usually introduced to start crystal formation, the seed centres are known as nuclei and if these are increased they enhance crystallisation. Sometimes they result from an excess of materials such as calcia or magnesia which would normally be included as fluxes or stabilisers. Sometimes materials such as titanium dioxide and phosphorous pentoxide are deliberately introduced. Sometimes crystals occur simply because the glaze has been held for too long in the cooling cycle and sometimes dust on the glass particles will act as nuclei and promote the development of crystals. To form crystals during the cooling cycle it is essential that the nuclei are developed at a suitable rate and that the crystals also grow from these nuclei at an appropriate rate. In the formation of glass ceramics the articles are often produced by normal glassmaking processes but are then reheated in order to first produce the nuclei and to then develop the crystals.

A point of confusion sometimes arises in both glazes and glass because opaque or matt results may be produced which have not been created by crystals at all but occur because of the colloidal effect of the presence of small bubbles in the glass or glaze.

There are various forms of crystal shape and orientation. Some are flat such as those promoted by zinc silicate and some are more like needles. Some are formed largely by materials which migrate from the clay body and others simply develop within the glaze. Wood ashes within a glaze, with their wide variety of oxides, etc, often provide seed materials which help to develop crystals. In many cases they are so fine that they produce no more than pleasant matt or semi-matt surfaces. On the other hand the results of developing within a glaze large crystal clusters, which may be up to as much as two inches (10 cm) across, can be spectacular but the results are often more of technical rather than of great aesthetic interest. Materials introduced to form large crystal clusters include calcium and magnesium silicates, zinc titanate and zinc silicate, manganese silicate, molybdenum and tungsten trioxide, and vanadium pentoxide.

These crystalline glazes can be achieved by establishing various criteria:-

(1) They should contain very little or no alumina

(2) Ideally, they should have a very slow cooling cycle or be held at a specific temperature at some stage, not necessarily during cooling, to allow the crystals to develop (see also Devitrification, page 106)

(3) They often need some seed material to help to form the crystals. These are usually zinc oxide, titanium dioxide, lithia, ort can be those mentioned at the end of the preceding chapter, used alone or together

(4) If they are to be aventurines, they also need what would normally be considered excessive amounts of colouring oxides (for example, 5 to 9% iron oxide is quite common)

The lack of alumina makes these glazes very fluid so any ware which has this type of crystalline glaze must be set upon a form of separator such as a wad of ceramic fibre in order to avoid the piece cementing itself to the kiln shelf with glaze which has run off from the surface during the firing.

A typical modern crystalline glaze formula maturing at 1240°C is (by weight):-

CaO	0·9
Na_2O	3·0
CuO	4·4
K_2O	2·3
PbO	27·8
B_2O_3	3·6
Al_2O_3	2·5
SiO_2	37·7
TiO_2	11
V_2O_5	3·9

In this case the titanium dioxide promotes the crystal development and the vanadium pentoxide the colour. Titanium dioxide and some other minerals such as phosphorous pentoxide promote the development of crystals by acting as nuclei. The greater the number of nuclei formed the greater the possibilities for the development of crystals. Dust and scratches on glass often have a similar effect and cause the misty effects which often develop when two or more pieces of glass are fused together. The translucency and occasional opacity of *pate de verre* is usually caused by surface crystallisation and is largely the effect of the dusty surfaces on the glass particles as they are fused together.

Aventurine glazes and aventurine glass derive their name from a form of feldspar (aventurine) containing minute crystals of iron oxide which gives a characteristic sparkle to the mineral. The glaze is often a basic crystalline glaze as described previously but not necessarily so. In common with aventurine glass it usually contains excessive amounts of colouring oxides. In aventurine glazes based upon an excess of iron oxide it can be beneficial to introduce some ilmenite. This contributes some iron oxide but the titanium dioxide is an effective seed material for promoting the growth of the crystals.

A typical formula for an aventurine glaze is (in parts by weight):-

Feldspar or Cornish stone	25
China clay	6
Flint	15
Colemanite	5
Borax	25
Sodium bicarbonate	10
Zinc oxide	5
Iron oxide	9

Early attempts to make aventurine glass in France were carried out by adding iron and/or brass filings to the molten glass in the furnace which was covered with hot ashes and then turned off. After very slow cooling, the furnace was cracked open and blocks of aventurine glass removed. Similar material was made in the USA by saturating a high lead glass with chrome oxide. Copper has become a popular metal to be used in this way. If an excess of metallic oxide is introduced into a glass to the extent that it cannot remain in solution, crystals are formed which are large enough to reflect light and give the characteristic aventurine appearance.

Two old batch recipes for aventurine glasses originating in Italy are (in parts by weight):-

Green aventurine

Silica sand	100
Soda	8
Potash	15
lead oxide	45
Borax	23
Saltpetre	5
Potassium dichromate	25

Golden brown aventurine

Silica sand	100
Soda	20
Potash	18
Limestone	16
Copper oxide	15
Tin oxide	6
Iron oxide	8
Borax	3

Rods of aventurine glass which are used to produce flashed aventurine layers on glassware are available in the Czech Republic.

Opal glass has been in evidence for many years. The Venetians certainly produced an opal glass which is known as Lattimo. Tin oxide, titania and zirconia tend to be used to produce the so-called enamel type of opal which is usually a dense white because of the slow solution into the parent glass leaving sufficient particles remaining in suspension to reflect the light.

Zircon is becoming very popular in this context because it is cheaper than tin oxide and is much less likely to react with other materials. This type of opacity is in contrast to the rather milky translucent appearance of the opals produced by arsenic, antimony, the phosphates and the fluorides where the crystals are formed during the cooling process. Other similar opacifiers include niobium pentoxide, zinc sulphide, cryolite, fluorspar (calcium fluoride) and bone ash. In more recent years sodium fluorosilicate (Na_2SiF_6) has become readily available as a by product of the fertiliser industry and is now commonly used for the production of fluoride opals.

Making and handling opals in a studio has always seemed to produce problems. Phosphate opals probably present the least of these but much depends on the nature of the base glass. Because bone ash is essentially calcium phosphate, introducing quantities of it into a soda–lime–silica glass could easily introduce a surfeit of calcia into the melt with the result that it becomes too stiff to work easily. Phosphorous pentoxide has a tendency to volatilise from the melt so barium and zinc glasses have become popular as base glasses for phosphate opals as they seem to be able to hold the phosphate in solution. Lithia is thought to help the melting of opal glasses considerably. The amount of bone ash required can also vary a great deal from one base glass to another. Whereas about 7% might be required for a glass containing barium and zinc, as little as 2% would produce similar results in a high lead glass. Bone ash as supplied is a bit of a variable feast and industry often needs to turn to a chemically prepared product to ensure continuity of stable production.

Opal glasses are notorious for changing as they are worked. When gathered there can be a normal transparent parison which will start to strike towards translucency in the reheating. Continuing reheating creates more crystals and develops those that are already there resulting in the glass gradually becoming more and more opaque and too stiff to work.

In normal production phosphate opals tend to be translucent rather than being truly opaque and in order to achieve a dense opal some manufacturers add a little tin oxide. Fluoride opals are also usually translucent but present different problems. Most of these result from the fact that whilst a suitable batch can be calculated, there is a continuing loss of fluorine from the melt both during the founding and whilst the glass is standing or being worked. As is the case of many of the volatiles which are released from a glass melt, all the necessary safety precautions must be taken (see Safety, page 233). They also seem to react strangely to modifications when these are introduced to change the expansion of the base glass to suit another glass, possibly due to changes in the nature of the phase separation caused by the new materials.

A list of opacifying agents is included in the table of raw materials in the appendix at the end of the book.

The following are various old batch recipes for opal glass originating in Germany (parts by weight):-

(1) *Phosphate opal*		(2) *Milk white opal*	
Sand	100	Sand	100
Soda	20	Soda	20
Feldspar	35	Fluorspar	12
Limestone	15	Feldspar	20
Bone ash	18	Bone ash	8
Saltpetre	2	Lead oxide	12
Arsenic	0·5	Arsenic	1

The first recipe is a straightforward phosphate opal but the second is an opal combining fluorine and phosphorous pentoxide.

Some opals involve the use of the mineral cryolite (Na_3AlF_6) to provide the fluorine and some of the sodium. The first example shown below is again an old German recipe for milk white opal whereas the second is an American recipe which again produces an opal based on a mixture of both fluorine and phosphorous pentoxide.

(1) Milk white opal		(2) Opal glass	
Sand	100	Sand	150
Soda	15	Soda	40
Cryolite	14	Saltpetre	5
Lead oxide	10	Fluorspar	10
Saltpetre	4	Feldspar	10
Arsenic	1	Bone ash	1
		Cryolite	10
		Arsenic	0·5

Sometimes the so-called opals were made more opaque by the introduction of materials such as tin oxide which remained in suspension. In the following example there are again three opacifiers, bone ash, arsenic and tin oxide.

Column, stone and glass

A recipe for this type of glass is (parts by weight):-

Sand	100
Potash	30
Lead oxide	65
Bone ash	12
Tin oxide	10
Borax	5
Saltpetre	5
Arsenic	10

Some old recipes for opal glass were just as simple as those to which we have become accustomed in glazes.

For example (parts by weight):-

(1) Sand	100	(2) Sand	100
Cryolite	43	Bone ash	30
Zinc oxide	20	Soda	50
		Potash	5

XX.
Safety

Aspects of safety in studios, workshops and factories was given scant consideration for many years but latterly it has become an area which is attracting a
great deal of attention.

Both national and international authorities have shown considerable concern with safety over recent years and with providing the necessary legislation
which it has been necessary to introduce and to constantly update. Much of
this legislation provides what is often simple and possibly obvious common
sense precautions but there are a surprising number of occasions when it has
the added advantage of pointing out particular hazards which are not known.

It is often assumed that the person operating on his or her studio or
workshop is not affected by Health and Safety regulations but this is not so
in Britain and it is certain that the same rules apply in many other countries. There is also a legal responsibility for anybody who might visit or use,
the studio.

When establishing or taking over the running of a studio or workshop it is
essential to take the trouble to explore the relevant regulations and responsi-
bilities. Some of those affecting people working in, Britain and the European
Community can be obtained from the Health & Safety Executive.

There are several areas of concern to people working in glass or clay, notably:-

    1. The effects of heat and infrared radiation from the kiln, furnace or
    glory hole

    2. Fire or explosion arising from the fuel and burner system

    3. The handling of potentially toxic, corrosive or irritant materials

    4. Fume from volatile materials in the melting or firing processes, from
    irridising processes, acid etching, from exhaust gases and from the effects
    of heat on various mediums and solvents

    5. Dust from, grinding, polishing, batch mixing, glazing, decorating, clean-
    ing, fettling and sandblasting operations

    6. Deficiencies in the provision of electrical safety

    7. Adequate storage for inflammable and toxic materials

    8. Suitable provision for the safe and legal removal of waste products

Working at a furnace can cause problems either from heat exhaustion or
from the effect of radiation from the infrared, ultraviolet and soda wavelengths
on the eyes and on the skin. Burns from contact with hot materials are very
rare but burns and eye conditions which develop from exposure to infrared
radiation often occur. This produces skin damage similar to that which results
from excessive exposure to the sun. The damage to the eyes is usually a much
more long term problem resulting from regular exposure to what can be relatively small amounts of infrared radiation. This means that the problem is not

confined to glassmakers who work at a furnace but can easily affect potters who regularly peer through a spyhole to judge the effects of a firing or to check heat cones. This type of exposure tends to cause some inflammation but can also damage the lens of the eye, causing it to gradually become opaque. Because of its known effect on glassblowers this condition is known as "glassblowers cataract" or simply as "heat cataract".

It is advisable not to spend too much time in front of the furnace, to use reflective screens and to develop the habit of constantly wearing appropriate eye protection.

Glass furnaces, glory holes and to a lesser extent, kilns give off a great deal of heat. When people are not acclimatised to heat, problems of heat stress can easily develop. Even healthy adults take some time to become acclimatised so whilst the glassblower or potter working continually in a heat environment may not be greatly affected, the person who works only occasionally or people with medical conditions such as heart and kidney difficulties, or who may be older and overweight, can be much more susceptible. Heat stress often takes the form of feeling faint because of the lack of blood reaching the brain. This is a relatively minor condition which initially is easily remedied by moving into a cool area but another form of heat stress known as heat stroke can be much more serious. Rising body temperature can lead to delirium, eventual loss of consciousness, and, if the temperature rise is not stopped, a fatal coma.

Gas and oil fired kilns and furnaces give off considerable amounts of carbon dioxide, oxides of nitrogen and under circumstances of inadequate combustion, toxic carbon monoxide They also release various volatiles from clay, glaze or glass batch materials as fume during the firing and founding processes, some of which can be toxic and/or corrosive. For example, some clays release acidic sulphurous fumes which in contact with water will form sulphuric acid. It is essential that the exhaust gases are properly ventilated.

Spraying a solution of tin nitrate or tin chloride on to the hot glass has become a popular method of irridising ware this must be carried out in a purpose built extractor facility which is efficient in completely removing the fumes that are released when these chemicals hit the hot glass.

Inflammable liquids need to be stored in a cool place away from any source of combustion.

They include lustres and liquid metals, turpentine, screen printing media and decorating oils.

Many of the techniques carried out on cutting and engraving lathes, polishing machines, etc, can create a hazard because of the possibility of glass breaking if the material being worked has not been properly annealed. Because of this, safety goggles are essential. As most of these operations are wet the danger from dust is minimal but particular care should be taken when handling dry Tripoli powder as this is highly siliceous and prudence demands the use of a suitable dust mask.

Sand is now rarely used in sandblasting as more effective materials such as carborundum or alumina grains are readily available. It is imperative that the dust collector in the sandblasting unit is working efficiently and that the cabinet door is well sealed. Similar precautions need to be taken when spraying glaze as even though the glaze is wet there is likely to be a very fine dispersion and many of the materials in glaze are either siliceous and/or toxic.

Many of the batch materials used in ceramics and glassmaking are either siliceous, irritant or toxic by ingestion, by inhalation or through the skin. Whenever possible glass and glaze batch should be mixed in a closed container and an appropriate mask and protective clothing worn when handling the various materials. Ideally, a shower unit should be available for use after glass batch mixing and founding. As glaze batch is usually mixed wet the problem is not so acute but appropriate care is still necessary when handling the dry materials being introduced into the water or those which may build up in a glaze spraying area. If glaze or decorating materials are being sprayed on to pots the operation must be carried out in an efficient and appropriate extractor unit and suitable dust masks must be used.

Eating or drinking in the studio or workshop, particularly in the batch mixing, glazing and decorating areas must be avoided.

Fumes

There has been a great deal of concern and legislation over recent times relating to the release of fumes, particularly during the glass founding and kiln firing processes. Most of the emissions coming from glass furnaces is simply water vapour and carbon dioxide which comes mainly from the conversion of the various carbonates. There are, however, many chemical changes in melting and firing and a wide range of volatile materials can be involved. Some of these continue to release fume after the glass has been founded and is being used. The firing of clay and glazes can also lead to the release of hazardous fumes.

Some of the major elements concerned are:-

nitrogen monoxide and nitrogen dioxide, carbon monoxide and carbon dioxide - from combustion processes and from the conversion of the various carbonates

sulphur dioxide - from saltcake, barytes, clay and from oil. Together with water vapour this can form sulphurous and/or sulphuric acid

lead - from making lead crystal and lead based glasses

Rather less common fumes arise from:-

fluorine - from making fluorine opals, a highly corrosive and toxic gas. This eventually becomes evident from its matting effect on windows in the vicinity

cadmium - from making red and yellow glass and glaze, a cumulative poison which attacks the kidneys

Fume is also released during the firing of lustres and, perhaps more obviously, during the process of producing iridescent surfaces by fuming.

Metal release from glass and glazed ware

There has been much concern and legislation for many years about the nature of metal release from ceramic glazes.

The principal metals concerned are lead and cadmium compounds but others are:-

antimony oxide
arsenic oxide
barium carbonate
beryllia
selenium compounds
copper oxide and carbonate
potassium dichromate
zinc oxide

In glazes the greatest danger appears to evolve from low or underfired glazes and enamels which have been exposed to the action of acidic liquids such as vinegar or fruit juices.

Stringent regulations exist in most countries and ware must withstand exposure to 4% acetic acid for 24 hours at room temperature for flat or storage vessels and to withstand boiling of acetic acid for two hours followed by a cooling period of 24 hours for ware which is to be used for cooking. This standard is being changed in some countries by the use of weak hydrochloric acid to replace the 4% acetic acid. A standard of parts per million of metal released, according to the regulations of the particular country must not be exceeded.

In Britain these are the current regulations:-

For flatware	Lead 20 parts per million
	Cadmium 2 parts per million
For hollow ware	Lead 7 ppm
	Cadmium 0·7 ppm
Storage vessels with a capacity of over 1100 millilitres	
	Lead 2 ppm
	Cadmium 0·2 ppm
For cooking ware	Lead 7 ppm
	Cadmium 0·5 ppm

Many potters buy ready made glazes and then modify them to suit their individual needs. It must be remembered that even small alterations to the formulation of a glaze can have significant effects on metal release. Additions of copper, zinc, lead or cadmium to low solubility glazes are of particular concern in this respect but other factors can also affect metal release. In particular, the firing of a glaze must be such that the glaze and/or added decoration reaches maturity. Glazes which have a high proportion of soda or potash are likely to be subject to acid attack. Glazes which have been compounded from a mixture of a lead frit such as lead bisilicate and a borax frit may have less resistance than lead bisilicate on its own. Glaze stains, particularly when fritted into the basic glaze batch, onglaze colour and underglaze colour can have significant effects on metal release.

Messrs Podmore of Stoke on Trent, manufacturers and suppliers of ceramic materials released some information on the effects of various additions on lead release. There have been several issues of similar information from various sources and all the results correspond very well. Part of this information is shown in the following tables.

The effect of colouring oxide on lead release using glazes of different lead bisilicate content is:-

| | Lead bisilicate | | |
	90%	*50%*	*25%*
With no addition	0·2 ppm	0·1 ppm	0·1 ppm
1% copper oxide	0·8 ppm	12·8 ppm	2·1 ppm
5% copper oxide	16·6 ppm	21·0 ppm	40·1 ppm
10% copper oxide	36·7 ppm	20·4 ppm	41·8 ppm
Copper oxide painted onglaze	3·2 ppm	4·6 ppm	17·3 ppm
Copper oxide painted underglaze	18·6 ppm	10·0 ppm	19·0 ppm
5% chrome based glaze stain	0·2 ppm	0·1 ppm	0·1 ppm

The next table indicates the effect of stain addition when it is incorporated into the frit and when it is added to the glaze. Addition of copper oxide is also given for comparison:-

	Stain included in the frit	*Stain added to glaze*
Lead bisilicate + 5% copper oxide	105·0 ppm	16·6 ppm
Lead bisilicate + 5% chrome green stain	1·9 ppm	0·2 ppm

Glass does not present problems to the extent of that experienced with ceramic glazes as the melting process is much more likely to produce a stable material. Nevertheless, there is some disquiet, particularly in the USA about the possibility of the release of lead in lead crystal ware, particularly that used for storage, and as a result there has been a considerable reduction in demand for high quality lead glass which has forced a change in the nature of batch being melted in many studio and industrial workshops. Fortunately there has been a surge of activity in researching suitable batches containing little or no lead but which produce glass with similar qualities of clarity and brilliance.

Appendix I.
Tables

There is an increasing movement, particularly in Europe, towards the use of metric measurement for indicating grain or grit sizes rather than the traditionally accepted wire mesh standard. With this in mind the following table gives an approximation of the relevant micron sizes equivalent to the standard mesh numbers.

Mesh No.	Size in microns (μm)
80	191
100	150
120	125
150	105
180	87
220	68
240	63
280	54
320	43
400	30
600	20

A micron is equal to a thousandth of a millimetre.

25 μm = one thousandth part of an inch.

Grain sizes for abrasives

Grain sizes for abrasives in Europe are defined by FEPA (Federation of European Producers of Abrasives) The list ranges from F8 (2000–2830 μm) to F220 (44–74 μm) but the sizes most likely to be use by glassworkers are:-

F80	(149–210	μm)
F90	(125–177	μm)
F100	(105–149	μm)
F120	(88–125	μm)
F150	(63–105	μm)
F180	(63–88	μm)
F220	(44–74	μm)

Diamond grain sizes as per FEPA standard.

D151	(125–150	μm)	very coarse
D126	(106–125	μm)	
D107	(90–106	μm)	
D91	(75–90	μm)	
D76	(63–75	μm)	
D64	(53–63	μm)	medium
D54	(45–53	μm)	
D46	(38–45	μm)	
D35	(32–38	μm)	
D25	(25–32	μm)	
D20	(20–25	μm)	very fine

CERAMICS AND GLASS: A BASIC TECHNOLOGY

Metric conversions
Grinding wheel diameters and thicknesses.

Metric (mm)	Nominal Imperial inches
6	0·25
8	0·3125
10	0·375
13	0·5
16	0·625
20	0·75
25	1·00
32	1·25
40	1·5
50	2·00
57	2·25
63	2·5
80	3·00
90	3·5
100	4·00
114	4·5
125	5·00
150	6·00
180	7·00
200	8·00
230	9·00
250	10·00
300	12·00
356	14·00
406	16·00

Units of capacity. Relative values
It is essential to understand that there are differences in the volumes indicated in Imperial or United Kingdom gallons, pints and fluid ounces to those indicated by the same terms but in US measure.

It should also be noted that whilst there are 8 pints in each of the US and UK gallons there are 20 fluid ounces in the UK pint whilst there are 16 fluid ounces in the US pint.

One cubic metre	= 1000 litres or one stere
One litre	= 1000 cc
	= 0·2199 UK gallons
	= 1·7598 U K pints
	= 35·196 UK fl. oz
	= 0·2642 US gallons
	= 2·1132 US pints
	= 33·8112 US fl. oz
	= 61·025 cubic inches
One cubic yard	= 27 cubic feet

One cubic foot	= 1728 cubic inches
	= 28·317 litres
	= 6·237 UK gallons
	= 7·481 US gallons

One cubic inch	= 16·387 cc
	= 0·5768 UK fl. oz
	= 0·5539 US fl. oz

One UK gallon	= 4 UK quarts
	= 8 UK pints
	= 4·5461 litres
	= 0·1603 cubic feet
	= 1·201 US gallons

One UK Pint	= 20 UK fl. oz
	= 0·5683 litres
	= 568·5 cc
	= 1·201 US pints
	= 19·22 US fl. oz
	= 34·677 cubic inches

One UK fl. oz	= 28·122 cc
	= 0·961 US fl. oz
	= 1·734 cubic inches

One US gallon	= 8 US pints
	= 3·7853 litres
	= 0·8327 UK gallons
	= 231 cubic inches

One US pint	= 0·4732 litres
	= 473·2 cc
	= 0·8237 UK pints
	= 16·6528 UK fl. oz
	= 28·875 cubic inches

One US fl. oz	= 29·573 cc
	= 1·0408 UK fl. oz
	= 1·805 cubic inches

One cc	= 0·06102 cubic inches
	= 0·0352 UK fl. oz
	= 0·0338 US fl. oz

Length equivalents

1 metre	= 100 centimetre	= 39·3696 inches
1 centimetre	= 100 millimetres	= 0·3937 inches
1 yard	= 3 feet	= 0·9144 metres
1 foot	= 12 inches	= 30·489 centimetre
1 inch	= 0·0833 feet	= 2·54 centimetres

Weight equivalents

1 tonne	= 1000 kg	= 2204·61 lb
1 kg	= 1000 g	= 2·2046 lb
1 g	= 0·001 kg	= 0·0353 oz

There are differences in some of the UK (Imperial) weights and those of the USA.

1 ton	= 20 cwt	
2240 lb (UK)	= 1016·06 kg	
2000 lb (US)	= 907·18 kg	
1 cwt	= 112 lb (UK)	= 50·803 kg
	= 100 lb (US)	= 45·359 kg
1 lb	= 16 oz	= 453·6 g
1 oz	= 0·0625 lb	= 28·35 g

Conversion factors for glass batch materials

Material (formula)	Molecular weight	Oxides supplied	% by weight	Material to oxide	Oxide to material
Raw materials					
Alumina (Al_2O_3)	102	Al_2O_3	100	1·000	1·000
Borax hydrated ($Na_2 B_4O_7 10H_2O$)	381·4	$B_2 O_3$	36·5	0·365	2·739
		Na_2O	16·3	0·163	6·154
Boric acid (H_3BO_3)	61·8	B_2O_3	56·3	0·563	1·776
Sand (SiO_2)	60·1	SiO_2	100	1·000	1·000
Barium carbonate ($BaCO_3$)	197·4	BaO	77·7	0·777	1·288
Dolomite ($CaO.MgO.2CO_2$)	84·4	CaO	30·4	0·304	3·290
		MgO	21·9	0·219	4·574
Feldspar (potash) ($K_2O.Al_2O_3.6SiO_2$)	556·7	K_2O	16·9	0·169	5·910
		Al_2O_3	18·3	0·183	5·460
		SiO_2	64·8	0·648	1·544
Limestone ($CaCO_3$)	100·1	CaO	56·0	0·560	1·785
Litharge (PbO)	23·2	PbO	100·0	1·000	1·000
Lithium carbonate (Li_2CO_3)	73·9	Li_2O	40·4	0·404	2·473
Magnesium carbonate ($MgCO_3$)	84·3	MgO	47·8	0·478	2·092
Potash (K_2CO_3)	138·2	K_2O	68·2	0·682	1·467
Potassium hydrate (KOH)	112·2	K_2O	83·9	0·839	1·191
Potassium nitrate (KNO_3)	101·1	K_2O	46·6	0·466	2·147
Red lead (Pb_3O_4)	685·6	PbO	97·7	0·977	1·024
Soda ash ($NaCO_3$)	106·0	Na_2O	58·5	0·585	1·710
Sodium nitrate ($NaNO_3$)	85	Na_2O	36·5	0·365	2·743
Strontium carbonate ($SrCO_3$)	47·6	SrO	70·2	0·702	1·425
Zinc carbonate ($ZnCO_3$)	25·4	ZnO	64·9	0·649	1·541

Material (formula)	Molecular weight	Oxides supplied	% by weight	Material to oxide	Oxide to material
Refining agents					
Ammonium nitrate (NH_4O_3)	80	decomposes			
Antimony oxide (Sb_2O_3)	291·5	Sb_2O_3	100	1·000	1·000
White arsenic (As_2O_3)	197·8	As_2O_3	116·2	1·162	0·861
Colouring materials					
Cadmium sulphide (CdS)	44·4	CdO	88·9	0·889	1·125
Cobalt oxide (Co_3O_4)	240·8	CoO	93·4	0·934	1·070
Chromic oxide (Cr_2O_3)	152·0	CrO_3	131·6	1·316	0·760
Chromium trioxide (CrO_3)	100	CrO_3	76·0	0·760	1·316
Gold chloride ($AuCl_3$)	303·4	Au	64·0	0·640	1·540
Manganese dioxide (MnO_2)	86·9	MnO_2	Rarely contains more than 85% MnO_2		
Nickel oxide (Ni_2O_3)	165·4	NiO	90·3	0·903	1·109
Potassium chromate (K_2CrO_4)	194·2	Cr_2O_3	39·1	0·391	2·555
		K_2O	48·5	0·485	2·062
Potassium dichromate ($K_2Cr_2O_7$)	294·2	CrO_3	68·0	0·680	1·471
		Cr_2O_3	51·7	0·517	1·935
		K_2O	32·0	0·320	3·122
Selenium (Se)	79	Considerable volatile loss in founding. Usually impure			
Silver nitrate ($AgNO_3$)	169·9	Ag_2O	68·2	0·682	1·466
Vanadium pentoxide (V_2O_5)	182·0	V_2O_5	100·0	1·000	1·000
Opacifying agents					
Calcium fluoride (CaF)	78·1	CaO	71·8	0·178	1·392
		F_2	46·7	Volatilisation loss	
Cryolite (Na_3AlF_6)	210·0	Na_2O	44·3	0·443	2·258
		Al_2O_3	24·3	0·243	4·118
		F_2	54·3	Volatilisation loss	
Calcium phosphate ($Ca_3(PO_4)_2$)	310·2	CaO	54·2	0·542	1·844
		P_2O_5	45·8	0·458	2·185
Tin oxide (SnO_2)	150·7	SnO_2	100	1·000	1·000
Zirconium dioxide (ZrO_2)	123·2	ZrO_2	100	1·000	1·000

Mohs' scale of hardness

1	Talc
2	Gypsum
3	Calcite
4	Fluorspar
5	Apatite
6	Orthoclase
7	Quartz
8	Topaz
9	Corundum
10	Diamond

Squatting temperatures for large Orton pyrometric cones when heated at:-

Cone no.	60°C/h	108°F/h	150°C/h	270°F/h
	°C	°F	°C	°F
022	576	1069	586	1086
021	602	1116	614	1137
020	625	1157	635	1175
019	668	1234	683	1161
018	696	1285	717	1323
017	727	1341	747	1377
016	764	1407	792	1458
015	790	1454	804	1479
014	834	1533	838	1540
013	836	1537	861	1582
012	856	1573	872	1602
011	872	1602	883	1621
010	880	1616	890	1634
09	913	1679	923	1693
08	945	1733	955	1751
07	973	1783	984	1803
06	991	1816	999	1830
05	1031	1888	1046	1915
04	1050	1922	1060	1940
03	1086	1987	1101	2014
02	1101	2014	1120	2048
01	1117	2043	1137	2079
1	1136	2077	1154	2109
2	1142	2088	1162	2124
3	1152	2196	1168	2134
4	1168	2134	1186	2167
5	1177	2151	1196	2185
6	1201	2194	1222	2232
7	1215	2219	1240	2264
8	1236	2257	1263	2305
9	1260	2300	1280	2336
10	1285	2345	1305	2381
11	1294	2361	1315	2399
12	1306	2385	1326	2419
13	1321	2410	1346	2455
14	1388	2530	1366	2491

CERAMICS AND GLASS: A BASIC TECHNOLOGY

Squatting temperatures. Small Orton pyrometric cones when heated at:-

300°C/h		540°F/h
Cone no.	°C	°F
022	630	1135
021	643	1189
020	666	1231
019	723	1333
018	752	1386
017	784	1443
016	825	1517
015	843	1549
014	870	1596
013	880	1615
012	900	1650
011	915	1680
010	919	1686
09	955	1751
08	983	1801
07	1008	1846
06	1023	1873
05	1062	1944
04	1098	2008
03	1131	2068
02	1148	2098
01	1178	2152
1	1179	2154
2	1179	2154
3	1196	2185
4	1209	2208
5	1221	2230
6	1255	2291
7	1264	2307
8	1300	2372
9	1317	2403
10	1330	2426
11	1336	2437
12	1355	2471

Squatting temperatures for large Seger cones when heated at 150°C/h (270°F/h)

Cone number	°C	°F
022	595	1103
021	640	1184
020	660	1220
019	685	1265
018	705	1301
017	730	1346
016	755	1391
015a	780	1436
014a	805	1481
013a	835	1535
012a	860	1580
011a	900	1652
010a	920	1688
09a	935	1715
08a	955	1751
07a	970	1778
06a	990	1814
05a	1000	1832
04a	1025	1877
03a	1055	1931
02a	1085	1985
01a	1105	2021
1a	1125	2057
2a	1150	2102
3a	1170	2138
4a	1195	2183
5a	1215	2219
6a	1240	2264
7	1260	2300
8	1280	2336
9	1300	2372
10	1320	2408
11	1340	2444
12	1360	2480
13	1380	2516
14	1400	2552

Squatting temperatures for small Seger cones when heated at 150°C/h (270°F/h)

Cone number	°C	°F
022	605	1121
021	650	1202
020	675	1247
019	695	1283
018	715	1319
017	735	1355
016	760	1400
015a	785	1445
014a	815	1499
013a	845	1553
012a	890	1643
011a	900	1652
010a	925	1697
09a	940	1724
08a	965	1769
07a	975	1787
06a	995	1823
05a	1010	1850
04a	1055	1931
03a	1070	1958
02a	1100	2012
01a	1125	2057
1a	1145	2093
2a	1165	2129
3a	1185	2165
4a	1220	2228
5a	1230	2246
6a	1260	2300
7	1270	2318
8	1295	2363
9	1315	2399
10	1330	2426
11	1350	2462
12	1375	2507
13	1395	2543
14	1410	2570

Approximate calorific values of fuels used for studio kilns and furnaces

Fuel	Chemical analysis	Average value x	Amount of fuel per 1,000,000
Electricity		3413 Btu/kW	300 kWh
Town (coal) gas	H_2 50% CH_4 30% CO 10% others 10%	550 Btu/cub ft	1900 cub ft
Methane	CH_4 100%	990 Btu/cub ft	1010 cub ft
Natural gas	CH_4 90% C_2H_6 10%	1020 Btu/cub ft	980 cub ft
LPG propane	C_2H_8 100%	2500 Btu/cub ft	400 cub ft
LPG butane	C_4H_{10} 100%	3200 Btu/cub ft	315 cub ft

Approximate analysis of various refractories

One of the items which tend to confuse the situation is that firebricks are generally classified by the percentage of alumina that they contain. Thus a firebrick 52 would contain 52% alumina. High temperature insulation bricks (HTIs) are classified according to their hot face temperature in Fahrenheit. This means that an HTI 25 will stand a hot face temperature of 2500°F. Unfortunately, ceramic fibre insulation materials are classified in Europe by their hot face temperature in centigrade so a ceramic fibre board or mat 1260 will stand a hot face of 1260°C.

Refractory	Al_2O_3	SiO_2	TiO_2	Fe_2O_3	ZrO	Cr_2O_3	Others
42 Firebrick	42	52	1·5	2·7		1·8	
52 firebrick	52	41	1·7	3·1		2·2	
AZS 33	50	15			33	1	
AZS 41	46	12			41	1	
AZSC	32	13			26	26	3
High alumina	95	1		4			
High zirconia	1	4·5			94		0·5
Insulation refractories							
HTI 23	43	57					
HTI 26	58	42					
HTI 30	72	28					
Ceramic fibre 1260		48	52				
Ceramic fibre 1400	35	50		15			
Microtherm	2·37	64·68	31·90		1·05		

Abbreviations

A	ampere
Å	Ångstrom, 10^{-10} m
At No.	atomic number
AW	atomic weight
BS	British standard
°C	degrees centigrade or Celsius
CF	conversion factor
D	density
EMF	electromotive force
°F	degrees Fahrenheit
H	hardness on Mohs' scale
Hz	Hertz
J	Joule
K	degrees Kelvin
MF	molecular formula
MW	molecular weight
N	Newton
SG	specific gravity
°TW	degrees Twaddell
UK	United Kingdom
US or USA	United States of America
V	volts
W	Watts
cm	centimetre
cub	cubic
cwt	hundredweight
fl oz	fluid ounce
ft	foot/feet
gall	gallon
gm or g	gram
imp	imperial measure
in	inches
kg	kilogram
l	litre
lb	pound
lm	lumen
lx	lux
m	metre
ml	millilitre
mm	millimetres
mol	mole
oz	ounce
pt	pint
qt	quart
s	second
wt	weight
yd	yard

Decimal multiples and sub multiples

Multiple	Prefix	Symbol
10	deca	da
10^2	hecto	h
10^3	kilo	k
10^6	mega	M
10^9	giga	G
10^{12}	tera	T
10^{15}	peta	P
10^{18}	exa	E

Sub multiple	Prefix	Symbol
10^{-1}	deci	d
10^{-2}	centi	c
10^{-3}	milli	m
10^{-6}	micro	μ
10^{-9}	nano	n
10^{-12}	pico	p
10^{-15}	femto	f
10^{-18}	atto	a

The following is a list of the elements showing symbols, atomic weights and various valencies. It offers an alternative method to conveying the information to that of the periodic table.

Table of elements

Element	Symbol	Atomic weight	Valency
Aluminium	Al	27	3
Antimony	Sb	121·8	3
Arsenic	As	74·9	3
Barium	Ba	137·3	2
Beryllium	Be	9·0	2
Bismuth	Bi	209·0	3
Boron	B	10·8	3
Cadmium	Cd	112·4	2
Calcium	Ca	40·1	2
Carbon	C	12	2 and 4
Cerium	Ce	140·1	4
Chlorine	Cl	35·5	1
Chromium	Cr	52	3
Cobalt	Co	58·9	2 and 3
Copper	Cu	63·5	1 and 2
Fluorine	F	19	1
Germanium	Ge	72·6	4
Gold	Au	197	-
Hydrogen	H	1	1
Iron	Fe	55·8	2 and 3
Lead	Pb	207·2	2 and 4
Lithium	Li	6·9	1
Magnesium	Mg	24·3	2
Manganese	Mn	54·9	2, 3 and 4
Nickel	Ni	58·7	2 and 4
Nitrogen	N	14	3
Oxygen	O	16	2
Phosphorous	P	31	3 and 5
Platinum	Pt	195·1	-
Potassium	K	39·1	1
Praseodymium	Pr	140·9	4
Selenium	Se	79	2, 4 and 6
Silicon	Si	28·1	4
Silver	Ag	107·9	1
Sodium	Na	23·	1
Strontium	Sr	87·6	2
Sulphur	S	31·1	2 and 4
Tin	Sn	118·7	4
Titanium	Ti	47·9	4
Uranium	U	238	3, 4 and 5
Vanadium	V	50·9	2, 3, 4 and 5
Zinc	Zn	65·4	2
Zirconium	Zr	91·2	4

There are many elements and compounds which are released as gases wholly or in part during a kiln firing or during a glass founding. The approximate temperature at which volatilisation begins to take place is shown below though it must be remembered that these temperatures can be modified considerably by reactions with other materials (see Eutectics on page 103).

Those which volatilise completely are:-

Water	H_2O	100°C
Nitrogen	N	200°C
Chlorine	Cl	200°C
Hydroxyls	OH	500°C
Oxides of carbon	CO, CO_2	700°C
Oxides of sulphur	SO_2, SO_3	900°C
Fluorine	F	1000°C

Those from which there may be a significant loss:-

Selenium	Se	
Zinc oxide	ZnO	950°C
Lead oxide	PbO	1000°C
Soda	Na_2O	1100°C
Boric oxide	B_2O_3	1150°C

Those from which there is a slight loss:-

Copper oxide	CuO	1000°C
Chromium	Cr_2O_3	1050°C
Cobalt oxide	CoO	1100°C
Barium oxide	BaO	1200°C
Manganous oxide	MnO	1200°C
Potash	K_2O	1200°C

Appendix II.
Glass recipes

The following glass making recipes are taken from various sources. Some are indicated in batch quantities whilst others are shown as chemical percentages. The first two recipes have both.

Details of the methods of finding the batch or chemical percentages from one or the other are shown in the chapter on batch calculations on page 77.

The potash and zinc in the following batch help both colour and brilliance and the apparently low calcia content is balanced by the inclusion of magnesia and zinc oxide to give long, easy working:-

Sand	60·8	SiO_2	68
Sodium carbonate	23·2	Na_2O	15
Feldspar	10·8	K_2O	5
Dolomite	4·6	CaO	3
Zinc oxide	4·0	ZnO	4
Potassium carbonate	3·9	Al_2O_3	2
Potassium nitrate	2·1	MgO	1
Sodium nitrate	2·7	B_2O_3	1
Borax	2·7	BaO	1

A basic soda–lime–silica glass which has been improved by the inclusion of some lead, potash, borax, magnesia, baria and zinc oxide is as follows. Again it should be good for colour and brilliance and should be easy to work:-

Sand	70	SiO_2	70
Soda ash	22·2	Na_2O	14·98
Dolomite	9·2	CaO	4·7
Borax	5·5	B_2O_3	2
Litharge	3·0	PbO	3
Potassium carbonate	2·9	K_2O	1·9
Barium carbonate	1·3	BaO	1·1
Zinc oxide	1·0	ZnO	1
Sodium nitrate	2·7	MgO	2
Lime	2·6		

The recipe below is for a basic soda–lime–silica glass for hand working:-

SiO_2	70·5%
Na_2O	16·5
CaO	5·5
MgO	3·0
K_2O	1·2
B_2O_3	0·5
Al_2O_3	2·5

A batch given by Klaus Kugler for a soda–lime–silica glass to match his coloured rods is:-

Sand	100
Soda ash	34
Lime	15
Potash	5

This appears to have a high calcia content for a hand working glass and might be improved by introducing some magnesia or zinc oxide in place of part of the lime. The high lime content would also have a tendency to promote devitrification.

A basic high lead glass designed for cutting and engraving is:-

SiO_2	55·5
PbO	33·0
K_2O	11·0

Another high lead glass with excellent working characteristics and compatible with most Kugler type colours is:-

SiO_2	56·5
Al_2O_3	1·4
PbO	29
Na_2O	4·25
K_2O	8·25

Batch for full lead crystal:-

Sand	59·5
Soda ash	6
Potassium carbonate (calcined)	10
Potassium nitrate	4
Litharge	31

Batch for lead crystal:-

Sand	60·2
Sodium carbonate	4
Potassium carbonate (calcined)	14·8
Sodium nitrate	2
Limespar	1·8
Litharge	25·9

Batch for a Pyrex type batch:-

Sand	75
Boric acid	12·5
Borax	14
Potassium nitrate	4·5
Calcined alumina	2

Batch for a soft glass for making jewellery and ornaments:-

Sand	68
Soda ash	26·5
Hydrated lime	9·5
Calcined alumina	3

Batch for a lead free long working studio glass:-

Sand	62·5
Soda ash	26·5
Lime	3
Barium carbonate	3·5
Zinc oxide	3·5
Anhydrite	0·5

Batch for an opalescent glass:-

Sand	60
Soda ash	23·5
Calcined alumina	3·5
Zinc oxide	4·8
Fluorspar	4·5
Sodium silico fluoride	1·6
Sodium nitrate	1·2
Salt	0·7

Matching clear glass for the above:-

Sand	63
Soda ash	26·2
Limestone	3
Barium carbonate	3·6
Zinc oxide	3·6
Calcium sulphate	0·6

Various other glass recipes

Lead based glasses

	(1)	(2)	(3)	(4)
		(full crystal)		(low lead)
Sand	57·5	56·5	100	50
Calcined alumina		1·4		
Soda ash	6	7·25		10
Calcined potash	10	12·1	36	11·5
Potassium nitrate	4		5	1
Lead oxide	31·5	29	22	
Lead bisilicate				6
Lime			12	9
Dehydrated borax				4
Arsenic			0·5	0·25

Soda–lime–silica glass

	(1)	(2)	(3)	(4)
Sand	100	210	56·5	71·5
Calcined alumina			1	
Soda ash	24	88	27·5	29
Sodium nitrate	2			2·5
Potash	12			
Dolomite				14
Lime	25	10	12·5	
Zinc oxide	6	12		
Barium carbonate		12		
Saltcake				0·5
Potash feldspar			16·5	
Anhydrite		2		
Arsenous oxide	0·5		0·5	0·25

Borosilicate glasses

	(1)	(2)	(3)
Sand	75	49	66
Boric acid	12·5	22·5	22·7
Soda ash			11·6
Dehydrated borax	14	4·6	
Potassium nitrate	4·5	1	
Calcined alumina	2		4·5
Barium carbonate		3·25	
Zinc oxide		1·9	
Potash		3·5	
Sodium silico fluoride		1	
Nepheline syenite		25	
Lime		0·5	

Photochromic glasses

	(1)	(2)	(3)
Silica (sand)	96·94	100	100
Sodium carbonate	43·4	34·31	34·31
Alumina	17·7		
Borax	3		
Barium carbonate	15·5	17	
Gold (10%)	0·08	0·014	
Ceric oxalate	0·0385	1·03	1·03
Sodium fluoride	12·87		
Silver nitrate		0·166	0·166
Antimony oxide		0·02	0·02
Zinc oxide			13

Appendix III.
Bibliography

Bohemian Glass. Sylva Petrova and Jean-Luc Olivie. Flammarion.
Coloured Glasses. W. A. Weyl. Society of Glass Technology.
The Potter's Dictionary. Frank and Janet Hamer. A & C Black.
A Dictionary of Glass. C. Bray. A & C Black.
Ceramics in the Modern World. Maurice Chandler. Aldus Books.
Conservation of Glass. R. G. Newton and S. Davison. Butterworth-Heinemann.
Conservation of Ceramics. Victoria Oakley and Susan Buys. Butterworth-Heinemann.
Contemporary Glass. Suzanne Franks. Harry N. Abrams, New York.
Ceramic glazes. F. Singer and W. F. German. Borax Consolidated.
Ceramic Glazes. C. W. Parmelee. Chicago Industrial Publications.
Ceramic faults. Harry Fraser. A & C Black.
Ceramic Technology. Yvonne Cuff. A & C Black.
Characteristics of Ceramics. Hench and Gould. Marcel Dekker Inc.
Chinese Glazes. Nigel Wood. A &C Black.
Ceramics. Richard Zakin. A & C Black.
Cooper's Book of Glaze Recipes. Emmanuel Cooper. Batsford.
Clay and glazes for the potter. Daniel Rhodes. Pitman.
Dangerous Properties of Industrial Materials. Sax. Van Nostrand-Reinhold.
Electric Kiln Construction for Potters. Robert Fournier. Van Nostrand Reinhold.
Fine Ceramics. F. H. Norton. McGraw Hill.
Glass and Glassmaking. Roger Dodsworth. Shire Publications.
Glass Engraving. J. Matcham & P. Dreiser. Batsford.
Glasses. Borax Consolidated Ltd, London.
Glass in Architecture and Decoration. Raymond McGrath and A. C. Frost. The Architectural Press, London.
Glass Ceramics. P. W. McMillan. Academic Press.
Glassmaking today. Doyle. Portcullis.
Glass Notes. Henry Halem. Franklin Mills Press.
Glass in the Modern World. Terence Mahoney. Aldus Books.
Glassschliff in Deutschland. Gernot Merker. Bergbau und Industrie Museum, Ostbayern, Germany.
Glazes for the Craft Potter. Harry Fraser. A & C Black.
Glazes and Glazing Techniques. Greg Daly. A & C Black.
Inorganic Glass forming Systems. H. Rawson. Academic Press.
The identification of stones in glass. H. E. Taylor and D. K. Hill. University of Sheffield.
Introduction to Glass Science and Technology. James E. Shelby. Royal Society of Chemistry.
Illustrated Dictionary of Practical Pottery. Robert Fournier. A & C Black.

International modern glass. Geoffrey Beard. Barrie & Jenkins.

Trechniques of Kiln Formed Glass. Keith Cummings. A & C Black.

Scandinavian. Ceramics and Glass of the Twentieth Century. Victoria and Albert Museum.

Modern Glass. Ada Polak. Faber and Faber.

Studio Glassmaking. R. Flavell and R. Smale. Van Nostrand Reinhold.

Rezptbuch fur die praktische glasschmelche. Wilhelm Schmidt. Arnstadt.

Le Vitrail. Nicole Blondel. Imprimerie Nationale, Paris.

Les arts du Verre. Centre Internationale du Vitrail, Chartes, France.

The Condensed Chemical Dictionary. Van Nostrand-Reinhold.

Toxicity of Industrial Metals. Browning. Butterworth.

Oriental Glazes. Nigel Wood. Pitman/Watson Guptil.

A Potters Book. Bernard Leach. Translantic Arts, New York.

An introduction to the technology of pottery. Paul Rado. Pergammon Press.

Schott Guide to Glass. Heinz G Pfaender. Van Rostrand Reinhold Co.

Materials Science. J. C. Anderson and K. D. Leaver. Nelson.

Whitewares. W. Ryan and C. Radford. Pergammon Press.

World Ceramics. Robert J. Charleston. Hamlyn.

Porcelain. Jan Axel and Karen McCready. Watson-Guptil.

The Art of Firing. Frederick Olsen. A & C Black.

Lustre Pottery. Robert Fournier. A & C Black.

Raku. Steve Branfman. A & C Black.

The Effect of Heat on Ceramics. W. F. Ford. P Maclaren & Sons Ltd.

Concise inorganic chemistry. J. D. Lee. Van Nostrand Reinhold.

Modern Glass Practice. S. R. Scholes. Industrial Publications Inc.

Raw materials for glassmaking. Bo Simmingsköld. Society of Glass Technology.

Soda Glazing. R. Tudball. A & C Black Ltd.

Glazes and glazing techniques. G. Daly. A & C Black Ltd.

Potter's Question and Answer Book. G. Bliss. A & C Black Ltd.

Glazes for the Craft Potter. H. Fraser. A & C Black Ltd.

Appendix IV.
Periodicals

Journal of the Society of Glass Technology, *Glass Technology* and *Physics and Chemistry of Glasses*, The Society of Glass Technology, Don Valley House, Saville St East, Sheffield S4 7UQ, UK.

Crafts Magazine. Crafts Council, 44a Pentonville Rd. London N1 9BY, UK.

American Crafts, The American Crafts Council. New York, USA.

American Ceramics. 15, W 44th Street. NY 10036, USA.

Craft Australia. Crafts Council of Australia, 27 King Street, Sydney, NSW 2000, USA.

Crafft. Welsh Arts Council, Museum Place, Cardiff, CF1 3NX, Wales UK.

Ceramic Review, 21 Carnaby Street, London, W1V 1PH, UK.

Ceramics Monthly, Box 12448, Columbus, Ohio 43212, UK.

Studio Potter, Box 172, Warner, New Hampshire 03278, USA.

Pottery Quarterly, Northfield Studio, Northfields Tring, Herts, UK.

New Zealand Potter, Box 147, Albany, New Zealand.

Neue Keramik, Unter Den Eichen 90, D-1000 Berlin 45, Germany.

Neues Glas, Verlagsgesellschaft Ritterbach mbH, Rodolf Diesel Strasse, Postfach 1820, D 50226 Frechen, Germany.
This Magazine also publishes the annual *New Glass Review* from the Corning Museum of Glass.

Glasswork. Japanese publication dealing with both Japanese and International Studio Glass. The text is in both Japanese and English. Fax +81 74223 6364 for details.

New Work. Quarterly publication of studio glass by the New York Experimental Glass Workshop. Tel +1212 966 1808 for details.

Glass Art Society Journal. Tel +1 206 382 1305 for details.

Glas and Keramik, Voorstraat 21, 4147 CA Asperen, The Netherlands.

La Revue de la Ceramique et du Verre, 61 Rue de Marconi, 62880 Vendin-le-Vieil, France.

Appendix V.
Organisations and Societies

The addresses of some societies tend to change from time to time as they often relate to that of the current secretary. If there is any difficulty, the Crafts Council at 44A Pentonville Road, London N1 9BY Telephone number 020 7278 7700 have an information service and can give appropriate addresses and telephone numbers of societies and individual artists based in Britain on request.

The Crafts Councils of the various countries usually have an information service to provide addresses/telephone numbers, details etc. of artists and organisations operating within their areas.

The Crafts Council, 44A Pentonville Rd, London N1 9BY, UK. Tel. +44(0)20 7278 7700.

The Crafts Council of Australia, 100 George Street, Sydney, New South Wales 2000, Australia. Tel +2 241 1701.

The Canadian Crafts Council, 46 Elgin Street, Suite 16 Ottawa, Canada K1P 5K6. Tel. +613, 235 8200.

Crafts Council of Japan, 503 Yoyogi 4-28-8, Shibuya-Ku, Tokyo 151, Japan.

Crafts Council of New Zealand, 22 The Terrace, PO Box 498, Wellington 1, New Zealand. Tel +44 727 018.

American Crafts Council, 40 West 53rd Street, New York, NY 14830, USA. Tel +212 956 5371.

INT Nat. de Nouvel Objet Visuel, 27 Rue de l'Universite, F75007 Paris, France.

The Glass Association, Broadfield House, Glass Museum, Barnett Lane, Kingswinford, West Midlands, DY6 9QA, UK.

The Contemporary Glass Society c/o Broadfield House Glass Museum. Barnett Lane, Kingswinford, West Midlands DY6 9QA, UK.

The Glass Circle, The Old Rectory, Walderslade, Dover, KT15 5AT, UK.

British Society of Master Glass Painters, 11 Landsdowne Road, Muswell Hill, London N10 2AX, UK.

The Society of Friends of Modern Glass, Singel 123A, 3112 Schieldam, The Netherlands.

Worshipful Company of Glaziers and Painters of Glass, Glaziers Hall, 9 Montague Close, London Bridge, London SE1 9DD, UK.

British Glass Manufacturers Confederation, Northumberland Road, Sheffield S10 2UA, UK. Tel +44(0)114 268 6201.

The Scottish Glass Society, Dorich, Glen Derby, Kirkmichael, Perthshire, Scotland, UK.

The Society of Glass Technology, Don Valley House, Savile Street East, Sheffield S4 7UQ, UK. Tel +114 263 4455.

Guild of Glass Engravers, Unit 27D, Thames House, South Bank Business Centre, 140 Battersea Park Rd, London SW11 4NB, UK.

The British Society of Scientific Glassblowers, 15 Crompton Street, Chelmsford, Essex CM1 3BW, UK. Tel +44(0)1245 355981.

British Ceramic Confederation, Federation House, Station Road, Stoke on Trent, ST4 2SA, UK.

British Ceramic Research Association, Queens Road, Penkhull, Stoke on Trent, ST4 7IQ, UK.

Other addresses:-

Artists in Stained Glass (AISG) Canada, c/o Ontario Crafts Council, 35 McCaul Street, Toronto M5T 1V7, Canada. Tel +416 977 3511.

Districta de l'Exempio Adjunctament de Barcelona, Casa Elizaldo, Valencia 302, Spain.

The Glass Art Society Inc, PO Box 1364, Corning, NY 14830, USA. Tel +607 936 0530

The Stained Glass Association of America, 4050 Broadway, Suite 219, Kansas City, MO 64111, USA. Tel +816 561 4404.

National Institute for Occupational Safety and Hygiene (NIOSH), 4676 Columbia Parkway, Cincinatti, Ohio, USA.

Occupational Safety and Health Administration (OSHA), 200 Constitution Avenue NW, Washington, DC 20210, USA.

Appendix VI.
List of figures

Index

Feldspar 15, 85
Feldspars 18, 63
Feldspathic rock 11
Feldspathoids 26
Ferric chloride 220
Fine matt 107
Fining 139, 175
Fining agents 140
Firebrick particles 141
Firebricks 22, 104, 157, 161, 248
Fireclays 21, 22, 26, 48, 146, 157, 169
Fired clay 35
Firing 13, 21, 25, 90, 92, 136, 167
Firing clay 25
Firing cycle 50, 134, 216
Firing range 45, 55
Firing schedules 118, 146, 174
Firing strategy 50
Firing temperature
    23, 24, 35, 38, 45, 46, 47, 51, 56, 216
Flake 122
Flaking 30, 117, 126, 134
Flameproof 46
Flash fire 222
Flash firing 218
Flashing 119, 135
Flint glass 75
Flocculants 31
Flocculation 29
Flocks 28
Fluidity 33, 119, 128
Fluoride opals 230
Flux 57, 59
Fluxes 12
Fluxing 25
Forest glass 66
Founding 90, 92, 106, 126, 139, 175
Fracture 148
Fraxbond 191
French chalk 184
Friable 24
Frit glaze 53, 55
Frits 27, 63
Fritting 72
Full lead crystal 254
Fume extraction 234
Fumes 235
Furnace atmosphere 90, 101, 200
Furnace crowns 83
Furnace refractories 67, 83
Furnaces 5, 153
Fused alumina 157
Fused borosilicate glass 137
Fused silica 132

Fusing 107
Fusion cast refractories 159

G

Gaolin 20
Gas fired kilns 168
Gels 193
Gibbsite 11, 86
Girasole glass 212
Glass 7, 27, 62, 73
Glass batch 63, 77, 101, 211, 227, 242
Glass ceramics 5, 67, 108, 114
Glass decay 102, 146
Glass faults 139
Glass fibre 9
Glass formers 7, 59, 62
Glass forming 178
Glass forming kiln 165
Glass founding 175, 252
Glass furnace 126, 153
Glass glazes 196
Glass lustres 222
Glass making recipes 253
Glass melting 57
Glass pots 154
Glass recipes 253
Glass rot 144
Glass tubing 201
Glassblowers cataract 234
Glassblowing 106, 199
Glasshouse pots 158
Glassmaking 57, 62
Glassmaking sands 16
Glaze 8, 27, 62, 195, 212, 226
Glaze batch 63, 77, 226
Glaze faults 130
Glaze firing 123, 127, 135, 171
Glaze fit 130, 132
Glaze formula 47
Glaze formulae 78
Glaze frits 71
Glaze making 57
Glaze materials 68
Glaze mixture 101
Glaze recipe 55
Glaze recipes 68
Glaze slop 27
Glaze stains 215
Glaze temperature 130
Glaze tests 209
Glazed ware 37, 236
Glazes 5, 13
Glory hole 156, 164

O

Obsidian 9
Ochre 54
Oil spot 55
Once fired ware 55
Opacifiers 199, 217, 227
Opacifying agents 231, 243
Opacity 107, 200, 225, 229
Opal glass 230, 231
Opalescence 62, 194, 212
Opalescent glass 255
Opaque white 53
Optical glass 74, 149, 223, 224
Orange 195, 199, 201
Orange peel 48, 52
Organisations and Societies 261
Oriental glazes 107
Orthoclase 18, 26
Orton pyrometric cones 244, 245
Ovenware 46
Overfiring 136
Overgrindin 135
Oxide washes 207
Oxidising atmosphere 197
Oxy-fuel burners 154

P

Painting 215
Parian ware 45
Partridge feather 55
Pate de verre 183, 229
Peacock Ware 219
Peeling 119, 134
Pegmatite 19
Pelletised batch 145
Periodic table 92, 97, 251
Periodicals 260
Permeability 33, 119
Petalite 27, 67
Phase separation 113
Phosphate opal 231
Phosphate opals 230
Phosphorous pentoxide 62, 69, 131
Photochromic glasses 257
Pinholes 119, 129, 136
Pink 198, 200, 204
Pitting 119
Plant ash 66
Plaster of Paris 177
Plastic flow 61
Plasticiser 24, 89
Plasticity 11, 16, 20, 38, 42, 88, 104

Polishing 178
Polyester resins 186
Polymerised carbohydrate pastes 89
Porcelain 8, 20, 35, 40, 46, 71, 146, 171
Porcelain slips 48
Porosity 35, 36, 135, 177
Pot furnace 167
Pot making 91
Potash 9, 57, 59, 66
Potash feldspar 18, 26, 85
Potassa 94
Potassium bichromate 196
Potassium carbonate 9, 66, 112, 138
Potassium chloride 50
Potassium dichromate 54, 200, 236
Potassium oxide 9, 57, 59, 66, 94, 131
Potassium permanganate 196
Potters 5
Pottery 13
Primary clays 16, 20, 22
Protons 97
Pumice 9
Purple 53, 56, 194, 197, 204
Purple of Cassius 209
Purple-red 205

Q

Quartz 15
Quick setting adhesive 190
Quicklime 10

R

Raku 52, 91
Raku firing 172
Random networks 11, 57, 85, 103
Ravenscroft, George 66, 75
Raw glazed ware 55
Raw glazing 171
Raw materials 62, 242
Recuperators 154
Red 53, 195, 197, 199, 201, 209
Red clays 24
Red-orange 200
Redox reactions 51
Reduced stoneware 91
Reducing atmosphere 39, 197, 202
Reducing/oxidising atmosphere 51
Reduction 54, 90
Refining 175
Refining agents 62, 68, 243
Reflected light 195
Reflectivity 59

Vitrified 9
Vitrified hotelware 35
Volatilisation 252

W

Waldglas 66, 203
Waste energy 153
Water of crystallisation 87
Waterproofing 189
Weathering 24, 89
Weathering crusts 144
Wetting 138
White 53, 230
Wood ash 55, 66, 69
Wood ash glaze 70
Working life 67
Working point 61

Working temperature 60, 72, 157

Y

Yellow 52, 53, 54, 194, 195, 199, 200, 205, 214
Yellow green 56, 200

Z

Zinc chloride 50
Zinc oxide
    59, 67, 131, 134, 138, 227, 236
Zinc silicate 227, 228
Zinc titanate 228
Zircon/alumina based refractory 109
Zirconia 138
Zirconium oxide 132, 205
Zirconium silicate 159